Voltaire's

CANDIDE

and the Critics

Wadsworth Guides to Literary Study
Maurice Beebe, General Editor

Voltaire's

CANDIDE

and the Critics

edited by Milton P. Foster
Eastern Michigan University

WADSWORTH PUBLISHING COMPANY, INC.
BELMONT, CALIFORNIA

Second printing, August 1964

L.C. Cat. Card No.: 62–19154
Printed in the United States of
America

CONTENTS

PREFACE

Voltaire was a man who liked to oppose. We can say of him, as Emerson said of Thoreau, that it was "as if he did not feel himself except in opposition." When he was a young student, he successfully resisted his father's efforts to make a lawyer of him. As a young man he enjoyed the company of other Parisian freethinkers, with whom he attacked religious orthodoxy and social customs. He acquired such a reputation for satire that he was exiled from Paris at this time for allegedly writing an attack in verse on evils in the state. Later he was forced to spend nearly a year in the Bastille on charges that he wrote satirically against the Duke of Orleans, the Regent of France.

After his release from prison he was busily and happily engaged in a successful writing career, and he gained many friends in the upper levels of society; but his pleasant life did not cause him to forget his habit of opposing. He used his wit to assail clergy, kings, and others in authority. He soon found himself in a dispute with an arrogant nobleman, the Chevalier de Rohan-Chabot, who was piqued by the intrusion of bourgeois Voltaire into aristocratic circles. When Voltaire challenged the Chevalier to a duel for having his servants beat him, the nobleman had Voltaire thrown into the Bastille for a second time.

His stay in prison this time was brief, but it was followed by enforced exile from France. In England, where he chose to spend his exile, Voltaire saw much to admire in the way of a more democratic government and more freedom of press, speech, and religion than he was used to at home. One result of these experiences was the publication of his *Letters on the English Nation,* a work that indirectly combats abuses in France by praising social conditions in England. After his return to France Voltaire was soon banished from Paris again because of this criticism.

In the next period of his life he offended conventional morality by living openly with his mistress, Madame du Châtelet, and her husband at their estate at Cirey. This well-educated and scientifically minded woman encouraged Voltaire to lead a serene life of scholarship for fifteen years, free from his usual tendency to engage in controversy. She was not able, however, to stifle his gradually increasing opposition to the philosophy of optimism, which many intellectuals of the day accepted. Madame du Châtelet herself agreed with the optimistic teachings of Gottfried Wilhelm von Leibniz and Alexander Pope, and Voltaire also was attracted to their ideas at first; but as time passed, and Voltaire's personal and vicarious sufferings increased, he became a vigorous opponent of optimism, as we see in *Candide.*

One example of his personal suffering was the death of Madame du Châtelet in 1749 (she died bearing the illegitimate child of a rival of Voltaire's for her love). Also his relations with King Louis XV of France were poor at this time because of the sharpness of Voltaire's satirical writings. Voltaire looked for a happier existence at the court of Frederick the Great of Prussia, to which Frederick himself invited him. For a while the Prussian king and the French writer got along well, but soon Voltaire displayed his old rebelliousness when Frederick became too tyrannical. They broke their friendship, and Voltaire became an exile again, living first in Geneva, Switzerland, and then in the part of France nearest the Swiss border.

Here he fought with his pen against the optimists, using the terrible suffering brought on by the Lisbon earthquake of 1755 as one of his chief arguments to prove that all is not well and that this is not the best of all possible worlds. He entered into a dispute with Jean-Jacques Rousseau about divine Providence and the Lisbon earthquake, and eventually the two men became bitter enemies. He wrote his most devastating thrust against optimism, *Candide,* at this time. He also found time to quarrel with the authorities of Protestant Geneva, who objected on moral grounds to his putting on plays at his estate, Les Délices.

In his old age Voltaire did not retire from opposition. Using *"Ecrasez l'infame"* ("Crush the infamous thing") as his war cry, he attacked the church for its persecution of alleged heretics and disbelievers. He wrote and acted in behalf of Jean Calas, a Protestant who was tortured and executed because he was accused of killing his son to prevent him from becoming a Catholic. Later Voltaire bitterly censured the authorities for decapitating an eighteen-year-old boy named La Barre on the charge of sacrilege. In these and in similar cases Voltaire expressed indignation because of the lack of real evidence against the accused. To the end of his life Voltaire opposed any act of intolerance or inhumanity that came to his attention.

Candide is Voltaire's most successful act of opposition. His unmerciful ridicule in this novel defeated eighteenth-century optimism, but the book would not still be read and admired today if it were only the author's negative reaction to a view of life. It has endured because it also possesses positive values. Its sparkling wit, its breath-taking pace, its clever ironies and paradoxes keep it fresh. Its confrontation of the problem of evil gives it depth and makes it relevant to the lives of human beings in all ages. And many readers have found in Candide's final remark that "we must cultivate our garden" a sane and constructive doctrine of work that counteracts despair.

From the time of its first publication *Candide* has aroused differences of opinion. It grew out of and contributed to the eighteenth-century philosophical argument between optimists and antioptimists about the problem of evil—a controversy involving several leading thinkers of the period: Leibniz, Christian Wolff, Bernard Mandeville, Pope, Kant, Rousseau, Voltaire, and others. In other respects also, *Candide* has given rise to critical controversy—with critics discussing and giving varied interpretations of such features as the elements of wit and literary artistry in the novel; the exact nature of Voltaire's vision of evil; the significance of the chapters on the utopian community Eldorado; the full implications of the final pronouncement, "we must cultivate our garden." These lively criticisms of *Candide* over the many years have contributed to our understanding and appreciation of the novel.

The purpose of this volume on *"Candide* and the Critics" is to provide materials that will enhance the reader's understanding of the novel and the controversies connected with it. The materials include a complete text of the novel, an introductory essay on the general background, and some of the best criticism on *Candide* and the optimism controversy. Significant dates and events in Voltaire's life and the literary-philosophical climate surrounding him are listed in the Chronology on pages ix–x. For those who will use the book for research papers in composition or literature courses in college, research topics and a bibliography are included at the end of the volume. The thematic organization of the book is designed to make subjects for discussion and research more evident—the various sections calling attention to the main problems concerning *Candide.* The book offers handy reference material for any course in which *Candide* might be studied, such as courses in the novel, comparative literature, humanities, or philosophy.

For some selections in this book, the editor has renumbered footnotes; and in some instances—because many users of this book probably will not have studied French—he has added footnotes containing translations of passages quoted in French. All such footnotes have been bracketed to indicate that they were added by the editor, who takes full responsibility for the translations found in them. Any other footnotes appearing in brackets are also additions by the editor. Original page numbers of the selections are given in raised brackets. When a page in the original text ends with part of a word, the page number has been placed at the end of the word. Spaced ellipses (. . .) indicate the editor's omissions; unspaced ellipses (...) indicate those in the original material.

The editor makes grateful acknowledgment to the authors, editors, and publishers who so kindly gave him permission to reprint selections. He is especially thankful to Catherine Foster, Betsi Foster, Sally Foster, Alice Bensen, William F. Bottiglia, and Maurice Beebe for the assistance, advice, and encouragement they gave him.

Milton P. Foster

CHRONOLOGY OF IMPORTANT EVENTS IN VOLTAIRE'S LIFE AND TIMES

1694   François-Marie Arouet born in Paris to middle-class parents; his father a lawyer.

1704   Entered the Jesuit school of Louis-le-Grand.

1710   Gottfried Wilhelm von Leibniz published *Theodicy*.

1711   Arouet left school.

1713   Sent by his father to Holland because he was spending time with literary friends instead of attending to the study of law.

1716   Banished from Paris for allegedly writing satirical verses.

1717   Began eleven-month imprisonment in the Bastille on charge that he wrote against the Regent of France, Philippe d'Orleans.

1718   Added "de Voltaire" to his name to make it sound more aristocratic. His tragedy *Oedipe* produced in Paris.

1723   Published first version of *La Henriade*, a long poem praising a tolerant monarch, Henry IV.

1726   In the Bastille again for two weeks for challenging the Chevalier de Rohan-Chabot to a duel. Began three-year exile, mostly in England, where he met the great English writers of the day and was favorably impressed by English culture and freedom. Jonathan Swift's *Gulliver's Travels* published in England.

1731   Published *History of Charles XII, King of Sweden*, in which he urged kings to strive for peace.

1732   Produced *Zaïre*, a tragedy.

1733–34   Published his *Letters on the English Nation* (also known as *Philosophical Letters*), in which he indirectly criticized conditions in France. Alexander Pope's *An Essay on Man* published in England.

1734   Banished again from Paris, Voltaire began living with Madame du Châtelet at Cirey in Champagne. Here for approximately fifteen years he studied science, history, and philosophy and wrote poems, dramas, essays, and philosophical tales. Became interested in the optimistic philosophy of Leibniz.

1746   Elected to the French Academy.

1749   Death of Madame du Châtelet.

1750   Accepted invitation of Frederick the Great of Prussia to live at his court in Potsdam.

1751   Published *The Age of Louis XIV*, a cultural history.

1752   Published *Poem on the Natural Law* and *Micromégas*, a philosophical tale.

1753   Quarreled with Frederick over Frederick's use of power. Left Potsdam in anger.

1755   Moved to an estate at Geneva, Switzerland, which he called "Les Délices." The Lisbon earthquake took place, causing many deaths.

1756   Published *Poem on the Lisbon Earthquake* and *Universal History (Essai sur les moeurs)*. Received *Letter on Providence* from Jean-Jacques Rousseau in reply to his *Poem on the Lisbon Earthquake*.

1759   Left Geneva because of opposition to theatrical performances at Les Délices by Swiss Protestants. Moved to an estate at Ferney in France just across the border from Switzerland. Published *Candide*.

1763   Wrote *Treatise on Tolerance* in defense of Jean Calas, who had been tortured and executed as a result of a religious controversy.

1764   Published *Philosophical Dictionary*, in which he set forth the main ideas of rationalism.

1766   Wrote *Account of the Death of the Chevalier de la Barre* in defense of a young boy executed for alleged sacrilege.

1778   After approximately twenty years at Ferney—where he developed a beautiful and profitable rural community, wrote unceasingly, advocated humanitarian reforms, and was visited by famous people from many countries—Voltaire finally returned to Paris in triumph. Here he died at the age of eighty-four after receiving much acclaim.

CANDIDE

or Optimism*

Translated from the German of Dr. Ralph[1]

With the Additions Found in the Doctor's Pocket When He Died at Minden in the Year of Our Lord 1759

1 How Candide Was Brought Up in a Fine Castle, and How He Was Expelled Therefrom

In Westphalia, in the castle of My Lord the Baron of Thunder-ten-tronckh, there was a young man whom nature had endowed with the gentlest of characters. His face bespoke his soul. His judgment was rather sound and his mind of the simplest; this is the reason, I think, why he was named Candide. The old servants of the house suspected that he was the son of My Lord the Baron's sister and of a good and honorable gentleman of the neighborhood whom that lady never would marry because he could prove only seventy-one quarterings[2] and the rest of his genealogical tree had been lost by the injuries of time.

My Lord the Baron was one of the most powerful lords in Westphalia, for his castle had a door and windows. His great hall was even adorned with a piece of tapestry. All the dogs of his stable yards formed a pack of hounds when necessary; his grooms were his huntsmen; the village vicar was his Grand Almoner. They all called him My Lord, and they laughed at the stories he told.

My Lady the Baroness, who weighed about three hundred and

---

* Reprinted from *Voltaire: Candide, Zadig and Other Stories*, translated by Donald M. Frame. Copyright © 1961 by Donald M. Frame. Reprinted by permission of The New American Library of World Literature, Inc., New York. Frame's footnotes are retained, and some notes from his glossary are included, necessitating some renumbering of notes. [Ed.]

1 For some weeks after its publication Voltaire denied authorship of *Candide*, as he often did with works potentially dangerous to himself.

2 Divisions on a coat of arms indicating degrees of nobility. Sixty-four was considered the maximum.

fifty pounds, attracted very great consideration by that fact, and did the honors of the house with a dignity that made her even more respectable. Her daughter Cunégonde, aged seventeen, was rosy-complexioned, fresh, plump, appetizing. The Baron's son appeared in all respects worthy of his father. The tutor Pangloss[3] was the oracle of the house, and little Candide listened to his lessons with all the candor of his age and character.

Pangloss taught metaphysico-theologo-cosmolo-nigology.[4] He proved admirably that there is no effect without a cause and that, in this best of all possible worlds,[5] My Lord the Baron's castle was the finest of castles, and My Lady the best of all possible Baronesses.

"It is demonstrated," he said, "that things cannot be otherwise, for, everything being made for an end, everything is necessarily for the best end. Note that noses were made to wear spectacles, and so we have spectacles. Legs were visibly instituted to be breeched, and we have breeches. Stones were formed to be cut and to make into castles; so My Lord has a very handsome castle; the greatest baron in the province should be the best housed; and, pigs being made to be eaten, we eat pork all year round: consequently, those who have asserted that all is well have said a foolish thing; they should have said that all is for the best."

Candide listened attentively and believed innocently; for he thought Mademoiselle Cunégonde extremely beautiful, though he never made bold to tell her so. He concluded that after the happiness of being born Baron of Thunder-ten-tronckh, the second degree of happiness was to be Mademoiselle Cunégonde; the third, to see her every day; and the fourth, to listen to Doctor Pangloss, the greatest philosopher in the province and consequently in the whole world.

One day Cunégonde, walking near the castle in the little wood they called The Park, saw in the bushes Doctor Pangloss giving a lesson in experimental physics to her mother's chambermaid, a very pretty and very docile little brunette. Since Mademoiselle Cunégonde had much inclination for the sciences, she observed breathlessly the repeated experiments of which she was a witness; she clearly saw the Doctor's sufficient reason, the effects and the causes, and returned home all agitated, all pensive, all filled with the desire to be learned, thinking that she might well be the sufficient reason of young Candide, who might equally well be hers.

She met Candide on the way back to the castle, and blushed; Candide blushed too; she said good morning to him in a faltering voice; and Candide spoke to her without knowing what he was saying. The next day, after dinner, as everyone was leaving the table, Cuné-

---

3 From the Greek: "all tongue."

4 The "-nigo-" suggests the French *nigaud*, "booby."

5 The systematic optimism ridiculed throughout *Candide* is a caricature of that of Leibniz (1646–1716), popularized by Alexander Pope in his *Essay on Man* (1733-1734), and systematized by Christian Wolff (1679-1754).

gonde and Candide found themselves behind a screen; Cunégonde dropped her handkerchief, Candide picked it up, she innocently took his hand, the young man innocently kissed the young lady's hand with a very special vivacity, sensibility, and grace; their lips met, their eyes glowed, their knees trembled, their hands wandered. My Lord the Baron of Thunder-ten-tronckh passed near the screen and, seeing this cause and this effect, expelled Candide from the castle with great kicks in the behind; Cunégonde swooned; she was slapped in the face by My Lady the Baroness as soon as she had come to herself; and all was in consternation in the finest and most agreeable of all possible castles.

2 What Became of Candide among the Bulgarians[1]

Candide, expelled from the earthly paradise, walked for a long time without knowing where, weeping, raising his eyes to heaven, turning them often toward the finest of castles, which enclosed the most beautiful of future Baronesses; he lay down to sleep without supper in the midst of the fields between two furrows; the snow was falling in fat flakes. The next day Candide, frozen, dragged himself toward the neighboring town, which was named Valdberghoff-trarbk-dikdorff, with no money, dying of hunger and fatigue. He stopped sadly at the door of an inn. Two men dressed in blue noticed him.

"Comrade," said one, "there's a very well-built young man, and he's of the right height."

They advanced toward Candide and very civilly invited him to dinner.

"Gentlemen," said Candide with charming modesty, "you do me great honor, but I haven't the money to pay my bill."

"Ah, sir," said one of the men in blue, "persons of your figure and merit never pay for anything; aren't you five feet five?"

"Yes, gentlemen, that is my height," he said with a bow.

"Ah, sir, sit down to table; not only will we pay your expenses, but we will never allow a man like you to lack money; men are made only to help one another."

"You are right," said Candide. "That is what Monsieur Pangloss always told me, and I clearly see that all is for the best."

They urge him to accept a few crowns, he takes them and wants to make out a promissory note: they want none, they all sit down to table.

---

1 Voltaire chose this name to represent the Prussians of Frederick the Great because he had reason to think that Frederick was a pederast and because the French *bougre*, like the English "bugger," comes from *Bulgare* (Bulgarian). Note the treatment of the Baron's son in Chapter 4 and his adventures narrated in Chapters 15 and 28.

"Don't you love tenderly . . . ?"

"Oh yes," he replied, "I love Mademoiselle Cunégonde tenderly."

"No," said one of the gentlemen, "we are asking you whether you do not tenderly love the King of the Bulgarians."

"Not at all," he said, "for I have never seen him."

"What! He is the most charming of Kings, and you must drink his health."

"Oh! most gladly, gentlemen"; and he drinks.

"That is sufficient," they say to him, "you are now the prop, the support, the defender, the hero of the Bulgarians; your fortune is made, and your glory is assured."

They immediately put irons on his legs and they take him to the regiment. They make him turn right, turn left, raise the ramrod, return the ramrod, take aim, fire, march on the double, and they give him thirty strokes with a stick; the next day he drills a little less badly and he gets only twenty strokes; the day after they give him only ten, and he is regarded as a prodigy by his comrades.

Candide, completely stupefied, could not yet understand too well how he was a hero. He took it into his head one fine spring day to go for a stroll, walking straight ahead, believing that it was a privilege of the race of humans, as of the race of animals, to use their legs as they please.[2] He had not gone two leagues when up came four other heroes, six feet tall; they overtake him, they bind him, they put him in a dungeon. He was asked, juridically, which he liked better, to be beaten thirty-six times by the whole regiment, or to receive twelve lead bullets at once in his brain. In vain he told them that the will is free and that he wanted neither of these; he had to make a choice. By virtue of the gift of God that is called *liberty,* he decided to run the gantlet thirty-six times; he did it twice. The regiment was made up of two thousand men. That gave him four thousand strokes of the ramrod, which laid open his muscles and nerves from the nape of his neck to his rump. As they were about to proceed to the third run, Candide, at the end of his rope, asked them as a favor to be kind enough to smash in his head; he obtained this favor. They bandage his eyes; they make him kneel; at that moment the King of the Bulgarians passes, inquires about the victim's crime; and since this King was a man of great genius, he understood, from all he learned about Candide, that this was a young metaphysician very ignorant of the ways of this world, and he granted him his pardon with a clemency that will be praised in all newspapers and in all ages. A worthy surgeon cured Candide in three weeks with the emollients prescribed by Dioscorides. He already had a little bit of skin, and could walk, when the King of the Bulgarians gave battle to the King of the Abarians.[3]

---

[2] This whole chapter satirizes the drillmastership of Frederick the Great. The desertion is suggested by Voltaire's memory of a Frenchman named Courtilz, whose release from prison into a hospital Voltaire had procured from Frederick.

[3] This name, which designates a Scythian tribe, represents the French, who were involved in the Seven Years' War (1756–1763) opposite the Prussians.

3 How Candide Escaped from among the Bulgarians, and What Became of Him

Nothing could be so beautiful, so smart, so brilliant, so well drilled as the two armies. Trumpets, fifes, oboes, drums, cannons formed a harmony such as was never heard even in hell. First the cannons felled about six thousand men on each side; then the musketry removed from the best of worlds some nine or ten thousand scoundrels who infected its surface. The bayonet also was the sufficient reason for the death of some thousands of men. The whole might well amount to about thirty thousand souls. Candide, trembling like a philosopher, hid himself as best he could during this heroic butchery.

Finally, while both kings were having *Te Deums* sung, each in his own camp, he decided to go reason elsewhere about effects and causes. He passed over heaps of dead and dying and first reached a neighboring village; it was in ashes; it was an Abarian village which the Bulgarians had burned in accordance with the rules of international law. Here, old men riddled with wounds watched their wives die, with their throats cut, holding their children to their bleeding breasts; there, girls, disemboweled after satisfying the natural needs of a few heroes, were gasping their last sighs; others, half-burned, screamed to be given the *coup de grâce*. Brains were spattered over the ground beside severed arms and legs.

Candide fled full speed to another village; it belonged to some Bulgarians, and the Abarian heroes had treated it in the same way. Candide, still treading on quivering limbs or through ruins, arrived at last outside the theater of war, carrying a few small provisions in his knapsack, and never forgetting Mademoiselle Cunégonde. His provisions ran out when he was in Holland; but having heard that everyone in that country was rich, and that they were Christians, he had no doubt that he would be treated as well as he had been in the castle of My Lord the Baron before he had been expelled from it on account of the lovely eyes of Mademoiselle Cunégonde.

He asked alms of several grave personages, who all replied that if he continued that practice he would be shut up in a house of correction to teach him how to live.

He then addressed a man who had just talked about charity for one solid hour unaided in a large assembly. This orator, looking askance at him, said to him: "What brings you here? Are you here for the good cause?"

"There is no effect without a cause," replied Candide modestly, "everything is linked by necessity and arranged for the best. It was necessary for me to be expelled from the presence of Mademoiselle Cunégonde and to run the gantlet, and now to beg my bread until I can earn it; all this could not happen differently."

"My friend," said the orator to him, "do you believe that the Pope is antichrist?"

"I had never heard that before," replied Candide; "but whether he is or not, I have no bread."

"You do not deserve to eat any," said the other. "Hence, scoundrel; hence, wretch; never come near me again in your life."

The orator's wife, who had put her head out the window, seeing a man who doubted that the Pope was antichrist, poured out on his head a full ... O Heavens! to what excess is religious zeal carried in ladies!

A man who had not been baptized, a good Anabaptist named Jacques, saw the cruel and ignominious treatment accorded to one of his brethren, a two-footed featherless creature with a soul;[1] he took him home, cleaned him up, gave him some bread and some beer, made him a present of two florins, and even volunteered to teach him to work in his factories of Persian cloth that is made in Holland. Candide, wanting to fall prostrate at his feet, cried:

"Doctor Pangloss was certainly right to tell me that all is for the best in this world, for I am infinitely more touched by your extreme generosity than by the harshness of that gentleman in the black coat and of my lady his wife."

The next day on a walk he met a beggar all covered with sores, his eyes dull as death, the end of his nose eaten away, his mouth awry, his teeth black, talking out of his throat, tormented with a violent cough, and spitting out a tooth at each spasm.

---

[1] The phrase goes back to Plato's so-called *Definitions*.

4 How Candide Met His Old Philosophy Teacher, Doctor Pangloss, and What Happened

Candide, moved even more by compassion than by horror, gave this frightful beggar the two florins he had received from his honest Anabaptist Jacques. The phantom gazed fixedly at him, shed tears, and threw his arms around his neck. Candide recoiled in terror.

"Alas!" said the wretch to the other wretch, "don't you recognize your dear Pangloss any more?"

"What do I hear? You, my dear master! You in this horrible state! Why, what misfortune has happened to you? Why are you no longer in the finest of castles? What has become of Mademoiselle Cunégonde, the pearl of young ladies, the masterpiece of nature?"

"I am exhausted," said Pangloss.

Immediately Candide took him into the Anabaptist's stable, where he had him eat a little bread; and when Pangloss had recovered: "Well," he said, "Cunégonde?"

"She is dead," the other replied.

Candide swooned at these words; his friend restored him to his senses with a little bad vinegar that happened to be in the stable. Candide opened his eyes.

"Cunégonde is dead! Ah, best of worlds, where are you? But what illness did she die of? Could it have been for having seen me expelled with great kicks from the fine castle of My Lord, her father?"

"No," said Pangloss, "she was disemboweled by Bulgarian soldiers after being raped as much as anyone can be; they smashed in the head of My Lord the Baron, who tried to defend her; My Lady the Baroness was cut to pieces; my poor pupil was treated precisely like his sister; and as for the castle, not a stone is left standing upon another, not a barn, not a sheep, not a duck, not a tree; but we have been well avenged, for the Abarians did as much in a neighboring barony that belonged to a Bulgarian lord."

At this account Candide swooned again; but having come back to his senses and said all that was appropriate, he inquired about the cause and effect, the sufficient reason, which had put Pangloss in such a piteous state.

"Alas!" said Pangloss, "it is love; love, the consoler of the human race, the preserver of the universe, the soul of all emotional beings, tender love."

"Alas!" said Candide, "I have known this love, this sovereign of hearts, this soul of our soul; all it has ever brought me was one kiss and twenty kicks in the ass. How could this beautiful cause produce in you so abominable an effect?"

Pangloss answered in these terms:

"O my dear Candide! You knew Paquette, that pretty attendant upon our august Baroness; I tasted in her arms the delights of paradise, which produced these torments of hell by which you see me devoured; she was infected and she may have died of it. Paquette had received this present from a very learned Franciscan, who had gone back to the source; for he had got it from an old countess, who had received it from a cavalry captain, who owed it to a marquise, who had it from a page, who had received it from a Jesuit, who as a novice had got it in a direct line from one of the companions of Christopher Columbus. For my part I shall give it to no one, for I am dying."

"O Pangloss!" exclaimed Candide, "that is a strange genealogy! Wasn't the devil the root of it?"

"Not at all," replied the great man. "It was an indispensable thing in the best of worlds, a necessary ingredient; for if Columbus had not caught, in an island in America, this disease which poisons the source of generation, which often even prevents generation, and which is obviously opposed to the great purpose of nature, we would not have either chocolate or cochineal. It should also be noted that to this day this malady is peculiar to us in our continent, like religious controversy. The Turks, the Indians, the Persians, the Chinese, the Siamese, the Japanese are not yet acquainted with it; but there is sufficient reason for their making its acquaintance, in their turn, within a few centuries. Meanwhile it has made marvelous progress among us, and especially in those great armies composed of decent, well-brought-up mercenaries, which decide the destiny of states; one may confidently assert that when thirty thousand men fight a pitched battle against an equal number of troops, there are about twenty thousand on each side with the pox."

"That is admirable," said Candide, "but we must get you cured."

"How can I be?" said Pangloss. "I haven't a sou, my friend; and in the whole area of this globe you cannot be bled or given an enema without paying, or without someone paying for you."

This last speech made up Candide's mind; he went and threw himself at the feet of his charitable Anabaptist Jacques and painted him such a touching picture of the state to which his friend was reduced that the good man had no hesitation in taking in Doctor Pangloss; he had him cured at his own expense. In the cure Pangloss lost only one eye and one ear. He wrote a good hand and knew arithmetic perfectly. The Anabaptist Jacques made him his bookkeeper.

Two months later, having to go to Lisbon on business, he took his two philosophers on his ship with him. Pangloss explained to him how everything was for the very best. Jacques was not of this opinion.

"Surely," he said, "men must have corrupted nature a little, for they were not born wolves, and they have become wolves; God gave them neither twenty-four-pounder cannon nor bayonets, and they have made bayonets and cannon to destroy one another. I could put bankruptcies into account, and the justice which seizes the goods of the bankrupt to defraud their creditors of them."

"All that was indispensable," replied the one-eyed Doctor, "and private misfortunes make up the general good; so that the more private misfortunes there are, the more all is well."

While he was reasoning, the air darkened, the winds blew from the four corners of the world, and the ship was assaulted by the most horrible tempest in sight of the port of Lisbon.

5 *Tempest, Shipwreck, Earthquake,*
   and What Happened to Doctor Pangloss,
   Candide, and the Anabaptist Jacques

Half the passengers, weakened, nearly dying of those inconceivable tortures that the rolling of a ship imparts to the nerves and all the humors of a body tossed in opposite directions, had not even the strength to worry about the danger. The other half were uttering screams and prayers; the sails were torn, the masts shattered, the vessel split open. Those who could worked, no one co-operated, no one commanded. The Anabaptist was helping a little with the work; he was on the main deck; a frenzied sailor struck him a hard blow and stretched him on the planks, but got such a jolt from the blow he gave him that he fell out of the ship headfirst. He was caught on a piece of broken mast and remained dangling from it. The good Jacques runs to his aid, helps him to climb back up, and by this effort is flung headfirst into the sea in full view of the sailor, who lets him perish without even deigning to look at him. Candide approaches, sees his benefactor come up again for a moment and then be swallowed up forever. He wants to throw himself into the sea after him; the philosopher Pangloss stops him, proving to him that the Lisbon roads had been formed expressly for this Anabaptist to be drowned in. While he was proving this a priori, the ship splits open and everyone perishes with the exception of Pangloss, Candide, and that brute of a sailor who had drowned the virtuous Anabaptist; the scoundrel swam successfully ashore and Pangloss and Candide were carried there on a plank.

When they had recovered themselves a little, they walked toward Lisbon; they had a little money left, with which they hoped to be saved from hunger after escaping from the tempest.

Hardly have they set foot in the city, weeping over the death of their benefactor, when they feel the earth tremble under their feet; the sea rises boiling in the port and shatters the vessels that are at anchor.[1] Whirlwinds of flame and ashes cover the streets and public squares, the houses crumble, the roofs are tumbled down upon the foundations, and the foundations disintegrate; thirty thousand inhabitants of every age and of either sex are crushed beneath the ruins. Said the sailor, whistling and swearing: "There'll be something to pick up here." Said Pangloss: "What can be the sufficient reason for this phenomenon?" "It is the end of the world," exclaimed Candide.

The sailor runs headlong into the midst of the debris, braves death to find money, finds some, seizes it, gets drunk, and when he has slept it off buys the favors of the first girl of good will he meets upon the ruins of demolished houses and in the midst of the dying and the dead. Pangloss meanwhile was tugging at his sleeve: "My friend," he said, "this is not good, you are departing from universal reason, you are choosing your time badly."

" 'Sblood and zounds!" the other replied. "I am a sailor, and born in Batavia; I have stamped on the crucifix four times on four trips to Japan,[2] you certainly picked the right man, you and your universal reason!"

Candide had been wounded by some splinters of stone; he was stretched out in the street and covered with debris. He said to Pangloss: "Alas! get me a little wine and oil, I am dying."

---

[1] The Lisbon earthquake and fire (November 1, 1755), which killed over 30,000 people and reduced the city to ruins, led Voltaire to make strong attacks on philosophical optimism, especially in his *Poem on the Lisbon Disaster* (written in 1755) and in *Candide*.

[2] To discourage trade with the Christians, the Japanese required European merchants to stamp on the cross as a sign of rejection of Christianity.

"This earthquake is not a new thing," replied Pangloss. "The town of Lima suffered the same shocks in America last year; same causes, same effects; there is certainly a vein of sulfur underground from Lima to Lisbon."

"Nothing is more probable," said Candide, "but for the love of God, a little oil and wine."

"What do you mean, probable?" replied the philosopher. "I maintain that the matter is proved." Candide lost consciousness, and Pangloss brought him a little water from a neighboring fountain.

The next day, having found a few victuals as they slipped through the ruins, they restored their strength a bit. Then they worked like the rest to relieve the inhabitants who had escaped death. A few citizens whom they had helped gave them as good a dinner as could be provided in such a disaster. True, the meal was sad, the guests watered their bread with their tears; but Pangloss consoled them by assuring them that things could not be otherwise.

"For," he said, "all this is for the very best. For if there is a volcano in Lisbon, it could not be anywhere else. For it is impossible that things should not be where they are. For all is well."

A little dark man, a familiar of the Inquisition, who was beside him, spoke up politely and said: "Apparently the gentleman does not believe in original sin; for, if all is for the best, then there has been neither fall nor punishment."

"I very humbly beg Your Excellency's pardon," replied Pangloss still more politely, "for the fall of man and the curse necessarily entered into the best of possible worlds."

"Then the gentleman does not believe in free will?" said the familiar.

"Your Excellency will excuse me," said Pangloss; "free will can coexist with absolute necessity, for it was necessary that we should be free; for after all, predetermined will . . ."

Pangloss was in the middle of his sentence when the familiar gave a nod to his armed attendant, who was pouring him out some port, or Oporto, wine.

6 *How They Held a Fine Auto-da-Fé*
   to Prevent Earthquakes,
   and How Candide Was Flogged

After the earthquake, which had destroyed three-quarters of Lisbon, the country's wise men had found no more efficacious means of preventing total ruin than to give the people a fine auto-da-fé;[1] it was decided by the University of Coimbra that the spectacle of a few

---

[1] From the Portuguese, "act of the faith": the ceremony attendant to a judgment by the Inquisition; hence the burning of heretics as a result of such a judgment.

persons burned by a slow fire in great ceremony is an infallible secret for keeping the earth from quaking.

They had consequently seized a Biscayan convicted of having married his godchild's godmother, and two Portuguese who when eating a chicken had taken out the bacon;[2] after dinner they came and bound Doctor Pangloss and his disciple Candide, the one for having spoken, and the other for having listened with an air of approbation; both were taken separately into extremely cool apartments in which one was never bothered by the sun;[3] a week later they were each clad in a sanbenito,[4] and their heads were adorned with paper miters; Candide's miter and sanbenito were painted with flames upside down and with devils that had neither tails nor claws; but Pangloss's devils wore claws and tails, and his flames were right side up.

Thus dressed, they marched in procession and heard a very pathetic sermon followed by some beautiful music in a droning plain song. Candide was flogged in time to the singing, the Biscayan and the two men who wouldn't eat the bacon were burned, and Pangloss was hanged although this is not the custom. On the same day the earth quaked again with a fearful crash.

Candide, terrified, dumfounded, bewildered, bleeding and quivering all over, said to himself:

"If this is the best of all possible worlds, then what are the others? I could let it pass if I had only been flogged, that happened also with the Bulgarians; but, O my dear Pangloss, greatest of philosophers, was it necessary that I see you hanged without knowing why! O my dear Anabaptist, best of men, was it necessary that you be drowned in the port! O Mademoiselle Cunégonde, pearl of young ladies, was it necessary that your belly be slit open!"

He was going back, barely supporting himself, preached at, flogged, absolved and blessed, when an old woman accosted him and said: "My son, take courage, follow me."

---

2 Thus showing that they were Jews still secretly faithful to Judaism.
3 Prison cells.
4 A yellow robe worn by heretics condemned to the stake by the Inquisition.

7   *How an Old Woman Took Care of
Candide, and How He Recovered That
Which He Loved*

Candide did not take courage, but he followed the old woman into a hovel; she gave him a jar of ointment to rub on and left him food and drink; she showed him a fairly clean little bed; beside the bed there was a suit of clothes.

"Eat, drink, sleep," she said, "and may Our Lady of Atocha, My Lord Saint Anthony of Padua, and My Lord Saint James of Compostela take care of you. I shall come back tomorrow."

Candide, still astounded at all he had seen, at all he had suffered, and even more at the old woman's charity, tried to kiss her hand.
"It is not my hand you should kiss," said the old woman. "I
shall come back tomorrow. Rub yourself with ointment, eat, and
sleep."

Candide for all his misfortunes ate and slept. The next day the
old woman brings him some breakfast, examines his back, rubs it
herself with another ointment; later she brings him dinner; she returns toward evening and brings supper. The day after, she again
performed the same ceremonies.

"Who are you?" Candide kept asking her. "Who has inspired
you with such kindness? How can I possibly thank you?"

The good woman never made any answer; she returned toward
evening and brought no supper. "Come with me," she said, "and
don't say a word."

She takes him by the arm and walks with him into the country
for about a quarter of a mile; they arrive at an isolated house surrounded with gardens and canals. The old woman knocks on a little
door. It is opened; she takes Candide by a hidden staircase into a
gilded boudoir, leaves him on a brocaded sofa, closes the door, and
goes away. Candide thought he was dreaming and considered his whole
life as a sinister dream and the present moment as a sweet dream.

The old woman soon reappeared; she was supporting with difficulty a trembling woman of majestic stature, gleaming with precious
stones and covered with a veil. "Remove that veil," said the old
woman to Candide. The young man approaches, he lifts the veil with
a timid hand. What a moment! What a surprise! He thinks he sees
Mademoiselle Cunégonde, he did indeed see her, it was she herself.
His strength fails him, he cannot utter a word, he falls at her feet.
Cunégonde falls on the sofa. The old woman plies them copiously
with aromatic spirits; they regain their senses, they speak to each
other; at first it is only disconnected words, questions and answers at
cross purposes, sighs, tears, cries. The old woman recommends that
they make less noise, and leaves them by themselves.

"What! Is it you?" said Candide. "You are alive! I find you
again here in Portugal! Then you were not raped? Your belly was
not slit open, as the philosopher Pangloss had assured me?"

"Oh yes," said the fair Cunégonde, "but people do not always
die of those two accidents."

"But were your father and mother killed?"

" 'Tis only too true," said Cunégonde, weeping.

"And your brother?"

"My brother was killed too."

"And why are you in Portugal, and how did you learn I was
here, and by what strange adventure did you have me brought to
this house?"

"I will tell you all that," replied the lady; "but first you must tell me everything that has happened to you since the innocent kiss that you gave me and the kicks that you received."

Candide obeyed her with profound respect; and though he was dumfounded, though his voice was weak and trembling, though his spine still hurt a little, he told her in the most naïve manner all that he had undergone since the moment of their separation. Cunégonde kept raising her eyes to heaven; she shed tears at the death of the good Anabaptist and of Pangloss; after which she spoke in these terms to Candide, who did not miss a word and devoured her with his eyes.

8 Cunégonde's Story

"I was in bed and fast asleep when it pleased Heaven to send the Bulgarians to our fine castle of Thunder-ten-tronckh; they slaughtered my father and brother and cut my mother into pieces. A big Bulgarian six feet tall, seeing that I had lost consciousness at the sight of this, set about raping me; this brought me to, I regained my senses, I screamed, I struggled, I bit, I scratched, I tried to tear that big Bulgarian's eyes out, not knowing that all that was happening in my father's castle was a matter of custom; the brute stabbed me with a knife in the left side and I still bear the mark." "Alas! I certainly hope I shall see it," said the naïve Candide. "You shall see it," said Cunégonde, "but let me go on." "Go on," said Candide.

She took up the thread of her story thus:

"A Bulgarian captain came in, he saw me all bleeding, and the soldier did not disturb himself. The captain grew angry at the lack of respect this brute showed him, and killed him upon my body. Then he had my wounds dressed and took me to his quarters as a prisoner of war. I laundered the few shirts he had, I did his cooking; he found me very pretty, I must admit; and I shall not deny that he was very well built and had soft white skin; for the rest little wit, little philosophy; it was easy to see that he had not been brought up by Doctor Pangloss. After three months, having lost all his money as well as his taste for me, he sold me to a Jew named Don Issachar, who traded in Holland and Portugal and had a passionate love of women. This Jew grew much attached to my person but could not triumph over it; I resisted him better than I did the Bulgarian soldier. A person of honor may have been raped once, but her virtue gains strength from it. The Jew, to tame me, brought me to this country house that you see. I had thought until then that there was nothing on earth so splendid as the castle of Thunder-ten-tronckh. I was undeceived.

"The Grand Inquisitor noticed me one day at Mass; he eyed me a great deal, and sent word to me that he had secret affairs to speak to me about. I was taken to his palace, I informed him of my birth; he pointed out to me how much it was beneath my rank to belong to an Israelite. On his behalf it was proposed to Don Issachar to yield me

to His Lordship. Don Issachar, who is the court banker and a man
of influence, would do no such thing. The Inquisitor threatened him
with an auto-da-fé. Finally my Jew, intimidated, made a bargain by
which the house and I would belong to them both in common, the
Jew would have Monday, Wednesday, and the Sabbath day for him,
and the Inquisitor would have the other days of the week. This agreement has lasted for six months. It has not been without quarrels, for it
has often been undecided whether the night between Saturday and
Sunday belongs to the old law or the new. For my part, thus far I have
resisted them both, and I think that is the reason why I have still
been loved.

"Finally, to turn aside the scourge of earthquakes and to in-
timidate Don Issachar, My Lord the Inquisitor was pleased to cele-
brate an auto-da-fé. He did me the honor of inviting me. I had a very
good seat; they served the ladies with refreshments between the Mass
and the execution. Truly I was seized with horror on seeing them
burn those two Jews and that worthy Biscayan who had married the
godmother of his godchild; but what was my surprise, my fright, my
distress, when I saw, in a sanbenito and under a miter, a face resembling that of Pangloss! I rubbed my eyes, I looked attentively, I
saw him hanged; I fell into a faint; hardly was I regaining my senses
when I saw you stripped stark naked; that was the height of horror,
consternation, grief, despair. I will tell you truthfully that your skin
is even whiter and more perfectly rosy than that of my Bulgarian
captain. This sight redoubled all the feelings that crushed me, that
devoured me. I cried out, I tried to say 'Stop, barbarians!' but my
voice failed me, and my cries would have been useless. When you had
been well flogged, I said: 'How can it be that the charming Candide
and the wise Pangloss are in Lisbon, one to receive a hundred lashes,
and the other to be hanged by order of My Lord the Inquisitor, whose
dearly beloved I am? Then Pangloss deceived me most cruelly when
he told me that all is for the very best.'

"Agitated, bewildered, now beside myself and now ready to die
of faintness, I had my mind filled with the massacre of my father,
mother, and brother, the insolence of my horrid Bulgarian soldier, the
stab he gave me, my slavery, my work as a cook, my Bulgarian captain, my horrid Don Issachar, my abominable Inquisitor, the hanging
of Doctor Pangloss, that long *miserere* in droning plain song during
which they were whipping you, and above all the kiss I gave you behind a screen the day I saw you for the last time. I praised God, who
was bringing you back to me through so many trials. I charged my
old woman to take care of you and to bring you here as soon as she
could. She has carried out my commission very well; I have enjoyed
the inexpressible pleasure of seeing you again, hearing you, speaking
to you. You must be ravenously hungry; my appetite is good; let's
begin with supper."

So they both sit down to table, and after supper resume their places on that handsome sofa that has been already mentioned; they were there when Señor Don Issachar, one of the masters of the house, arrived. It was the Sabbath day. He was coming to enjoy his rights and expound his tender love.

9 What Happened to Cunégonde, Candide, the Grand Inquisitor, and a Jew

This Issachar was the most choleric Hebrew ever seen in Israel since the Babylonian captivity.

"What!" he said. "Bitch of a Galilean, My Lord the Inquisitor isn't enough? This scoundrel must share with me too?"

So saying, he draws a long dagger which he always carried and, not thinking that his adversary was armed, throws himself upon Candide; but our good Westphalian had received a fine sword from the old woman together with the suit. He draws his sword, although he had a very gentle character, and stretches out the Israelite stone dead on the floor at the feet of the fair Cunégonde.

"Holy Virgin!" she cried, "what is to become of us? A man killed in my house! If the law comes, we are lost."

"If Pangloss had not been hanged," said Candide, "he would give us good advice in this extremity, for he was a great philosopher. Failing him, let us consult the old woman."

She was very prudent, and was beginning to state her advice, when another little door opened. It was one hour after midnight, it was the beginning of Sunday. That day belonged to My Lord the Inquisitor. He came in and saw the flogged Candide sword in hand, a dead man stretched on the floor, Cunégonde terrified, and the old woman giving advice.

Here is what went on in that moment in Candide's soul, and how he reasoned: "If this holy man calls for help, he will have me burned without fail; he may do as much to Cunégonde; he has had me pitilessly whipped; he is my rival; I have started killing, there is no hesitating."

This reasoning was clear-cut and swift, and without giving the Inquisitor the time to recover from his surprise, he pierces him through and through and tosses him beside the Jew.

"Now here's another one," said Cunégonde; "there is no more chance of pardon; we are excommunicated, our last hour is come. How could you, who were born so mild, manage to kill one Jew and one Inquisitor in two minutes?"

"My fair lady," replied Candide, "when a man is in love, jealous, and whipped by the Inquisition, he is out of his mind."

The old woman then spoke up and said: "There are three Andalusian horses in the stable with their saddles and bridles; let the brave Candide prepare them; My Lady has moidores and diamonds; let us mount quickly, although I can ride on only one buttock, and let us go to Cádiz; the weather could not be finer, and it is a great pleasure to travel in the cool of the night."

Immediately Candide saddles the three horses. Cunégonde, the old woman, and he do thirty miles at one stretch. While they were riding away, the Holy Hermandad[1] arrives in the house; they bury His Lordship in a beautiful church and they toss Don Issachar on the dump.

Candide, Cunégonde, and the old woman were already in the little town of Avacena in the midst of the mountains of the Sierra Morena; and they were talking as follows in an inn.

---

[1] The Holy Brotherhood, an association formed in Spain with a police force to track down criminals.

10   In What Distress Candide, Cunégonde, and the Old Woman Arrive at Cádiz; and About Their Embarkation

"Now who can have stolen my pistoles and my diamonds?" said Cunégonde, weeping. "What shall we live on? What shall we do? Where shall we find Inquisitors and Jews to give me others?"

"Alas!" said the old woman. "I strongly suspect a reverend Franciscan father who slept in the same inn with us yesterday at Badajoz; God keep me from forming a rash judgment, but he came into our room twice and he left long before us."

"Alas!" said Candide, "the good Pangloss had often proved to me that the goods of the earth are common to all men, that each has an equal right to them. That Franciscan, according to these principles, should certainly have left us enough to complete our trip. Have you nothing at all left then, my fair Cunégonde?"

"Not a maravedi," said she. "What should we do?" said Candide. "Let's sell one of the horses," said the old woman. "I'll ride on the crupper behind my lady, although I can ride on only one buttock, and we will get to Cádiz."

In the same hostelry there was a Benedictine prior; he bought the horse at a bargain. Candide, Cunégonde, and the old woman passed through Lucena, Chillas, Lebrixa, and at last reached Cádiz. There a fleet was being equipped and troops assembled to bring to terms the reverend Jesuit Fathers in Paraguay, who were accused of causing one of their tribes, near the town of San Sacramento, to revolt against the kings of Spain and Portugal.[1] Candide, having served with the Bulgarians, performed the Bulgarian drill before the general of the little army with so much grace, celerity, skill, pride, and agility,

---

[1] This revolt occurred in 1756.

that they gave him an infantry company to command. Here he is a captain; he embarks with Mademoiselle Cunégonde, the old woman, two valets, and the two Andalusian horses that had belonged to His Lordship the Grand Inquisitor of Portugal.

During the whole crossing they reasoned a great deal about the philosophy of poor Pangloss.

"We are going to another universe," said Candide; "no doubt it is in that one that all is well. For it must be admitted that one might groan a little over what happens in the physical and the moral domain in ours."

"I love you with all my heart," said Cunégonde, "but my soul is still frightened by what I have seen, what I have undergone."

"All will be well," replied Candide; "the sea of this new world is already better than the seas of our Europe; it is calmer, the winds are more constant. It is certainly the new world that is the best of possible universes."

"God grant it," said Cunégonde; "but I have been so horribly unhappy in mine that my heart is almost closed to hope."

"You complain," the old woman said to them. "Alas! You have not undergone misfortunes such as mine."

Cunégonde almost burst out laughing, and thought this good woman very comical to claim to be more unfortunate than herself.

"Alas!" she said to her, "my dear woman, unless you have been raped by two Bulgarians, been stabbed twice in the belly, had two of your castles demolished and two mothers and two fathers slaughtered before your eyes, and seen two of your beloveds flogged in an auto-da-fé, I don't see that you can outdo me; plus the fact that I was born a Baroness with seventy-two quarterings, and now I have been a cook."

"My Lady," replied the old woman, "you do not know my birth, and if I showed you my bottom you would not speak as you do and you would suspend your judgment."

This speech aroused extreme curiosity in the minds of Cunégonde and Candide. The old woman spoke to them in these terms.

11 *The Old Woman's Story*

"My eyes were not always bloodshot and red-rimmed; my nose did not always touch my chin, and I was not always a servant. I am the daughter of Pope Urban X and the Princess of Palestrina.[1] Until the age of fourteen I was brought up in a palace to which all the castles of your German barons would not have served as stables, and one of my dresses was worth more than all the magnificence of West-

---

[1] Author's posthumous note: "Observe the author's extreme discretion. There has been up to now no Pope named Urban X. The author fears to assign a bastard daughter to a known Pope. What circumspection! What delicacy of conscience!"

phalia. I grew in beauty, graces, and talents, in the midst of pleasures, respect, and hopes. Already I inspired love, my bosom was forming; and what a bosom! White, firm, sculptured like that of the Venus de Medici. And what eyes! What eyelids! What black eyebrows! What flames shone in my two irises and dimmed the glistening of the stars, as the neighborhood poets used to tell me. The women who dressed and undressed me fell into ecstasies when they looked at me in front and behind, and all the men would have liked to be in their place.

"I was betrothed to a sovereign prince of Massa-Carrara. What a prince! As handsome as I, formed of sweetness and charms, agleam with wit and afire with love. I loved him as one loves for the first time, with idolatrous frenzy. The nuptials were prepared. The pomp, the magnificence were unheard of; there were continual festivities, tournaments, comic operas, and all Italy composed for me sonnets not one of which was passable.

"The moment of my happiness was at hand when an old marquise who had been my prince's mistress invited him to have some chocolate at her house. He died in less than two hours in frightful convulsions. But that is only a trifle. My mother, in despair, yet much less afflicted than I, decided to tear herself away for a time from such a fateful place. She had a very beautiful estate near Gaeta. We embarked on a local galley, gilded like the altar of St. Peter's in Rome. Suddenly a pirate from Salé swoops down on us and boards us. Our soldiers defended themselves like soldiers of the Pope; they all fell on their knees, throwing away their arms, and begging the pirates for absolution *in articulo mortis*.[2]

"Immediately they stripped them naked as monkeys, and my mother too, our ladies of honor too, and me too. The diligence with which those gentlemen undress people is a wonderful thing. But what surprised me more was that they put their fingers in a place in all of us where we women ordinarily admit only the nozzle of a syringe. This ceremony seemed quite strange to me; that is how one judges of everything when one has never been out of one's country. I soon learned that this was to see whether we had not hidden some diamonds there; it is a custom established from time immemorial among the civilized nations that roam the seas. I learned that My Lords the religious Knights of Malta never fail to do this when they capture Turkish men and women; it is a rule of international law that has never been broken.

"I shall not tell you how hard it is for a young princess to be taken to Morocco as a slave with her mother. You can imagine well enough all that we had to suffer in the pirate ship. My mother was still very beautiful; our ladies of honor, our mere chambermaids had more charms than can be found in all Africa. As for me, I was ravishing, I was beauty and grace itself, and I was a virgin. I was not so for

---

2 At the point of death.

long: that flower that had been reserved for the handsome Prince of Massa-Carrara was ravished from me by the pirate captain. He was an abominable Negro who yet thought he was doing me much honor. Indeed My Lady the Princess of Palestrina and I had to be very strong to endure all we underwent until we arrived in Morocco. But let's get on; these are things so common that they are not worth speaking of.

"Morocco was swimming in blood when we arrived. Fifty sons of the Emperor Muley Ismael each had a faction; which produced in effect fifty civil wars, of blacks against blacks, blacks against tans, tans against tans, mulattoes against mulattoes. It was a continual carnage over the whole extent of the empire.

"Hardly had we landed when some blacks, of a faction hostile to that of my pirate, came up to take his booty from him. After the diamonds and the gold, we were the most precious thing he had. I was witness to a combat such as you never see in your European climates. The blood of the northern peoples is not ardent enough. They are not mad about women to the point that is common in Africa. It seems as though your Europeans have milk in their veins; it is vitriol, it is fire that flows in those of the inhabitants of Mount Atlas and the neighboring countries. They fought with the fury of the lions, tigers, and snakes of the country to see who should have us. One Moor seized my mother by the right arm, my captain's lieutenant held her back by the left arm; a Moorish soldier took her by one leg, one of our pirates held her by the other. In a moment nearly all our girls found themselves pulled in this way by four soldiers. My captain kept me hidden behind him. He had his scimitar in hand, and was killing everything that opposed his rage. Finally I saw all our Italian women and my mother torn, cut, massacred by the monsters who were fighting over them. My fellow captives, those who had captured them, soldiers, sailors, blacks, tans, whites, mulattoes, and finally my captain—all were killed, and I remained dying on a heap of dead. Similar scenes were taking place, as everyone knows, over an area of more than three hundred square leagues, without anyone failing to say the five prayers a day ordained by Mohammed.

"I extricated myself with great difficulty from the press of so many heaped-up bleeding corpses, and I dragged myself beneath a big orange tree at the edge of a nearby stream; there I fell down from fright, weariness, horror, despair, and hunger. Soon afterward my exhausted senses gave themselves up to a sleep that was more like a swoon than a rest. I was in this state of weakness and insensibility, between life and death, when I felt something pressing on me and moving on my body. I opened my eyes and saw a white man of good appearance who was sighing and muttering between his teeth: 'O che sciagura d'essere senza coglioni!' "[3]

---

[3] "Oh, what an affliction to be without testicles!"

12   Continuation of the Old Woman's Misfortunes

"Astounded and delighted to hear the language of my home-land, and no less surprised at the words this man was uttering, I re-plied that there were worse misfortunes than the one he was com-plaining of. I informed him in a few words of the horrors I had suffered, and I fell back into a faint. He took me into a neighboring house, had me put to bed and given food, served me, consoled me, flattered me, told me he had never seen anything as beautiful as I and that he had never so much regretted what no one could restore to him.

" 'I was born in Naples,' he told me; 'there they caponize two or three thousand boys every year; some die of it, others acquire a voice more beautiful than a woman's, others go and govern states. This operation was performed on me with great success, and I was a musician in the chapel of My Lady the Princess of Palestrina.'

" 'Of my mother!' I cried out.

" 'Of your mother!' he exclaimed, weeping. 'What! Can you be that young princess that I brought up until the age of six, and who already then promised to be as beautiful as you are?'

" 'I am indeed; my mother is four hundred yards from here, cut into quarters under a heap of dead.'

"I told him everything that had happened to me; he too told me his adventures, and informed me that he had been sent by a Christian power to the King of Morocco to conclude a treaty with that monarch by which he would be furnished with gunpowder, cannon, and ships to help him to exterminate the commerce of the other Christians. 'My mission is performed,' this honest eunuch said; 'I am going to embark at Ceuta and I will take you back to Italy. *Ma che sciagura d'essere senza coglioni!*'

"I thanked him with tears of emotion, and instead of taking me to Italy he conducted me to Algiers and sold me to the Dey of that province. Hardly was I sold when that plague which has spread all over Africa, Asia, and Europe broke out furiously in Algiers. You have seen earthquakes; but, My Lady, have you ever had the plague?"

"Never," replied the Baroness.

"If you had had it," the old woman went on, "you would admit that it is far worse than an earthquake. It is very common in Africa; I was struck with it. Imagine what a situation for the daughter of a Pope, aged fifteen, who in three months' time had undergone poverty and slavery, had been raped almost every day, had seen her mother cut into quarters, had endured hunger and war, and was now dying of the plague in Algiers. However, I did not die of it; but my eunuch and the Dey and almost all the seraglio of Algiers perished.

"When the first ravages of this frightful plague were over, the Dey's slaves were sold. A merchant bought me and took me to Tunis. He sold me to another merchant, who resold me at Tripoli; from Tripoli I was resold to Alexandria, from Alexandria resold to Smyrna, from Smyrna to Constantinople. I finally belonged to an Aga of the Janizaries,[1] who was soon ordered to go and defend Azov against the Russians who were besieging it.

"The Aga, who was a very gallant man, took his whole seraglio with him and lodged us in a little fort on the Maeotian Marsh, guarded by two black eunuchs and twenty soldiers. They killed a prodigious number of Russians, but these repaid us with interest. Azov was put to fire and sword, and there was no pardon for sex nor for age; nothing remained but our little fort; the enemy tried to take us by famine. The twenty Janizaries had sworn never to surrender. The extremities of hunger to which they were reduced forced them to eat our two eunuchs, for fear of violating their oath. A few days later they resolved to eat the women.

"We had with us a very pious and very compassionate imam, who preached them a fine sermon by which he persuaded them not to kill us completely. 'Just cut off one buttock from each of these ladies,' he said, 'you will make very good cheer; if you have to come back, you will have as much again in a few days; heaven will be pleased with you for so charitable an action, and you will be rescued.'

"He had great eloquence; he persuaded them. They performed this horrible operation on us. The imam applied to us the same balm that they put on children who have just been circumcised. We were all at the point of death.

"Scarcely had the Janizaries eaten the meal we had furnished them when the Russians arrived in flat-bottomed boats; not one Janizary escaped. The Russians paid no attention to the state we were in. There are French surgeons everywhere; one of them, who was very skillful, took care of us; he cured us; and I shall remember all my life that when my wounds were fully closed, he made propositions to me. For the rest, he told us all to console ourselves; he assured us that the same sort of thing had happened in many sieges and that it was a law of war.

"As soon as my companions could walk, they were sent to Moscow. I fell to the lot of a Boyar,[2] who made me his gardener and gave me twenty lashes a day. But when this lord was broken on the wheel two years later with some thirty other Boyars for some petty fuss at court, I profited by this adventure; I fled; I crossed the whole of Russia; I was long a servant in an inn at Riga, then at Rostock, at Wismar, at Leipzig, Cassel, Utrecht, Leyden, the Hague, Rotterdam; I have grown old in misery and opprobrium, having only half a

---
1 A high officer of the guards of the Turkish Sultan.
2 Russian nobleman.

backside, always remembering that I was the daughter of a Pope; a hundred times I wanted to kill myself, but I still loved life. This ridiculous foible is perhaps one of our most disastrous inclinations. For is there anything more stupid than to want to bear continually a burden that we always want to throw to the ground? To regard our being with horror, and to cling to our being? In fine, to caress the serpent that devours us until it has eaten up our heart?

"I have seen, in the countries that fate has driven me through and in the inns where I have served, a prodigious number of persons who loathed their existence; but I have seen only twelve who voluntarily put an end to their misery: three Negroes, four Englishmen, four Genevans, and a German professor named Robeck.[3] I ended up by being a servant to the Jew Don Issachar; he put me in your service, my fair young lady; I have attached myself to your destiny, and I have been more occupied with your adventures than with mine. I would never even have spoken to you of my misfortunes if you had not piqued me a little and if it were not customary on shipboard to tell stories to conquer boredom. In short, My Lady, I have experience, I know the world; have some fun, get each passenger to tell you his story; and if there is a single one who has not often cursed his life, who has not often said to himself that he was the unhappiest of men, throw me into the sea headfirst."

---

[3] Author of theses on the folly of loving life, who drowned himself in 1739 at the age of sixty-seven.

13   How Candide Was Obliged to Part from the Fair Cunégonde and the Old Woman

The fair Cunégonde, having heard the old woman's story, showed her all the courtesy due to a person of her rank and merit. She accepted the proposition and got all the passengers one after the other to tell her their adventures; Candide and she admitted that the old woman was right.

"It is a great pity," said Candide, "that the wise Pangloss was hanged contrary to custom in an auto-da-fé; he would tell us wonderful things about the physical evil and the moral evil that cover earth and sea, and I would feel strong enough to dare to offer him, respectfully, a few objections."

As each one was telling his story the vessel moved on. They landed in Buenos Aires. Cunégonde, Captain Candide, and the old woman called on the governor, Don Fernando d'Ibaraa y Figueora y Mascarenes y Lampourdos y Souza. This lord had the pride befitting a man who bore so many names. He spoke to men with the noblest disdain, bearing his nose so high, raising his voice so pitilessly, assuming so imposing a tone, affecting so lofty a bearing, that all who addressed him were tempted to give him a beating. He loved women with a frenzy. Cunégonde seemed to him the most beautiful thing he had ever seen. The first thing he did was ask if she were not the Captain's wife. The air with which he asked this question alarmed Candide; he did not dare say she was his wife because in fact she was not; he did not dare say she was his sister, because she was not that either; and although this diplomatic lie was once very fashionable among the ancients[1] and might be useful to the moderns, his soul was too pure to be disloyal to the truth. "Mademoiselle Cunégonde," he said, "is to do me the honor of marrying me, and we beseech Your Excellency to deign to perform our wedding ceremony."

Don Fernando d'Ibaraa y Figueora y Mascarenes y Lampourdos y Souza, twirling his mustache, smiled bitterly and ordered Captain Candide to go pass his company in review. Candide obeyed; the governor remained with Mademoiselle Cunégonde. He declared his passion to her, protested that the next day he would marry her publicly in church, or otherwise, as it might please her charms. Cunégonde asked him for a quarter of an hour to collect herself, to consult the old woman, and to make up her mind.

The old woman said to Cunégonde:

"My Lady, you have seventy-two quarterings and not a penny; it depends on you alone to be the wife of the greatest lord in South America, who has a very handsome mustache; is it for you to pride yourself on an invincible fidelity? You have been raped by the Bulgarians; a Jew and an Inquisitor have enjoyed your good graces. Misfortunes confer rights. I admit that if I were in your place, I would have no scruple over marrying My Lord the Governor and making the fortune of Captain Candide."

While the old woman was speaking with all the prudence that age and experience give, a little vessel was seen to enter the port; it brought an alcaide and some alguazils,[2] and here is what had happened.

The old woman had guessed correctly that it was a long-sleeved Franciscan who stole Cunégonde's money and jewels in the town of Badajoz when she was fleeing in haste with Candide. This monk tried to sell some of the precious stones to a jeweler. The merchant recognized them as belonging to the Grand Inquisitor. The Franciscan, before being hanged, admitted that he had stolen them; he indicated the persons and the route they were taking. The flight of Cunégonde and Candide was already known. They were followed to Cádiz; with no loss of time a ship was sent in pursuit of them. The ship was already in the port of Buenos Aires. The rumor spread that an alcaide

---

[1] A reference to Abraham and Sarah (Genesis 12:12–13 and again 20:2–3) and to Isaac and Rebekah (Genesis 26:7–9).

[2] A municipal officer and some police officers.

was about to land and that they were pursuing the murderers of His Lordship the Grand Inquisitor. The prudent old woman saw in an instant all that was to be done.

"You cannot flee," she said to Cunégonde, "and you have nothing to fear; it was not you that killed His Lordship; besides, the governor, who loves you, will not allow you to be maltreated; stay."

She immediately ran to Candide. "Flee," she said, "or you're going to be burned within an hour." There was not a moment to lose; but how could he part with Cunégonde, and where was he to take refuge?

14   How Candide and Cacambo Were Received by the Jesuits in Paraguay

Candide had brought from Cádiz a valet of a type often found on the coasts of Spain and in the colonies. He was one-quarter Spanish, born of a half-breed in Tucuman, he had been a choirboy, sacristan, sailor, monk, merchant's representative, soldier, lackey. His name was Cacambo, and he loved his master very much, because his master was a very good man. He saddled the two Andalusian horses as fast as possible.

"Come, master, let us take the old woman's advice, leave, and run for it without looking behind us."

Candide shed tears. "O my dear Cunégonde! Must I abandon you just when My Lord the Governor is going to perform our marriage! Cunégonde, brought here from so far, what will become of you?"

"She will get along as best she can," said Cacambo; "women are never at a loss; God looks after them; let's run for it."

"Where are you taking me? Where are we going? What shall we do without Cunégonde?" said Candide.

"By St. James of Compostela," said Cacambo, "you were going to make war on the Jesuits; let's make war for them; I know the roads well enough, I will take you to their kingdom, they will be delighted to have a captain who can drill Bulgarian style, you will make a prodigious fortune; when you don't get your due in one world you find it in another. It is a very great pleasure to see and do new things."

"Then you have already been in Paraguay?" said Candide.

"Oh yes indeed," said Cacambo, "I was a servant in the College of the Assumption, and I know the government of *Los Padres*[1] as well as I know the streets of Cádiz. It is an admirable thing, this government. The kingdom is already more than three hundred leagues in diameter; it is divided into thirty provinces; *Los Padres* have everything and the people nothing; it is the masterpiece of reason and justice. For my part, I know nothing so divine as *Los Padres*, who here

---

1 "The Fathers," i.e., the Jesuits.

make war on the King of Spain and the King of Portugal, and who in Europe confess those Kings; who here kill Spaniards, and in Madrid send them to heaven; this enchants me; let's get on; you are going to be the happiest of men. What pleasure *Los Padres* will have when they learn that a captain is coming to them who knows the Bulgarian drill!"

As soon as they had reached the first barrier, Cacambo told the outpost that a captain asked to speak to My Lord the Commandant. They went to notify the main guard. A Paraguayan officer ran to the feet of the Commandant to impart the news to him. First Candide and Cacambo were disarmed; their two Andalusian horses were seized. The two strangers were brought in between two ranks of soldiers; the Commandant was at the end, three-cornered hat on head, gown tucked up, sword at side, and a half-pike in hand. He made a sign; and immediately twenty-four soldiers surround the two newcomers. A sergeant tells them that they must wait, that the Commandant cannot speak to them, that the Reverend Provincial Father does not permit any Spaniard to open his mouth except in his presence or to remain more than three hours in the country.

"And where is the Reverend Provincial Father?" said Cacambo.

"He is at the parade after having said Mass," replied the sergeant, "and you will not be able to kiss his spurs until three hours from now."

"But," said Cacambo, "the captain, who is dying of hunger as I am, is not a Spaniard, he is a German; mightn't we have breakfast while waiting for His Reverence?"

The sergeant immediately went and reported this statement to the Commandant.

"Praise God!" said this lord. "Since he is a German I can speak to him; let him be brought to my arbor."

Candide was taken immediately into a leafy bower adorned with a very pretty colonnade in green and gold marble and with trellises which enclosed parrots, two kinds of humming birds, guinea fowl, and all the rarest of birds. An excellent breakfast stood prepared in vessels of gold; and while the Paraguayans ate corn out of wooden bowls in the open fields in the blaze of the sun, the Reverend Father Commandant entered the arbor.

He was a very handsome young man, full-faced, rather white-skinned, high-colored, with arched eyebrows, keen eyes, red ears, vermilion lips, his manner proud, but with a pride that was neither that of a Spaniard nor that of a Jesuit. Candide and Cacambo were given back their arms, which had been taken from them, as well as their two Andalusian horses; Cacambo fed them oats near the arbor and kept his eye constantly on them for fear of a surprise.

Candide first kissed the hem of the Commandant's robe, then they sat down to table.

"So you are a German?" the Jesuit said to him in that language.

"Yes, Reverend Father," said Candide.

Each one, as he pronounced these words, looked at the other with extreme surprise and an emotion which they could not master.

"And what part of Germany are you from?" said the Jesuit.

"From the filthy province of Westphalia," said Candide; "I was born in the castle of Thunder-ten-tronckh."

"Heavens! Is it possible!" cried the Commandant.

"What a miracle!" cried Candide.

"Can it be you?" said the Commandant.

"That is not possible," said Candide. They both fall over backwards, they embrace, they shed torrents of tears.

"What! Can that be you, Reverend Father? You, the brother of the fair Cunégonde! You, who were killed by the Bulgarians! You, the son of My Lord the Baron! You a Jesuit in Paraguay! I must admit that this world is a strange thing. O Pangloss! Pangloss! How happy you would be if you had not been hanged!"

The Commandant sent away the Negro slaves and the Paraguayans who were serving drink in rock-crystal goblets. He thanked God and St. Ignatius a thousand times; he clasped Candide in his arms; their faces were bathed in tears.

"You would be even more astounded, more touched, more beside yourself," said Candide, "if I told you that Mademoiselle Cunégonde your sister, whom you thought disemboweled, is in full health."

"Where?"

"In your neighborhood, with My Lord the Governor of Buenos Aires; and I was coming to make war on you."

Each word they uttered in this long conversation piled prodigy upon prodigy. Their whole souls flew from their tongues, listened in their ears, sparkled in their eyes. Since they were Germans, they stayed long at table, waiting for the Reverend Father Provincial; and the Commandant spoke thus to his dear Candide.

15   How Candide Killed the Brother
of His Dear Cunégonde

"All my life I shall have present in my memory the horrible day when I saw my father and mother killed and my sister raped. When the Bulgarians were withdrawn, that adorable sister was not found, and my mother, my father, and I, two serving girls and three little boys who had all been slaughtered were put into a cart to be taken and buried in a Jesuit chapel two leagues from the castle of my forefathers. A Jesuit threw holy water on us; it was horribly salt; a few drops got into my eyes; the father noticed a tiny movement in my eyelid; he put his hand on my heart and felt it beating; I was rescued, and after three weeks it was as if nothing had happened. You know, my dear Candide, that I was very pretty, I became even more so; so the Reverend Father Kroust, superior of the house, conceived the most tender friendship for me; he gave me the dress of a novice; some time later I was sent to Rome. The Father General needed some young German Jesuit recruits. The sovereigns of Paraguay receive as few Spanish Jesuits as they can; they prefer foreigners, since they feel more their masters. I was judged fit by the Reverend Father General to go and labor in this vineyard. We set out, a Pole, a Tyrolese, and I. On arriving, I was honored with a subdeaconate and a lieutenancy; today I am a colonel and priest. We shall give the King of Spain's troops a vigorous reception; I warrant you they will be excommunicated and beaten. Providence sends you here to second us. But is it really true that my dear sister Cunégonde is in the neighborhood with the Governor of Buenos Aires?"

Candide assured him on his oath that nothing could be truer. Their tears began to flow again.

The Baron seemed unable to tire of embracing Candide; he kept calling him his brother, his savior.

"Ah!" he said, "my dear Candide, perhaps we can enter the city together as conquerors and regain my sister Cunégonde."

"That is all I wish for," said Candide; "for I was counting on marrying her, and I still hope to."

"You, insolent wretch!" replied the Baron. "You would have the impudence to marry my sister who has seventy-two quarterings! I am amazed at your effrontery in daring to speak to me of so rash a plan!"

Candide, petrified at such a speech, replied: "Reverend Father, all the quarterings in the world have nothing to do with it; I have saved your sister from the arms of a Jew and an Inquisitor; she has obligations enough toward me, she wants to marry me; Doctor Pangloss always told me that men are equal, and certainly I shall marry her."

"We'll see about that, you scoundrel!" said the Jesuit Baron of Thunder-ten-tronckh, and at the same time he struck him a great blow on the face with the flat of his sword. That same instant Candide drew his own and thrust it up to the hilt in the Jesuit Baron's belly; but as he drew it out all smoking he began to weep: "Alas! Good Lord!" he said. "I have killed my former master, my friend, my brother-in-law; I am the kindest man in the world, and here I am killing three men already, and two of the three are priests."

Cacambo, who was standing watch at the door to the arbor, ran up.

"There is nothing left for us but to sell our lives dear," said his master to him. "No doubt they will be coming into the arbor, we must die arms in hand."

Cacambo, who had seen the likes of this before, did not lose his head; he took the Jesuit robe worn by the Baron, put it over Candide's body, gave him the dead man's square bonnet, and got him to mount his horse. All this was done in the twinkling of an eye. "Let's gallop, master. Everyone will take you for a Jesuit on his way to give orders, and we will have passed the frontiers before they can come after us." He was already in flight as he uttered these words, and shouted in Spanish: "Make way, make way for the Reverend Father Colonel."

16   What Happened to the Two Travelers with Two Girls, Two Monkeys, and the Savages Called Oreillons[1]

Candide and his valet were beyond the barriers, and as yet no one in the camp knew of the death of the German Jesuit. The vigilant Cacambo had taken care to fill his bag with bread, chocolate, ham, fruit, and a few bottles of wine. On their Andalusian horses they plunged into an unknown land where they found no road. Finally there appeared before them a beautiful meadow interlaced with streams. Our two travelers give food to their mounts. Cacambo proposes to his master that they eat, and sets the example.

"How," said Candide, "can you expect me to eat ham, when I have killed the son of My Lord the Baron and find myself condemned never to see the fair Cunégonde again in my life? What will it profit me to prolong my wretched days, since I must drag them out far from her in remorse and despair? And what will the *Journal de Trévoux*[2] say?"

As he spoke thus, he did not fail to eat. The sun was setting. The two wanderers heard a few little cries that seemed to be uttered by women. They did not know whether these were cries of pain or of joy; but they jumped to their feet hastily with the anxiety and alarm that everything inspires in an unknown country. These sounds came from two girls, stark naked, who were running lightly along the edge of the meadow, while two monkeys followed them and bit their buttocks. Candide was moved with pity; he had learned to shoot among the Bulgarians, and he could have knocked a nut off a bush without touching the leaves. He takes his double-barreled Spanish gun, fires, and kills the two monkeys.

"God be praised, my dear Cacambo, I have delivered these two poor creatures from great peril; if I committed a sin in killing an Inquisitor and a Jesuit, I have certainly made up for it by saving the lives of these two girls. Perhaps they are two young ladies of quality, and this adventure may earn us great advantages in this country."

He was going to continue, but his tongue was silenced when he saw these two girls tenderly embrace the two monkeys, burst into tears over their bodies, and fill the air with the most grievous cries.

---

[1] From the Spanish *Orejones*, suggesting "pierced ears" or "big ears." The French name likewise suggests *oreilles*, "ears."

[2] The Jesuit journal, founded in 1701 and edited for many years by Guillaume-François Berthier.

"I was not expecting such goodness of soul," he said at last to Cacambo, who answered him: "You've done a fine piece of work there, my master; you have killed the two lovers of these young ladies."

"Their lovers! Can this be possible? You are making fun of me, Cacambo; how can I believe you?"

"My dear master," replied Cacambo, "you are always astonished at everything; why do you find it so strange that in some countries there are monkeys who obtain the good graces of the ladies? They are one-quarter men as I am one-quarter Spaniard."

"Alas!" replied Candide, "I remember hearing Doctor Pangloss say that in other times similar accidents had happened and that these mixtures had produced Aegipans, fauns, and satyrs; that many great personages of antiquity had seen them; but I took that for fables."

"You ought to be convinced now," said Cacambo, "that it is the truth, and you see how people behave who have not received a certain education; all I fear is that these ladies may get us into bad trouble."

These solid reflections led Candide to leave the meadow and plunge into a wood. There he ate supper with Cacambo, and they both, after cursing the Inquisitor of Portugal, the Governor of Buenos Aires, and the Baron, fell asleep on some moss. When they woke up they found that they could not move; the reason was that during the night the Oreillons, the inhabitants of the country, to whom the two ladies had denounced them, had bound them with ropes of bark. They were surrounded by about fifty stark-naked Oreillons armed with arrows and stone clubs and hatchets; some were boiling up a great caldron, others were preparing spits; and all were shouting: "It's a Jesuit, it's a Jesuit; we shall be avenged and we shall have a good meal; let's eat Jesuit, let's eat Jesuit."

"I told you so, my dear master," exclaimed Cacambo sadly; "I said that those two girls would do us a bad turn."

Candide, perceiving the caldron and the spits, exclaimed: "We are certainly going to be roasted or boiled. Ah! what would Doctor Pangloss say if he saw what the pure state of nature is like? All is well; so be it; but I confess it is very cruel to have lost Mademoiselle Cunégonde and to be put on a spit by the Oreillons."

Cacambo never lost his head. "Do not despair about anything," he said to the disconsolate Candide; "I understand a bit of the lingo of these people, I'm going to speak to them."

"Do not fail," said Candide, "to point out to them what frightful inhumanity it is to cook men and how unchristian it is."

"Gentlemen," said Cacambo, "so you are counting on eating a Jesuit today; that is a very good thing to do; nothing is more just than to treat one's enemies thus. In fact natural law teaches us to kill our neighbor, and this is how people behave all over the world. If we do not exercise our right to eat him, that is because we have other ingredients for a good meal; but you do not have the same resources as we do; certainly it is better to eat one's enemies than to abandon the fruits of victory to the crows and the ravens. But, gentlemen, you would not want to eat your friends. You think you are going to put a Jesuit on the spit, and it is your defender, it is the enemy of your enemies that you are about to roast. For my part I was born in your country; the gentleman you see here is my master; and far from being a Jesuit, he has just killed a Jesuit, he is wearing his spoils, that is the reason for your mistake. To verify what I am telling you, take his robe, carry it to the first barrier of the kingdom of *Los Padres,* find out whether my master has not killed a Jesuit officer. It won't take you long; you can still eat us if you find I have lied to you. But if I have told you the truth, you know the principles of international law, its customs and rules, too well not to spare us."

The Oreillons found this speech very reasonable; they deputized two notables to go with all diligence and find out the truth; the two deputies acquitted themselves of their commission like intelligent men and soon returned bearing good news. The Oreillons untied their two prisoners, paid them all sorts of courtesies, offered them girls, gave them refreshments, and conducted them all the way to the confines of their states, shouting joyfully: "He's not a Jesuit, he's not a Jesuit!"

Candide could not tire of wondering at the reason for his deliverance. "What a race!" he said. "What men! What customs! If I had not had the good fortune of giving a great sword thrust through the body of Mademoiselle Cunégonde's brother, I would have been eaten without mercy. But after all, the pure state of nature is good, since these people, instead of eating me, offered me a thousand courtesies as soon as they learned that I was not a Jesuit."

17 *Arrival of Candide and His Valet
in the Country of Eldorado,[1]
and What They Saw There*

When they were at the frontiers of the Oreillons, Cacambo said to Candide: "You see, this hemisphere is no better than the other; take my word for it, let's go back to Europe by the shortest route."

"How can we go back there?" said Candide. "And where could we go? If I go to my own country, the Bulgarians and Abarians are slaughtering everyone; if I go back to Portugal I am burned; if we stay in this country we run the risk at any moment of being put on the spit. But how can one bring oneself to leave the part of the world where Mademoiselle Cunégonde lives?"

"Let's turn toward Cayenne," said Cacambo; "there we will find Frenchmen; they go all over the world; they may help us; perhaps God will have pity on us."

It was not easy to go to Cayenne. They knew about what direc-

---

1 "The Golden (Country)," which a lieutenant of Pizarro claimed to have discovered.

tion they had to go, but mountains, rivers, precipices, brigands, savages, were terrible obstacles on all sides. Their horses died of fatigue; their provisions were used up. For a whole month they lived on wild fruits, and at last found themselves by a little river bordered with coconut trees, which supported their lives and hopes.

Cacambo, who always gave as good advice as the old woman, said to Candide: "We are at the end of our rope, we have walked far enough; I see an empty canoe on the bank, let us fill it with coconuts, cast ourselves into this little bark, and drift with the current; a river always leads to some inhabited spot. If we do not find pleasant things, at least we shall find new things."

"Let's go," said Candide, "let us recommend ourselves to Providence."

They drifted a few leagues between banks now flowery, now barren, now smooth, now rugged. The river kept getting wider; finally it disappeared under an arch of frightful rocks that rose to the heavens. The two travelers had the hardihood to abandon themselves to the waters underneath this arch. The river, at this point narrowed, carried them along with horrible rapidity and noise. After twenty-four hours they saw daylight again, but their canoe smashed on the reefs. They had to drag themselves from rock to rock for a whole league; finally they discovered an immense horizon bordered by inaccessible mountains. The country was cultivated for pleasure as well as for need; everywhere the useful was attractive. The roads were covered, or rather adorned, with carriages brilliant in form and material, bearing men and women of singular beauty, and drawn rapidly by big red sheep which in swiftness surpassed the finest horses of Andalusia, Tetuan, and Meknes.

"All the same," said Candide, "here is a country that is better than Westphalia." With Cacambo he set foot on land near the first village he came upon. A few village children covered with badly torn gold brocade were playing quoits at the entrance to the village. Our two men from the other world watched them with enjoyment. Their quoits were rather wide round pieces, yellow, red, and green, which shone with singular brilliance. The travelers took a notion to pick up a few of them; they were gold, emerald, and rubies, the least of which would have been the greatest ornament of the Mogul's throne.

"No doubt," said Cacambo, "these children are the sons of the King of the country playing quoits."

The village schoolmaster appeared at that moment, to call them back to school. "That," said Candide, "is the tutor of the royal family."

The little beggars immediately left their game, leaving on the ground their quoits and everything they had been playing with. Candide picks them up, runs to the tutor, and humbly presents them to him, giving him to understand by signs that Their Royal Highnesses had forgotten their gold and their precious stones. The village school-

master, smiling, threw them on the ground, looked at Candide's face
for a moment with much surprise, and continued on his way.

The travelers did not fail to pick up the gold, the rubies, and the
emeralds. "Where are we?" exclaimed Candide. "Kings' children must
be well brought up in this country, since they teach them to despise
gold and jewels." Cacambo was as surprised as Candide. Finally they
approached the first house in the village. It was built like a European
palace. A crowd of people was bustling at the door, and even more
inside the house. You could hear very pleasant music and smell a delicious odor of cooking. Cacambo approached the door and heard
them speaking Peruvian; it was his mother tongue; for everyone knows
that Cacambo was born in Tucuman in a village where only that
language was known. "I will serve as your interpreter," he said to
Candide; "let's go in, this is an inn."

Instantly two boys and two girls of the hostelry, dressed in cloth
of gold, their hair bound up with ribbons, invited them to sit at the
host's table. They served four soups each garnished with two parrots,
a boiled condor that weighed two hundred pounds, two roast monkeys
of excellent flavor; three hundred colibri hummingbirds on one plat-
ter and six hundred other hummingbirds on another; exquisite stews,
delicious pastries; all this on platters of a sort of rock crystal. The
boys and girls of the inn poured several liquors made of sugar cane.

The guests were for the most part merchants and coachmen, all
of the greatest politeness, who asked Cacambo many questions with the
most circumspect discretion and who answered his in a wholly satis-
factory manner.

When the meal was over, Cacambo, like Candide, thought to pay
his bill full well by throwing on the host's table two of those big gold
pieces that he had picked up; the host and hostess burst out laughing
and held their sides for quite a while. Finally they recovered themselves.

"Gentlemen," said the host, "we can easily see that you are foreigners; we are not accustomed to see any. Pardon us if we began to
laugh when you offered us in payment the pebbles of our highroads.
No doubt you have none of this country's money, but it is not necessary to have any in order to dine here. All the hostelries established
for the convenience of commerce are paid for by the government. You
had a bad meal here because this is a poor village; but everywhere else
you will be received as you deserve to be."

Cacambo explained to Candide all the host's remarks, and
Candide listened to them with the same amazement and the same be-
wilderment with which his friend Cacambo reported them. "What
kind of a country is this, then," they said to each other, "unknown to
the rest of the world, and where all nature is of a sort so different from
ours? Probably this is the country where all is well; for there absolutely must be one of that sort. And no matter what Doctor Pangloss
said about it, I often noticed that all was pretty bad in Westphalia."

18   *What They Saw in the Land of Eldorado*

Cacambo manifested all his curiosity to his host; the host said to him: "I am very ignorant, and I get along all right that way; but we have here an old man who has retired from the court, who is the most learned man in the kingdom and the most communicative." Immediately he took Cacambo to the old man. Candide was now playing only second fiddle and going along with his valet. They entered a house that was very simple, for the door was only of silver and the paneling in the apartments only of gold, but wrought with so much taste that the richest paneling did not eclipse it. True, the antechamber was encrusted only with rubies and emeralds, but the order in which everything was arranged fully made up for this extreme simplicity.

The old man received the two foreigners on a sofa stuffed with hummingbird feathers, and had them served liquors in diamond vases; after which he satisfied their curiosity in these terms:

"I am a hundred and seventy-two years old, and I learned from my late father, equerry to the King, of the astounding revolutions in Peru that he had witnessed. The kingdom we are in is the ancient homeland of the Incas, who left it very imprudently to go and subjugate part of the world, and who were finally destroyed by the Spaniards.

"The princes of their family who remained in their native country were wiser; they ordained, with the consent of the nation, that no inhabitant should ever leave our little kingdom; and that is what has preserved our innocence and happiness for us. The Spaniards gained some confused knowledge of this country; they called it El Dorado; and an Englishman named Lord Raleigh even came near it about a hundred years ago; but since we are surrounded by inaccessible rocks and precipices, we have up to now always been sheltered from the rapacity of the nations of Europe, who have an inconceivable rage for the pebbles and mud of our land, and who would kill us all to the last man to get some."

The conversation was long; it bore on the form of government, customs, women, public spectacles, arts. Finally Candide, who always had a taste for metaphysics, had Cacambo ask whether there was a religion in the country.

The old man blushed a little. "What," he said, "can you doubt it? Do you take us for ingrates?" Cacambo humbly asked what was the religion of Eldorado. The old man blushed again.

"Can there be two religions?" he said. "We have, I think, the religion of everyone; we worship God from morning till evening."

"Do you worship only one single God?" said Cacambo, who was still serving as interpreter for Candide's doubts.

"It appears," said the old man, "that there are not two, or three or four. I must admit that the people of your world ask very singular questions."

Candide could not tire of having this good old man questioned; he wanted to know how they prayed to God in Eldorado.

"We do not pray to him," said the good and respectable sage; "we have nothing to ask him for; he has given us all we need, we thank him without ceasing."

Candide had a curiosity to see some priests; he asked where they were. The good old man smiled.

"My friends," he said, "we are all priests; the King and all the heads of families solemnly sing hymns of thanksgiving every morning, and five or six thousand musicians accompany them."

"What! you have no monks to teach, to dispute, to govern, to intrigue, and to have people burned who are not of their opinion?"

"We would have to be crazy," said the old man; "we are all of the same opinion, and we do not understand what you mean with your monks."

At all these remarks Candide remained in ecstasy and said to himself:

"This is very different from Westphalia and the castle of My Lord the Baron; if our friend Pangloss had seen Eldorado, he would no longer have said that the castle of Thunder-ten-tronckh was the best thing on earth; travel is certainly necessary."

After this long conversation, the good old man had a carriage harnessed with six sheep and gave the two travelers twelve of his servants to take them to court. "Excuse me," he said to them, "if my age deprives me of the honor of accompanying you. The King will receive you in a way that will not leave you discontented, and you will doubtless pardon the customs of the country if there are some that displease you."

Candide and Cacambo climbed into the carriage, the six sheep flew, and in less than four hours they arrived at the King's palace, situated at one end of the capital. The portal was two hundred and twenty feet high and a hundred wide; it is impossible to describe what material it was. It is easy to see what prodigious superiority it must have had over those pebbles and sand that we call gold and precious stones.

Twenty beautiful girls of the watch received Candide and Cacambo as they got out of the carriage, took them to the baths, dressed them in robes woven from hummingbird down; after which the men and women grand officers of the crown took them to His Majesty's apartment between two files of a thousand musicians each, according to the ordinary custom. When they approached the throne room, Cacambo asked one grand officer how they should go about saluting His Majesty: whether you crawled on your knees or on your belly, whether you put your hands on your head or on your backside,

whether you licked the dust of the room, in short what the ceremony was.

"The custom," said the grand officer, "is to embrace the King
and kiss him on both cheeks."

Candide and Cacambo threw their arms around the neck of His
Majesty, who received them with all the grace imaginable and politely asked them to supper.

While waiting, they were shown the town, the public buildings
rising to the clouds, the market places adorned with a thousand columns, the fountains of pure water, those of rose water, and those of
cane-sugar liquors, which flowed continually in great squares paved
with a kind of precious stone which gave off a perfume like that of
cloves and cinnamon.

Candide asked to see the law courts; they told him that there
were none and that people never went to law. He inquired whether
there were prisons, and they told him no. What surprised him even
more and pleased him most was the Palace of Sciences, in which he
saw a great gallery two thousand paces long all full of instruments for
mathematics and physics.

After spending all afternoon touring about the thousandth part
of the city, they were taken back to the King's palace; Candide sat
down to table with His Majesty, his valet Cacambo, and several ladies.
Never was better cheer made, and never had a man more wit at supper
than His Majesty. Cacambo explained the King's witty remarks to
Candide, and even when translated they still appeared witty. Of all
that astounded Candide this was not what astounded him least.

They stayed a month in this hospitable place. Candide never
stopped saying to Cacambo:

"It is true, my friend, once again, that the castle where I was
born is not worth the country where we are now; but after all, Mademoiselle Cunégonde is not here, and no doubt you have some mistress
in Europe. If we stay here, we shall only be like the others, whereas if
we return to our own world with just twelve sheep laden with the
pebbles of Eldorado, we shall be richer than all the Kings put together, we shall have no more Inquisitors to fear, and we shall easily
be able to recover Mademoiselle Cunégonde."

Cacambo liked this idea; people are so fond of running about,
showing off before the folks at home, and parading what they have
seen on their travels, that the two happy men resolved to be so no
longer and to ask His Majesty for leave to go.

"You are doing a foolish thing," the King said to them. "I know
that my country is not much; but when a person is reasonably well off
somewhere he should stay there. I certainly have no right to detain
foreigners; that is a tyranny that does not exist either in our customs
or in our laws; all men are free; leave when you will, but the way out
is very difficult. It is impossible to go back up the rapid river on
which by a miracle you came here and which runs under arches of

rock. The mountains that surround my whole kingdom are ten thousand feet high and as perpendicular as walls; they are each more than ten leagues wide, you can descend them only by way of precipices. However, since you absolutely want to leave, I am going to give orders to the directors of machinery to make a machine that can transport you comfortably. When you have been taken to the other side of the mountains, no one will be able to accompany you farther; for my subjects have made a vow never to go beyond the mountain walls, and they are too wise to break their vow. Ask of me anything else you like."

"We ask of Your Majesty," said Cacambo, "only a few sheep loaded with victuals, pebbles, and some of the country's mud."

The King laughed. "I do not understand," he said, "the taste your people of Europe have for our yellow mud; but take as much as you want, and much good may it do you."

He immediately gave orders to his engineers to make a machine to hoist these two extraordinary men out of the kingdom. Three thousand good physicists worked on it; it was ready in two weeks and cost no more than twenty million pounds sterling in the money of the country. They put Candide and Cacambo on the machine; there were two big red sheep saddled and bridled to serve them as mounts when they had crossed the mountains; twenty pack sheep laden with victuals, thirty bearing presents of the most curious products of the country, and fifty laden with gold, precious stones, and diamonds. The King embraced the two wanderers tenderly.

A fine spectacle was their departure and the ingenious manner in which they and their sheep were hoisted to the top of the mountains. The physicists took leave of them after setting them down safely, and Candide was left with no other desire and object than to go and present his sheep to Mademoiselle Cunégonde.

"We have enough," he said, "to pay the Governor of Buenos Aires, if Mademoiselle Cunégonde can be ransomed. Let us head for Cayenne and take ship, and then we shall see what kingdom we can buy."

19   *What Happened to Them in Surinam,*
     and How Candide Made the
     Acquaintance of Martin

Our two travelers' first day was rather pleasant. They were encouraged by the idea of finding themselves possessors of more treasures than Asia, Europe, and Africa could assemble. Candide in transport wrote Cunégonde's name on the trees. On the second day two of their sheep got stuck in marshes and went down with their loads; two other sheep died of fatigue a few days later; seven or eight then died of hunger in a desert; a few days later some others fell from precipices. Finally, after a hundred days of travel, they had only two sheep left.

Candide said to Cacambo: "My friend, you see how perishable are the riches of this world; there is nothing solid but virtue and the happiness of seeing Mademoiselle Cunégonde again."

"I admit it," said Cacambo, "but we still have two sheep left with more treasures than the King of Spain will ever have, and I see in the distance a town that I suspect is Surinam, which belongs to the Dutch. We are at the end of our troubles and the beginning of our happiness."

As they approached the town they met a Negro stretched on the ground, with only half his clothes left, that is to say a pair of blue cloth shorts; the poor man had his left leg and his right hand missing. "Oh, good Lord!" said Candide to him in Dutch. "What are you doing there, my friend, in that horrible state I see you in?"

"I am waiting for my master Monsieur Vanderdendur, the famous merchant," the Negro replied.

"Was it Monsieur Vanderdendur," said Candide, "who treated you this way?"

"Yes, sir," said the Negro, "it is the custom. They give us a pair of cloth shorts twice a year for all our clothing. When we work in the sugar mills and we catch our finger in the millstone, they cut off our hand; when we try to run away, they cut off a leg; both things have happened to me. It is at this price that you eat sugar in Europe. However, when my mother sold me for ten patacóns on the Guinea coast, she said to me: 'My dear child, bless our fetishes, worship them always, they will make you live happily; you have the honor to be a slave to our lords the whites, and thereby you are making the fortune of your father and mother.' Alas! I don't know if I made their fortune, but they didn't make mine. Dogs, monkeys, parrots are a thousand times less miserable than we are. The Dutch fetishes who converted me tell me every Sunday that we are all, whites and blacks, children of Adam. I am no genealogist, but if those preachers are telling the truth, we are all second cousins. Now you must admit that no one could treat his relatives in a more horrible way."

"O Pangloss!" exclaimed Candide, "you had not guessed this abomination; this does it, at last I shall have to renounce your optimism."

"What is optimism?" said Cacambo.

"Alas," said Candide, "it is the mania of maintaining that all is well when we are miserable!" And he shed tears as he looked at his Negro, and he entered Surinam weeping.

The first thing they inquired about was whether there was not some ship in the port that could be sent to Buenos Aires. The man they addressed proved to be a Spanish ship's captain, who offered to make an honest bargain with them. He arranged to meet them at an inn. Candide and the faithful Cacambo went and waited for him there with their two sheep.

Candide, whose heart was on his lips, told the Spaniard all his adventures and admitted to him that he wanted to carry off Mademoiselle Cunégonde.

"I shall take good care not to take you to Buenos Aires," said the captain. "I would be hanged and you too. The fair Cunégonde is His Lordship's favorite mistress."

This was a bolt from the blue for Candide; he wept for a long time; finally he drew Cacambo aside.

"My dear friend," he said to him, "here is what you must do. We each have in our pockets five or six millions worth of diamonds; you are cleverer than I; go get Mademoiselle Cunégonde in Buenos Aires. If the Governor makes any difficulties, give him a million; if he still doesn't give in, give him two; you haven't killed an Inquisitor, they won't suspect you. I will fit out another ship; I will go to Venice and wait for you; it is a free country where there is nothing to fear either from Bulgarians, or Abarians, or Jews, or Inquisitors."

Cacambo applauded this wise resolution. He was in despair at parting from a good master who had become his intimate friend; but the pleasure of being useful to him overcame the grief of leaving him. They embraced, shedding tears. Candide recommended to him not to forget the good old woman. Cacambo left that very day. He was a very good man, this Cacambo.

Candide stayed on some time in Surinam and waited for another captain to be willing to take him to Italy, him and the two sheep he had left. He took servants and bought everything he needed for a long voyage. At last Monsieur Vanderdendur, master of a big ship, came to see him.

"How much do you want," he asked this man, "to take me straight to Venice, me, my men, my baggage, and the two sheep you see here?" The captain agreed to ten thousand piasters. Candide did not hesitate.

"Oho!" said the prudent Vanderdendur to himself, "this foreigner gives ten thousand piasters right away! He must be very rich." Then, returning a moment later, he signified that he could not sail for less than twenty thousand. "Very well, you shall have them," said Candide.

"Whew!" said the merchant softly to himself, "this man gives twenty thousand piasters as easily as ten thousand." He came back again and said that he could not take him to Venice for less than thirty thousand piasters. "Then you shall have thirty thousand," said Candide.

"Oho!" said the Dutch merchant to himself again, "thirty thousand piasters means nothing to this man; no doubt the two sheep are carrying immense treasures; let's not insist any further; let's get the thirty thousand piasters paid first, and then we shall see."

Candide sold two little diamonds the smaller of which was worth more than all the money the captain was asking. He paid him in advance. The two sheep were put aboard. Candide was following in a little boat to join the ship in the roads; the captain seizes his chance, sets sail, weighs anchor; the wind favors him. Candide, bewildered and stupefied, soon loses sight of him. "Alas!" he cried, "that's a trick worthy of the Old World." He returns to shore sunk in grief, for after all he had lost enough to make the fortune of twenty monarchs.

He goes to see the Dutch judge; and since he was somewhat upset, he knocks roughly on the door; he enters, expounds his adventure, and exclaims a little louder than was fitting. The judge began by making him pay ten thousand piasters for the noise he had made. Then he listened to him patiently, promised to look into his affair as soon as the merchant had returned, and charged him another ten thousand piasters for the costs of the hearing.

This procedure completed Candide's despair; true, he had endured misfortunes a thousand times more painful; but the cold-bloodedness of the judge, and of the captain by whom he had been robbed, inflamed his bile and plunged him into a black melancholy. The wickedness of men appeared to his mind in all its ugliness; he fed only on sad ideas.

Finally when a French ship was on the point of leaving for Bordeaux, since he had no more sheep laden with diamonds to put on board, he hired a cabin at a proper price and let it be known in the town that he would pay the passage and food and two thousand piasters to a decent man who would like to make the voyage with him, on condition that this man should be the most disgusted with his lot, and the most unfortunate in the province.

A throng of aspirants presented themselves that a fleet could not have held. Candide, wanting to choose among the most promising, picked out about twenty persons who seemed to him sociable enough and who all claimed to deserve the preference. He assembled them in his inn and gave them supper on condition that each would take an oath to tell his story faithfully; promising to choose the one who should seem to him the most to be pitied and the most discontented with his lot for the best reasons, and to give the others rewards.

The session lasted until four in the morning. Candide, as he listened to all their adventures, remembered what the old woman had said to him on the way to Buenos Aires, and the wager she had made that there was no one on the ship to whom very great misfortunes had not happened. At each adventure that was told him he thought of Pangloss.

"That Pangloss," said he, "would be much embarrassed to try to prove his system. I wish he were here. Certainly if all is well it is in Eldorado and not in the rest of the world."

Finally he made up his mind in favor of a poor scholar who had worked ten years for the booksellers in Amsterdam.[1] He judged

---

[1] Because of French censorship, Dutch freedom of the press, and the lack of international copyright laws, many French books were published piratically in Holland. Voltaire, among others, had suffered much from this pirating.

that there was no occupation in the world that a man should be more disgusted with.

This scholar, moreover, who was a good man, had been robbed by his wife, beaten by his son, and abandoned by his daughter, who had eloped with a Portuguese. He had just been deprived of a small job on which he lived, and the preachers of Surinam were persecuting him because they took him for a Socinian.[2] It must be admitted that the others were at least as unfortunate as he; but Candide hoped that the scholar would allay his boredom on the voyage. All his other rivals considered that Candide was doing them a great injustice, but he appeased them by giving them each a hundred piasters.

---

[2] A religious rationalist, denying the Trinity and the divinity of Christ.

20 *What Happened to Candide and Martin at Sea*

So the old scholar, whose name was Martin, embarked with Candide for Bordeaux. Both had seen much, and suffered much; and if the ship had been scheduled to set sail from Surinam to Japan by the Cape of Good Hope, they would have had enough to say about moral and physical evil to last the whole voyage.

However, Candide had one great advantage over Martin: he still hoped to see Mademoiselle Cunégonde again, and Martin had nothing to hope for; furthermore, he had gold and diamonds; and though he had lost a hundred big red sheep laden with the greatest treasures on earth, though he still had the knavery of the Dutch captain on his mind, nevertheless, when he thought about what he had left in his pockets, and when he talked about Cunégonde, especially toward the end of a meal, he still leaned toward the system of Pangloss.

"But you, Monsieur Martin," he said to the scholar, "what do you think of all that? What is your idea about moral and physical evil?"

"Sir," replied Martin, "my priests accused me of being a Socinian; but the truth of the matter is that I am a Manichean."[1]

"You are making fun of me," said Candide, "there are no more Manicheans in the world."

"There's me," said Martin; "I don't know what to do about it, but I cannot think any other way."

"You must be full of the devil," said Candide.

"He takes so much part in the affairs of this world," said Martin, "that I might well be full of him, just like everything else; but I must admit that when I cast my eyes over this globe, or rather over this globule, I think that God has abandoned it to some maleficent being—

---

[1] A follower of Mani or Manicheus, a third-century Persian who believed in two nearly equal forces, of good and of evil. The sect flourished in St. Augustine's time.

always excepting Eldorado. I have hardly seen a town that did not desire the ruin of the neighboring town, never a family that did not want to exterminate some other family. Everywhere the weak loathe the powerful before whom they crawl, and the powerful treat them like flocks whose wool and flesh are for sale. A million regimented assassins, ranging from one end of Europe to the other, practice murder and brigandage with discipline to earn their bread, because there is no more honest occupation; and in the towns that seem to enjoy peace and where the arts flourish, men are devoured with more envy, cares, and anxieties than the scourges suffered by a town besieged. Secret griefs are even more cruel than public miseries. In a word, I have seen so much, and undergone so much, that I am a Manichean."

"Yet there is some good," said Candide.

"That may be," said Martin, "but I do not know it."

In the midst of this dispute they heard the sound of cannon. The noise redoubles each moment. Everyone takes his spyglass. They see two ships fighting about three miles away. The wind brought them both so near the French ship that they had the pleasure of seeing the combat quite at their ease. Finally one of the two ships sent the other a broadside so low and so accurate as to sink it. Candide and Martin distinctly saw a hundred men on the main deck of the sinking ship; they all raised their hands to heaven and uttered frightful screams; in a moment all was swallowed up.

"Well," said Martin, "that is how men treat each other."

"It is true," said Candide, "that there is something diabolical in this affair."

So saying, he spied something bright red swimming near his ship. They launched the ship's boat to see what it could be; it was one of his sheep. Candide felt more joy on finding this sheep again than he had felt grief on losing a hundred all laden with big diamonds from Eldorado.

The French captain soon perceived that the captain of the ship that sank the other was a Spaniard and that the captain of the ship that sank was a Dutch pirate; he was the very one who had robbed Candide. The immense riches that this scoundrel had stolen were buried with him in the sea, and nothing but one sheep was saved.

"You see," said Candide to Martin, "that crime is sometimes punished; that rascal of a Dutch captain met the fate he deserved."

"Yes," said Martin, "but was it necessary that the passengers on his ship should perish also? God punished that knave, the devil drowned the others."

Meanwhile the French ship and the Spaniard continued on their way, and Candide continued his conversations with Martin. They argued for two weeks without stopping, and after two weeks they were as far advanced as the first day. But after all they were talking, they were exchanging ideas, they were consoling each other. Candide kept stroking his sheep. "Since I have found you again," he said, "I may well find Cunégonde again."

21   Candide and Martin Approach the Coast of France, Reasoning

At last they sighted the coast of France.

"Have you ever been in France, Monsieur Martin?" said Candide.

"Yes," said Martin, "I have been through several provinces. There are some where half the inhabitants are crazy, some where they are too tricky, others where they are usually rather gentle and rather stupid; others where they try to be witty; and in all of them the principal occupation is making love, the second talking slander, and the third talking nonsense."

"But, Monsieur Martin, have you seen Paris?"

"Yes, I have seen Paris; it is like all those kinds, it's a chaos, it's a crowd in which everyone seeks pleasure and in which almost no one finds it, at least so it appeared to me. I did not stay there long; on arrival I was robbed of all I had by pickpockets at the Saint-Germain fair. I was taken for a thief myself and I was in prison for a week; after which I became a printer's proofreader to earn enough to return on foot to Holland. I came to know the writing rabble, the intriguing rabble, and the convulsionary[1] rabble. They say there are some very polite persons in that city; I am willing to believe it."

"For my part, I have no curiosity to see France," said Candide. "You can easily guess that when a man has spent a month in Eldorado, he does not care about seeing anything else on earth, except Mademoiselle Cunégonde; I am going to wait for her in Venice; we will cross France on our way to Italy; won't you come along with me?"

"Very gladly," said Martin. "They say that Venice is good only for Venetian nobles, but that nevertheless they receive foreigners very well when they have a lot of money; I have none, you have, I will follow you anywhere."

"By the way," said Candide, "do you think that the earth was originally a sea, as we are assured in that big book[2] that belongs to the ship's captain?"

"I believe nothing of the sort," said Martin, "any more than all the daydreams that people have been trying to sell us for some time now."

"But then to what end was this world formed?" said Candide.

"To drive us mad," replied Martin.

"Aren't you quite astonished," Candide continued, "at the love of those two girls in the country of the Oreillons for those two monkeys, the adventure with whom I told you?"

---

[1] Manifestations of religious ecstasy or mania, like those of the Holy Rollers today. The Jansenists were noted for them.

[2] The "big book" presumably is the Bible; the theory had recently been advanced again in Buffon's *Théorie de la terre* (1749).

"Not at all," said Martin, "I don't see what is strange about that passion; I have seen so many extraordinary things that there is nothing extraordinary left."

"Do you think," said Candide, "that men have always massacred each other as they do today, always been liars, cheats, faithbreakers, ingrates, brigands, weaklings, rovers, cowards, enviers, gluttons, drunkards, misers, self-seekers, carnivores, calumniators, debauchees, fanatics, hypocrites, and fools?"

"Do you think," said Martin, "that sparrow hawks have always eaten pigeons when they found any?"

"Yes, no doubt," said Candide.

"Well," said Martin, "if sparrow hawks have always had the same character, why do you expect men to have changed theirs?"

"Oh!" said Candide, "there's a big difference, for free will ..."

Reasoning thus, they arrived at Bordeaux.

22 What Happened to Candide and Martin in France

Candide stopped in Bordeaux only as long as it took to sell a few pebbles from Eldorado and to provide himself with a good two-seated chaise; for he now could not do without his philosopher Martin; only he was very sorry to part with his sheep, which he left to the Bordeaux Academy of Science, which proposed, as the subject of that year's competition, to find out why this sheep's wool was red; and the prize was awarded to a scholar from the north, who proved by A plus B, minus C, divided by Z, that the sheep must be red and die of sheep pox.

Meanwhile all the travelers that Candide met in the inns on the road said to him: "We are going to Paris." This general eagerness finally gave him a hankering to see this capital; it was not much of a detour off the road to Venice.

He entered by the Faubourg Saint-Marceau[1] and thought he was in the ugliest village in Westphalia.

Hardly was Candide in his inn when he was attacked by a slight illness caused by his fatigue. Since he had an enormous diamond on his finger and a prodigiously heavy strongbox had been observed in his baggage, he immediately had at his side two doctors he had not called, some intimate friends who did not leave him, and two pious ladies heating up his broths.

Martin said: "I remember having been sick in Paris too on my first trip; I was very poor, so I had neither friends, nor pious ladies, nor doctors; and I got well."

However, by dint of medicines and bloodlettings, Candide's illness became serious. A neighborhood priest came and asked him gently

---

[1] In Voltaire's time an ugly, dirty suburb.

for a note payable to the bearer in the next world.[2] Candide wanted
no part of it; the pious ladies assured him that it was a new fashion.
Candide replied that he was not a man of fashion. Martin wanted to
throw the priest out the window. The cleric swore that Candide should
not be buried.[3] Martin swore that he would bury the cleric if he continued to bother them. The quarrel grew heated; Martin took him
by the shoulders and pushed him out roughly, which caused a great
scandal which led in turn to a legal report.

Candide got well, and during his convalescence he had very good
company to supper with him. They gambled for high stakes. Candide
was quite amazed that he never got any aces, and Martin was not
amazed at this at all.

Among those who did the honors of the town for him was a
little abbé from Périgord, one of those eager people, always alert,
always obliging, brazen, fawning, complaisant, who lie in wait for
strangers passing through, tell them the history of the town's scandals,
and offer them pleasures at any price. This man first took Candide
and Martin to the theater. They were playing a new tragedy. Candide
found himself seated next to some wits. This did not keep him from
weeping at certain perfectly played scenes. One of the reasoners beside him said to him during an intermission:

"You are very wrong to weep, for that actress is very bad, the
actor playing opposite her even worse, the play is even worse than
the actors: the author doesn't know a word of Arabic, and yet the
scene is in Arabia; and besides, he is a man who doesn't believe in
innate ideas;[4] tomorrow I will bring you twenty pamphlets against
him."

"Sir,[5] how many plays do you have in France?" said Candide to
the abbé, who replied: "Five or six thousand."

"That's a lot," said Candide. "How many of them are good?"

"Fifteen or sixteen," replied the other.

"That's a lot," said Martin.

Candide was very pleased with an actress who played Queen
Elizabeth in a rather dull tragedy that is sometimes performed.[6]

"I like this actress very much," he said to Martin; "she reminds
me of Mademoiselle Cunégonde; I would very much like to pay her
my respects."

---

[2] A reference to the *billets de confession* required from 1746 on, on pain of
refusal of absolution and the sacraments.

[3] That is, buried in consecrated ground. See below, note 7.

[4] Voltaire followed Locke's view of the mind at birth as a blank slate, rather
than Descartes's theory of innate ideas. Cf. *Memory's Adventure*, pp. 325–26 [of
Voltaire: Candide, Zadig and Selected Stories, trans. Donald M. Frame].

[5] Here begins a long passage added by Voltaire in 1761, which ends below,
p. 49.

[6] Presumably Thomas Corneille, *Le Comte d'Essex*.

The abbé from Périgord offered to take him to meet her. Candide, brought up in Germany, asked what the proper etiquette was, and how they treated queens of England in France.

"You have to make a distinction," said the abbé. "In the provinces they take them to a tavern, in Paris they respect them when they are beautiful and throw them on the dump when they are dead."

"Queens on the dump!" said Candide.

"Yes, really," said Martin; "the abbé is right; I was in Paris when Mademoiselle Monime[7] passed on, as they say, from this life to the next; she was refused what those people call the honors of burial, that is to say, of rotting with all the beggars of the district in an ugly cemetery; alone of her troupe, she was buried at the corner of the Rue de Bourgogne; which must have pained her extremely, for she had a very noble mind."

"That was very impolite," said Candide.

"What do you expect?" said Martin. "These people are made that way. Imagine all possible contradictions and incompatibilities, you will see them in the government, the tribunals, the churches, the entertainments of this queer nation."

"Is it true that people are always laughing in Paris?" said Candide.

"Yes," said the abbé, "but it is with rage in their hearts; for here people complain about everything with great bursts of laughter, and they even perform the most detestable actions with a laugh."

"Who," said Candide, "is that fat pig who was telling me so many bad things about the play at which I wept so much and about the actors who gave me such pleasure?"

"He is a living disease," replied the abbé, "who makes his living by saying bad things about all plays and all books; he hates anyone who succeeds, as eunuchs hate those who can enjoy sex; he is one of those serpents of literature who feed on filth and venom; he is a foliferous pamphleteer. ..."

"What do you mean by a foliferous pamphleteer?" said Candide.

"A producer of scribbled leaves," said the abbé, "a Fréron."

That is how Candide, Martin, and the Perigordian were talking on the staircase as they watched people file out after the play.

"Although I am very eager to see Mademoiselle Cunégonde again," said Candide, "still I would like to have supper with Mademoiselle Clairon,[8] for she seemed admirable to me."

The abbé was not the man to approach Mademoiselle Clairon, for she saw only good company. "She is engaged for this evening," he said, "but I shall have the honor of taking you to the house of a

---

7 Adrienne Lecouvreur (1690–1730), a distinguished actress who made her debut at the Comédie Française as Monime in Racine's *Mithridate*. Being an actress at her death, she was refused burial in consecrated ground.

8 A celebrated actress who played leading roles in many of Voltaire's plays.

lady of quality, and there you will come to know Paris as if you had been here four years."

Candide, who was naturally curious, let himself be taken to the lady's house, at the far end of the Faubourg Saint-Honoré;[9] they were busy playing faro; twelve sad punters[10] each held a small hand of cards, the foolish register of their misfortunes. A deep silence reigned, pallor sat on the punters' foreheads, anxiety on that of the banker; and the lady of the house, seated beside this pitiless banker, watched with a lynx's eyes all the underhand plays for double stakes or for three straight wins to pay seven times, for which each player turned up the corner of his cards;[11] she had them turned back down with severe but polite attention, and did not show any anger for fear of losing her customers; the lady called herself the Marquise de Parolignac.[12] Her daughter, aged fifteen, was one of the punters, and tipped her off with a wink to the cheating of those who were trying to repair the cruelties of fortune. The abbé from Périgord, Candide, and Martin entered, no one got up, greeted them, or looked at them; all were deeply preoccupied with their cards.

"My Lady the Baroness of Thunder-ten-tronckh was more civil," said Candide.

However, the abbé got the ear of the Marquise, who half rose, honored Candide with a gracious smile and Martin with a truly noble nod; she saw to it that a seat and a hand of cards were given to Candide, who lost fifty thousand francs in two deals; after which they had supper most gaily, and everyone was astounded that Candide was not moved by his loss; the lackeys said to one another in their lackey language: "He must be some English Milord."

The supper was like most suppers in Paris; first a silence; then a noise of undistinguishable words; then jokes, most of them insipid, false news, bad reasoning, a little politics, and a lot of slander; there was even some talk about new books.

"Have you seen," said the abbé from Périgord, "the novel by a certain Gauchat, Doctor of Theology?"

"Yes," replied one of the guests, "but I could not finish it. We have a host of nonsensical writings, but all of them together do not approach the nonsensicality of Gauchat, Doctor of Theology; I am so surfeited with this immense number of detestable books that inundate us that I have taken to punting at faro. ...."

"What about the *Mélanges* by Archdeacon Trublet? What do you say about them?" said the abbé.

---

9 An aristocratic quarter of Paris.

10 Faro is played by an unlimited number of punters against the banker.

11 To mark that he was making this bet—illegally, however.

12 From *paroli*, the doubled stakes alluded to above, and the *-gnac* ending common in the southwest of France, a great source of impoverished and spurious nobility.

"Oh!" said Madame de Parolignac, "what a tedious mortal! How assiduously he tells you what everybody knows! How ponderously he discusses what is not worth being noted lightly! With what absence of wit he appropriates the wit of others! How he spoils what he plunders! How he disgusts me! But he will not disgust me any more; it is enough to have read a few pages by the Archdeacon."

There was a learned man of taste at table who supported what the Marquise said. They talked of tragedies next; the lady asked why there were tragedies that were sometimes played and that could not be read. The man of taste explained very well how a play could have some interest and almost no merit; he proved in a few words that it was not enough to bring on one or two of those situations that you find in all novels and that always beguile the spectators, but that you have to be new without being bizarre, often sublime, and always natural, know the human heart and make it speak, be a great poet without letting any character in the play appear to be a poet, know the language perfectly, speak it with purity, with continual harmony, without ever rhyming at the expense of the sense.

"Anyone," he added, "who does not observe all these rules may compose one or two tragedies that win applause at the theater, but he will never be ranked among good writers; there are very few good tragedies; some are idyls in well-written and well-rhymed dialogue, others are political arguments that put you to sleep, or repulsive amplifications; still others are the dreams of enthusiasts, in a barbarous style; interrupted speeches, long apostrophes to the gods—because the author does not know how to speak to men—false maxims, bombastic commonplaces."

Candide listened attentively to this speech and formed a fine impression of the speaker; and since the Marquise had taken care to place him next to her, he got her ear and took the liberty of asking her who was that man who spoke so well.

"He is a learned man," said the lady, "who does not play faro and whom the abbé sometimes brings to supper with me; he is a perfect connoisseur of tragedies and books, and he has written a tragedy that was hissed and a book of which only one copy, which he dedicated to me, was ever seen outside his publisher's store."

"What a great man!" said Candide. "He is another Pangloss."

Then, turning toward him, he said to him:

"Sir, no doubt you think that all is for the best in the physical world and in the moral, and that nothing could have been otherwise?"

"I, sir," replied the scholar, "I think nothing of the sort; I think that everything goes awry with us, that no one knows his rank or his job or what he is doing or what he should do, and that except for supper, which is rather gay and where there seems to be a good deal of agreement, all the rest of the time is spent in senseless quarrels: Jansenists against Molinists, lawyers against churchmen, men of letters against men of letters, courtiers against courtiers, financiers against the people, wives against husbands, relatives against relatives—it's an eternal war."

Candide replied: "I have seen worse; but a sage, who has since had the misfortune to be hanged, taught me that all this is wonderful: these are shadows in a beautiful picture."

"Your hanged man was making fun of everybody," said Martin; "your shadows are horrible stains."

"It is men who make the stains," said Candide, "and they can't help it."

"Then it isn't their fault," said Martin.

Most of the gamblers, who understood nothing of this kind of talk, were drinking; and Martin talked theory with the scholar, and Candide told the lady of the house part of his adventures.

After supper the Marquise took Candide into her boudoir and sat him down on a sofa.

"Well," she said to him, "so you are still madly in love with Mademoiselle Cunégonde of Thunder-ten-tronckh!"

"Yes, Madame," answered Candide.

The Marquise replied to him with a tender smile: "You answer me like a young man from Westphalia; a Frenchman would have said to me: 'It is true that I have been in love with Mademoiselle Cunégonde, but when I see you, Madame, I fear I no longer love her.' "

"Alas! Madame," said Candide, "I will answer as you wish."

"Your passion for her," said the Marquise, "began when you picked up her handkerchief; I want you to pick up my garter."

"With all my heart," said Candide, and he picked it up.

"But I want you to put it back on me," said the lady, and Candide put it back on her.

"You see," said the lady, "you are a foreigner; I sometimes make my Parisian lovers languish for two weeks, but I give myself to you on the very first night, because one must do the honors of one's country to a young man from Westphalia."

The beauty, having perceived two enormous diamonds on her young foreigner's two hands, praised them so sincerely that they passed from Candide's fingers to the fingers of the Marquise.

When Candide went home with his Perigordian abbé, he felt some remorse at having been unfaithful to Mademoiselle Cunégonde; the abbé took part in his grief; he had got only a small share of the fifty thousand francs lost at gambling by Candide and of the value of the two brilliants half given, half extorted from him. His plan was to make all the profit he could from the advantages that his acquaintance with Candide might procure him. He talked to him a lot about Cunégonde, and Candide told him that he would certainly beg that fair lady's pardon for his infidelity when he saw her in Venice.

The Perigordian redoubled his courtesies and attentions, and took a tender interest in everything Candide said, everything he did, everything he wanted to do.[13]

"So you have a rendezvous in Venice, sir?" he said.

"Yes, Mr. Abbé," said Candide; "I absolutely must go and find Mademoiselle Cunégonde."

Then, led on by the pleasure of talking about the one he loved, he related, as was his custom, a part of his adventures with that illustrious lady of Westphalia.

"I suppose," said the abbé, "that Mademoiselle Cunégonde has a great deal of wit and writes charming letters?"

"I have never received any from her," said Candide, "for you must realize that having been expelled from the castle for love of her, I could not write her; that soon afterward I learned that she was dead, then I found her again, and then lost her; and that I have sent her a dispatch by special messenger two thousand five hundred leagues from here and am awaiting her reply."

The abbé listened attentively and seemed a bit thoughtful. He soon took leave of the two foreigners after embracing them tenderly. The next day Candide, on waking, received a letter couched in these terms:

"Sir, my very dear lover, I have been ill in this city for a week; now I learn that you are here. I would fly into your arms if I could move. I heard that you had passed through Bordeaux, I left the faithful Cacambo and the old woman there, and they are to follow me soon. The Governor of Buenos Aires took everything, but I still have your heart. Come, your presence will restore me to life or make me die of pleasure."

This charming letter, this unhoped-for letter, transported Candide with inexpressible joy; and the illness of his dear Cunégonde overwhelmed him with grief. Torn between these two feelings, he takes his gold and his diamonds and has himself driven with Martin to the hotel where Mademoiselle Cunégonde was staying. He enters, trembling with emotion; his heart beats, his voice sobs; he wants to open the bed curtains, he wants to have a light brought.

"Don't do anything of the sort," says the waiting maid, "light is the death of her"; and promptly she closes the curtains again.

"My dear Cunégonde," says Candide, weeping, "how are you feeling? If you cannot see me, at least speak to me."

"She cannot speak," says the maid.

The lady then stretches out of the bed a plump hand which Candide waters at length with his tears and which he then fills with diamonds, leaving a bag full of gold on the armchair.

In the midst of these transports a police officer arrives followed by the Perigordian abbé and a squad.

"So these are those two suspicious foreigners?" he says.

---

13 Here ends the addition of 1761 that began on p. 44.

He immediately has them arrested and orders his bravoes to drag them off to prison.

"This is not how they treat travelers in Eldorado," says Candide.

"I am more of a Manichean than ever," says Martin.

"But, sir, where are you taking us?" says Candide.

"To a deep dungeon," says the police officer.

Martin, having regained his coolness, decided that the lady who claimed to be Cunégonde was a fraud, the abbé from Périgord a fraud who had taken advantage of Candide's innocence as fast as he could, and the police officer another fraud of whom they could easily get rid.

Rather than expose himself to the processes of justice, Candide, enlightened by Martin's advice and moreover still impatient to see the real Mademoiselle Cunégonde again, suggests to the police officer three little diamonds worth about three thousand pistoles each.

"Ah, sir," says the man with the ivory baton, "even had you committed all the crimes imaginable, you are the finest man in the world. Three diamonds! Each worth three thousand pistoles! Sir, I would let myself be killed for you, instead of taking you to a dungeon. They arrest all foreigners here, but let me take care of things; I have a brother at Dieppe in Normandy, I'm going to take you there; and if you have an extra diamond to give him, he will take care of you just as I am doing myself."

"And why do they arrest all foreigners?" said Candide.

The abbé from Périgord then spoke up and said: "It is because a tramp from the region of Atrebatum[14] listened to foolish talk; this alone made him commit a parricide, not like that of May, 1610, but like that of December, 1594,[15] and like many others committed in other years and other months by other tramps who had listened to foolish talk."

The police officer then explained what it was all about.

"Oh, the monsters!" exclaimed Candide. "What! Such horrors in a nation that dances and sings! Can I not depart at once out of this country where monkeys incite tigers? I have seen bears in my own country; I have seen men only in Eldorado. In the name of God, Mr. Officer, take me to Venice, where I am to await Mademoiselle Cunégonde."

"I can take you only to Lower Normandy," said the officer.

Immediately he has his chains taken off, says he has made a mistake, sends his men away, and takes Candide and Martin to Dieppe and leaves them in the hands of his brother. There was a little Dutch ship in the roads. The Norman, having with the help of three other diamonds become the most obliging of men, embarks Candide and his

---

14 Latin name for Arras, home of Damiens, who attempted to assassinate Louis XV in 1757.

15 Two attempts on the life of Henry IV were the unsuccessful one by Châtel in 1594 and the successful one by Ravaillac in 1610.

men on the ship, which was about to set sail for Portsmouth in England. It was not the way to Venice; but Candide thought he was delivered from hell, and fully intended to get back on the way to Venice at the first opportunity.

23   *Candide and Martin Go to the Coast*
      of England; What They See There

"O Pangloss, Pangloss! O Martin, Martin! O my dear Cunégonde! What sort of a world is this?" said Candide on the Dutch ship.

"Something very mad and very abominable," replied Martin.

"You know England; are they as mad there as in France?"

"It's another kind of madness," said Martin. "You know that these two nations are at war over a few acres of snow out around Canada, and that they are spending on that fine war much more than all of Canada is worth. As for telling you precisely whether there are more people who need to be locked up in one country than another, that is something that my poor lights do not allow me to do. I only know that in general the people we are on our way to see are very gloomy."

While chatting thus, they arrived at Portsmouth; a multitude of people covered the shore and looked attentively at a rather fat man who was on his knees, his eyes bandaged, on the main deck of one of the ships of the fleet; four soldiers posted facing this man shot three bullets each into his skull as peacefully as can be, and the whole assemblage went back home extremely satisfied.

"What in the world is all this?" said Candide. "And what demon is exercising his domination everywhere?" He asked who was that fat man who had just been ceremoniously killed.

"An admiral,"[1] was the reply.

"And why kill this admiral?"

"Because," he was told, "he did not get enough people killed; he gave battle to a French admiral, and they decided that he was not close enough to him."

"But," said Candide, "the French admiral was as far from the English admiral as he was from him!"

"That is incontestable," was the reply; "but in this country it is a good thing to kill an admiral from time to time to encourage the others."

Candide was so stunned and so shocked at what he saw and what he heard that he would not even set foot on land, and made his bargain with the Dutch captain (even if he were to rob him like the one in Surinam) to take him to Venice without delay.

---

[1] Admiral Byng of England was executed on March 14, 1757, after a court-martial, for losing a naval battle to the French the year before. Voltaire had tried in vain to intervene to save his life.

Two days later the captain was ready. They sailed along the coast of France. They passed in sight of Lisbon, and Candide shuddered. They entered the Strait[2] and the Mediterranean. Finally they landed in Venice. "God be praised," said Candide, embracing Martin, "here is where I shall see the fair Cunégonde again. I count on Cacambo as on myself. All is well, all goes well, all goes as well as it possibly could."

---

2 Of Gibraltar.

24 *Paquette and Friar Giroflée*

As soon as he was in Venice, he had a search made for Cacambo in all the taverns, all the cafés, and among all the ladies of pleasure, and did not find him. Every day he sent to investigate all the ships and boats: no news of Cacambo.

"What!" he said to Martin. "I have had time to cross from Surinam to Bordeaux, to go from Bordeaux to Paris, from Paris to Dieppe, from Dieppe to Portsmouth, to skirt the coasts of Portugal and Spain, to cross the whole Mediterranean, to spend a few months in Venice, and the fair Cunégonde has not arrived! Instead of her I have met only a tricky wench and an abbé from Périgord! Cunégonde is beyond doubt dead, there is nothing left for me to do but die. Ah! it would have been better to remain in the paradise of Eldorado than to return to this accursed Europe. How right you are, my dear Martin! All is but illusion and calamity."

He fell into a black melancholy and took no part in the opera *à la mode* or the other diversions of the carnival; not one lady caused him the least temptation. Martin said to him:

"Truly you are very simple to imagine that a half-breed valet who has five or six millions in his pockets will go find your mistress at the end of the world and bring her to you in Venice. He will take her for himself if he finds her. If he does not find her, he will take another. I advise you to forget your valet Cacambo and your mistress Cunégonde."

Martin was not consoling. Candide's melancholy increased, and Martin never stopped proving to him that there was little virtue and little happiness on earth, except perhaps in Eldorado, where no one could go.

While arguing about this important matter and waiting for Cunégonde, Candide noticed a young Theatine monk in the Piazza San Marco arm-in-arm with a girl. The Theatine looked fresh, plump, vigorous; his eyes were brilliant, his manner assured, his head erect, his bearing proud. The girl was very pretty and was singing; she looked lovingly at her Theatine, and from time to time pinched his plump cheeks.

"You will admit to me at least," said Candide to Martin, "that these people are happy; up to now I have found, in all the habitable earth except Eldorado, nothing but unfortunates; but as for that girl and that Theatine, I wager they are very happy creatures."

"I wager they're not," said Martin.

"We have only to ask them to dinner," said Candide, "and you'll see whether I'm wrong."

Immediately he accosts them, pays them his compliments, and invites them to come to his inn and eat macaroni, Lombardy partridges, and caviar, and drink Montepulciano, Lacryma Christi, Cyprus and Samos wine. The lady blushed, the Theatine accepted the invitation, and the girl followed him, looking at Candide with eyes full of surprise and confusion and dimmed with a few tears. Hardly had she entered Candide's room when she said to him: "What! Monsieur Candide no longer recognizes Paquette!"

At these words Candide, who had not looked at her with any attention until then, because he was preoccupied only with Cunégonde, said to her:

"Alas! my poor child, so it was you who put Doctor Pangloss in the fine state in which I saw him?"

"Alas! sir, I myself," said Paquette; "I see that you are informed about everything. I learned about the frightful misfortunes that happened to the whole household of My Lady the Baroness and to the fair Cunégonde. I swear to you that my destiny has been hardly less sad. I was very innocent when you knew me. A Franciscan who was my confessor easily seduced me. The consequences were frightful; I was obliged to leave the castle a little while after My Lord the Baron had sent you away with great kicks in the backside. If a famous doctor had not taken pity on me I would have died. For some time out of gratitude I was that doctor's mistress. His wife, who was madly jealous, used to beat me pitilessly every day, she was a fury. This doctor was the ugliest of all men, and I the unhappiest of all creatures at being beaten continually because of a man I did not love. You know, sir, how dangerous it is for a shrewish woman to be a doctor's wife. This man, outraged at his wife's ways, one day gave her, to cure her of a little cold, a medicine so efficacious that she died of it in two hours' time in horrible convulsions. My lady's relatives brought a criminal suit against the gentleman; he took flight, and I was put in prison. My innocence would not have saved me if I had not been rather pretty. The judge turned me loose on condition that he would succeed the doctor. I was soon supplemented by a rival, tossed out with no compensation, and obliged to continue this abominable occupation which seems so amusing to you men and which for us is but an abyss of misery. I went to Venice to practice the profession. Ah! sir, if you could imagine what it is to be obliged to caress indiscriminately an old merchant, a lawyer, a monk, a gondolier, an abbé; to be exposed to every insult, every outrage; to be often reduced to borrowing a skirt in order to go have it lifted by some disgusting man; to be robbed by one of what you have earned with the other; to be forced by the officers of the law to buy protection, and to have in prospect nothing but a frightful old age, a hospital, and a dunghill—you would conclude that I am one of the unhappiest creatures in the world."

Thus Paquette opened her heart to the good Candide in a private room in the presence of Martin, who said to Candide:

"You see, I have already won half my wager."

Friar Giroflée had remained in the dining room and was having a drink while waiting for dinner.

"But," said Candide to Paquette, "you looked so gay, so happy, when I met you, you were singing, you were caressing the Theatine with natural complaisance; you seemed to me as happy as you claim to be unfortunate."

"Ah! sir," replied Paquette, "that is still another of the miseries of the trade. Yesterday I was robbed and beaten by an officer, and today I have to appear in a good humor to please a monk."

Candide had enough, he admitted that Martin was right. They sat down to table with Paquette and the Theatine; the meal was rather entertaining; and toward the end they talked to each other with some frankness.

"Father," said Candide to the monk, "you seem to me to enjoy a destiny that everyone must envy; the flower of health shines on your face,[1] your physiognomy bespeaks happiness, you have a very pretty girl for your recreation, and you seem very content with your condition as a Theatine."

"Faith, sir" said Friar Giroflée, "I wish all Theatines were at the bottom of the sea. I have been tempted a hundred times to set fire to the monastery and go turn Turk. My parents forced me at the age of fifteen to put on this detestable robe, in order to leave a greater fortune to an accursed older brother whom God confound! Jealousy, discord, rage inhabit the monastery. It is true, I have preached a few bad sermons that have brought me in a little money, half of which the prior steals from me; the rest serves me to keep girls; but when I go back to the monastery in the evening I am ready to smash my head against the dormitory walls; and all my colleagues are in the same state."

Martin, turning toward Candide with his customary coolness, said to him: "Well! Haven't I won the whole wager?"

Candide gave two thousand piasters to Paquette and a thousand piasters to Friar Giroflée. "I warrant you," he said, "with this they will be happy."

"I don't believe it in the very least," said Martin; "perhaps with these piasters you will make them much unhappier yet."

---

[1] In French, the monk's name means *gillyflower* or *wallflower*, while that of Paquette means *daisy*.

"That will be as it may," said Candide. "But one thing consoles me: I see that we often find people again whom we never thought to find; it may well be that having met up with my red sheep and Paquette, I shall also meet Cunégonde again."

"I hope," said Martin, "that she may someday be the making of your happiness; but that is something I strongly doubt."

"You are very hard," said Candide.

"That's because I have lived," said Martin.

"But look at these gondoliers," said Candide. "Aren't they always singing?"

"You don't see them at home, with their wives and their brats of children," said Martin. "The Doge has his troubles, the gondoliers have theirs. It is true that taken all in all the lot of a gondolier is preferable to that of a doge; but I think the difference is so slight that it is not worth examining."

"They speak," said Candide, "of Senator Pococurante,[2] who lives in that handsome palace on the Brenta, and who receives foreigners rather well. They claim he is a man who has never known grief."

"I would like to see so rare a species," said Martin.

Candide immediately sent to ask Lord Pococurante for permission to come to see him the next day.

---

2 From the Italian: "caring little."

25 Visit to the Venetian Nobleman, Lord Pococurante

Candide and Martin took a gondola onto the Brenta and arrived at the palace of the noble Pococurante. The gardens were well conceived and adorned with handsome marble statues; the architecture of the palace was fine. The master of the house, a man of sixty, very rich, received the two sight-seers very politely but with very little enthusiasm, which disconcerted Candide and did not displease Martin.

First two pretty, neatly dressed girls served chocolate, well prepared with whipped cream. Candide could not refrain from praising them for their beauty, their grace, and their skill.

"They are pretty good creatures," said Senator Pococurante; "I sometimes take them to bed with me, for I am very tired of the town ladies, their coquetries, their jealousies, their quarrels, their humors, their pettinesses, their pride, their follies, and the sonnets one must compose on order for them; but after all, these two girls are beginning to bore me a lot."

Candide, walking after breakfast in a long gallery, was surprised by the beauty of the pictures. He asked what master had painted the first two.

"They are by Raphael," said the senator; "I bought them a few years ago at a very high price out of vanity; they say they are the finest things in Italy, but I do not like them at all; their color has become very dark; the figures are not rounded enough and do not stand out enough; the draperies are not at all like cloth. In a word, no matter what they say, I do not find in them a true imitation of nature. I will like a picture only when I think I am seeing nature itself; and there are none of that kind. I have many pictures, but I no longer look at them."

While waiting for dinner, Pococurante had a concerto played for him. Candide found the music delightful.

"That noise," said Pococurante, "can be entertaining for half an hour, but if it lasts longer, it tires everyone, though no one dares admit it. Music today is merely the art of executing difficult things; and in the long run what is merely difficult is not pleasing. Perhaps I would like opera better, if they had not found the secret of making it a monster that revolts me. Let those who wish go to see bad tragedies set to music, where the scenes are composed only to bring in very clumsily two or three ridiculous songs which show off an actress's vocal cords. Let those who will, or who can, swoon with pleasure at seeing a eunuch hum the part of Caesar or Cato and tread the boards awkwardly. As for me, it has been a long time since I gave up these trivialities, which today are the glory of Italy and for which sovereigns pay so dear."

Candide argued a little, but with discretion. Martin was entirely in agreement with the senator.

They sat down to table, and after an excellent dinner they went into the library. Candide, seeing a magnificently bound Homer, praised the Illustrissimo for his good taste.

"That," he said, "is a book that was the delight of the great Pangloss, the best philosopher in Germany."

"It is no delight to me," said Pococurante coldly. "Once I was made to believe I took pleasure in reading it.[1] But that continual repetition of combats that are all alike, those gods that are always active and never do anything decisive, that Helen who is the subject of the war and who has hardly any part in the action, that Troy which is always besieged and never taken—all that caused me the most deadly boredom. I have sometimes asked learned men whether they were as bored as I was in reading it. All the sincere ones admitted to me that the book fell out of their hands, but that you always had to have it in your library, like an ancient monument, or like those rusty coins which cannot be used in commerce."

---

[1] Pococurante's opinions are not to be taken for Voltaire's, but they often express Voltaire's sense of the weaknesses of the great. Virgil was generally much preferred to Homer until the nineteenth century. Ariosto and Tasso were favorites of Voltaire's.

"Your Excellency does not think the same thing about Virgil?" said Candide.

"I admit," said Pococurante, "that the second, fourth, and sixth books of his *Aeneid* are excellent; but as for his pious Aeneas and strong Cloanthes and faithful Achates and little Ascanius and the imbecile King Latinus and middle-class Amata and insipid Lavinia, I do not believe there is anything so frigid or more disagreeable. I prefer Tasso and the fantastic fairy tales of Ariosto."

"Might I venture to ask you, sir," said Candide, "if you do not take great pleasure in reading Horace?"

"There are some maxims in him," said Pococurante, "that can profit a man of the world, and which, being compressed into energetic verses, engrave themselves the more easily on the memory. But I care very little about his journey to Brundisium or his description of a bad dinner, or the ruffians' quarrel between someone named Pupilus,[2] whose words, he said, were full of pus, and another whose words were vinegar. I have read only with extreme disgust his gross verses against old women and against witches; and I do not see what merit there can be in telling his friend Maecenas that if he is placed by him among the lyric poets he will strike the stars with his lofty brow. Fools admire everything in a noted author. I read only for myself, I like only what I have use for."

Candide, who had been brought up never to judge anything for himself, was greatly astonished at what he heard, and Martin considered Pococurante's way of thinking rather reasonable.

"Oh, here is a Cicero," said Candide. "Now as for that great man, I suppose you never tire of reading him?"

"I never read him," replied the Venetian. "What do I care whether he pleaded for Rabirius or for Cluentius? I have quite enough with the cases that I judge; I would have made out better with his philosophical works, but when I saw that he doubted everything, I concluded that I knew as much about it as he did, and that I did not need help from anyone in order to be ignorant."

"Ah, there are eighty volumes of proceedings of an Academy of Sciences," exclaimed Martin; "there may be something good there."

"There would be," said Pococurante, "if a single one of the authors of that rubbish had invented even the art of making pins; but in all those volumes there is nothing but empty systems and not a single useful thing."

"What a lot of plays I see here," said Candide, "in Italian, Spanish, and French!"

"Yes," said the senator, "there are three thousand of them and not three dozen good ones. As for these collections of sermons, which all together are not worth one page of Seneca, and all these great

---

2 Should be Rupilius. See *Satires*, I, vii.

volumes of theology, you may well suppose that I never open them, not I nor anyone else."

Martin noticed some shelves loaded with English books. "I suppose," he said, "a republican must enjoy most of those works written with so much freedom."

"Yes," replied Pococurante, "it is fine to write what you think; that is the privilege of man. In all this Italy of ours people write only what they do not think; those who inhabit the land of the Caesars and the Antonines dare not have an idea without the permission of a Dominican.[3] I would be glad of the freedom that inspires English geniuses, if passion and factionalism did not corrupt all that is estimable in that precious freedom."

Candide, noticing a Milton,[4] asked him if he did not regard that author as a great man.

"Who?" said Pococurante. "That barbarian who writes a long commentary on the first chapter of Genesis in ten books of harsh verses? That crude imitator of the Greeks, who disfigures the Creation and who, whereas Moses represents the eternal Being as producing the world by the word, has the Messiah take a great compass from a cupboard in Heaven to trace out his work? I should esteem the man who spoiled Tasso's Hell and Devil, who disguises Lucifer now as a toad, now as a pygmy, who has him repeat the same remarks a hundred times, who has him argue about theology, who, imitating in all seriousness the comical invention of firearms in Ariosto, has the devils fire cannon in Heaven? Not I, nor anyone in Italy has been able to enjoy all these sad eccentricities; and the marriage of Sin and Death, and the snakes that Sin gives birth to, make any man vomit who has a little delicacy of taste; and his long description of a hospital is good only for a gravedigger. This obscure, bizarre, and disgusting poem was despised at its birth; I treat it today as it was treated in its own country by its contemporaries. Besides, I say what I think, and I worry very little whether others think as I do."

Candide was distressed by these remarks. He respected Homer, and he rather liked Milton.

"Alas!" he whispered to Martin. "I'm very much afraid that this man may have a sovereign contempt for our German poets."

"There would be no great harm in that," said Martin.

"Oh, what a superior man!" said Candide under his breath. "What a great genius this Pococurante is! Nothing can please him."

After they had thus passed all the books in review, they went down into the garden. Candide praised all its beauties.

"I know of nothing in such bad taste," said the master; "we

---

[3] The Inquisition was in the hands of the Dominicans.

[4] Voltaire had much admiration for Milton, as he did for Shakespeare, but as time passed he became more and more critical of what he considered the barbarism of both.

have nothing but trifles here; but tomorrow I am going to have one planted on a nobler plan."

When the two sight-seers had taken leave of His Excellency, Candide said to Martin: "Well now, you will agree that there is the happiest of all men; for he is above everything he possesses."

"Don't you see," said Martin, "that he is disgusted with everything he possesses? Plato said a long time ago that the best stomachs are not those which refuse all food."

"But," said Candide, "isn't there pleasure in criticizing everything, in sensing defects where other men think they see beauties?"

"That is to say," retorted Martin, "that there is pleasure in taking no pleasure?"

"Oh well!" said Candide, "then there is no one happy except me —when I see Mademoiselle Cunégonde again."

"It is always a good thing to hope," said Martin.

However, the days, the weeks passed by; Cacambo still did not come back, and Candide was so sunk in his sorrow that he did not even notice that Paquette and Friar Giroflée had not so much as come to thank him.

26 *Of a Supper That Candide and Martin Had with Six Foreigners, and Who These Were*

One evening when Candide, followed by Martin, was going to sit down to table with the foreigners who were staying in the same hotel, a man with a soot-colored face came up to him from behind and, taking him by the arm, said: "Be ready to leave with us, do not fail."

He turns around and sees Cacambo. Only the sight of Cunégonde could have astounded and pleased him more. He was on the point of going mad with joy. He embraced his dear friend.

"Then doubtless Cunégonde is here? Where is she? Take me to her, let me die of joy with her."

"Cunégonde is not here," said Cacambo, "she is in Constantinople."

"Oh heavens! In Constantinople! But were she in China, I fly to her, let's go."

"We will leave after supper," said Cacambo; "I cannot tell you any more; I am a slave, my master is waiting for me, I must go and serve him at table. Don't say a word; have supper and be ready."

Candide, torn between joy and sorrow, charmed to see his faithful agent again, astounded to see him a slave, full of the idea of recovering his mistress, his heart agitated and his mind topsy-turvy, sat down to table with Martin, who observed all these adventures imperturbably, and with six foreigners who had come to spend the Carnival in Venice.

Cacambo, who was pouring drink for one of these six foreigners, got his master's ear toward the end of the meal and said to him: "Sire, Your Majesty will leave when you wish, the vessel is ready." Having said these words he went out.

The guests, astonished, looked at each other without uttering a single word, when another servant, coming up to his master, said to him: "Sire, Your Majesty's chaise is in Padua, and the boat is ready." The master made a sign, and the servant left.

All the guests looked at each other again, and the general surprise redoubled. A third valet, also approaching a third foreigner, said to him: "Sire, believe me, Your Majesty must not remain here any longer; I am going to prepare everything." And immediately he disappeared.

By now Candide and Martin had no doubt that this was a Carnival masquerade. A fourth servant said to the fourth master: "Your Majesty will leave when you please," and went out like the others. The fifth valet said as much to the fifth master. But the sixth valet spoke differently to the sixth foreigner who was sitting with Candide; he said to him: "Faith, Sire, they won't give Your Majesty credit any more, nor me either; and we could well be locked up tonight, you and me; I am going to see to my own affairs; farewell."

All the servants having disappeared, the six foreigners, Candide, and Martin remained in deep silence. Finally Candide broke it:

"Gentlemen," he said, "this is a singular jest. Why are you all kings? For myself, I admit that neither Martin nor I am."

Cacambo's master then spoke up gravely and said in Italian: "I am not jesting, my name is Ahmed III.[1] I was Grand Sultan for several years; I dethroned my brother; my nephew dethroned me; my viziers had their heads cut off; I am ending my days in the old seraglio. My nephew, the Grand Sultan Mahmud, allows me to travel sometimes for my health, and I have come to spend the Carnival in Venice."

A young man who was next to Ahmed spoke after him and said: "My name is Ivan; I was Emperor of all the Russians; I was dethroned in my cradle; my father and mother were locked up; I was brought up in prison; I sometimes have permission to travel, accompanied by those who guard me, and I have come to spend the Carnival in Venice."

The third said: "I am Charles Edward, King of England; my father ceded me his rights to the kingdom. I fought to maintain them; they tore the hearts out of eight hundred of my supporters and dashed them in their faces. I was put in prison; I am going to Rome to pay a visit to the King my father, who is dethroned like my grandfather and me; and I have come to spend the Carnival in Venice."

The fourth then took the floor and said: "I am King of the

---

[1] All these kings are real.

Poles; the fortunes of war have deprived me of my hereditary states; my father underwent the same reverses; I resign myself to Providence like Sultan Ahmed, Emperor Ivan, and King Charles Edward, whom God give long life; and I have come to spend the Carnival in Venice."

The fifth said: "I too am King of the Poles; I have lost my kingdom twice; but Providence has given me another state,[2] in which I have done more good than all the kings of the Sarmatians together have ever been able to do on the banks of the Vistula; I too resign myself to Providence; and I have come to spend the Carnival in Venice."

It remained for the sixth monarch to speak. "Gentlemen," said he, "I am not as great a lord as you; but even so I have been a King like anyone else. I am Theodore; I was elected King of Corsica; I have been called Your Majesty, and at present I am hardly called Sir. I have coined money, and I do not have a penny; I have had two secretaries of state, and I have scarcely a valet. I was once on a throne, and I was in prison for a long time in London, on the straw. I am much afraid I shall be treated the same way here, although I have come, like Your Majesties, to spend the Carnival in Venice."

The five other Kings listened to this speech with noble compassion. Each of them gave King Theodore twenty sequins to get clothes and shirts; and Candide presented him with a diamond worth two thousand sequins. "Who is this man," said the five Kings, "who is in a position to give a hundred times as much as each of us, and who gives it? Are you a King too, sir?"

"No, gentlemen, and I have no desire to be."[3]

At the moment when they were leaving the table, there arrived in the same hotel four Most Serene Highnesses, who had also lost their states by the fortunes of war, and who were coming to spend the rest of the Carnival in Venice. But Candide did not even take note of these newcomers; he was preoccupied only with going to find his dear Cunégonde in Constantinople.

---

2 Stanislas Leszczynski (1677–1766), father of the Queen of France, abdicated the throne of Poland in 1736, was made Duke of Lorraine, and did much good in and around Lunéville. The Sarmatians are the Slavs.

3 These three sentences (from " 'Who is this man' " on) are the final form that Voltaire intended, replacing the following:

" 'Who is this ordinary citizen,' said the five Kings, 'who is in a position to give a hundred times as much as each of us, and who gives it?' "

27 Candide's Voyage to Constantinople

The faithful Cacambo had already obtained an agreement with the Turkish captain who was about to take Sultan Ahmed back to Constantinople that he would take Candide and Martin on his ship. Both came on board after having prostrated themselves before his miserable Highness. On the way, Candide said to Martin:

"But those were six dethroned Kings that we had supper with, and besides, among those six Kings there was one to whom I gave alms. Maybe there are many other princes still more unfortunate. As for me, I have lost only a hundred sheep, and I am flying to Cunégonde's arms. My dear Martin, once again, Pangloss was right, all is well."

"I hope so," said Martin.

"But," said Candide, "that was a most implausible adventure we had in Venice. No one ever saw or heard of six dethroned Kings having supper together in an inn."

"That is no more extraordinary," said Martin, "than most of the things that have happened to us. It is very common for Kings to be dethroned; and as for the honor we had in having supper with them, it is a thing that does not deserve our attention. What does it matter whom you sup with, provided you make good cheer?"[1]

Scarcely was Candide in the ship when he threw his arms around the neck of his former valet, his friend Cacambo.

"Well," he said, "what is Cunégonde doing? Is she still a prodigy of beauty? Does she still love me? How is she? No doubt you bought her a palace in Constantinople?"

"My dear master," replied Cacambo, "Cunégonde is washing dishes on the banks of Propontis for a prince who has very few dishes; she is a slave in the household of a former sovereign named Ragotsky,[2] to whom the Grand Turk gives three crowns a day in his refuge; but what is much sadder is that she has lost her beauty and become horribly ugly."

"Ah! beautiful or ugly," said Candide, "I am an honorable man, and my duty is to love her always. But how can she be reduced to so abject a state with the five or six millions you brought her?"

"Well," said Cacambo, "did I not have to give two millions to Señor Don Fernando d'Ibaraa y Figueora y Mascarenes y Lampourdos y Souza, Governor of Buenos Aires, for permission to take Mademoiselle Cunégonde back? And did not a pirate bravely despoil us of all the rest? And did not that pirate take us to Cape Matapan, to Milo, to Nicaria, to Samos, to Petra, to the Dardanelles, to Marmora, to Scutari? Cunégonde and the old woman are servants with that prince I spoke to you about, and I am a slave of the dethroned Sultan."

"What a chain of frightful calamities one after another!" said Candide. "But after all, I still have a few diamonds. I shall easily deliver Cunégonde. It is a great pity that she has become so ugly."

Then, turning toward Martin, he said: "Which one do you think is the most to be pitied, Emperor Ahmed, Emperor Ivan, King Charles Edward, or I?"

---

[1] This passage, from "it is a thing" on, is another change intended by Voltaire to replace this: " 'it is a trifle that does not deserve our attention.' "

[2] A former prince of Transylvania.

"I know nothing about that," said Martin; "I would have to be inside your hearts to know."

"Ah!" said Candide, "if Pangloss were here, he would know and would tell us."

"I do not know," said Martin, "with what scales your Pangloss could have weighed the misfortunes of men and estimated their sorrows. All I presume is that there are millions of men on earth a hundred times more to be pitied than King Charles Edward, Emperor Ivan, and Sultan Ahmed."

"That might well be," said Candide.

They arrived in a few days in the Bosporus. Candide began by buying back Cacambo at a very high price; and without wasting time he flung himself into a galley with his companions to go to the shores of Propontis and find Cunégonde, however ugly she might be.

In the convict crew there were two galley slaves who rowed very badly, and from time to time the Levantine captain applied a few strokes of a bull's pizzle to their bare shoulders; Candide, from a natural impulse, looked at them more attentively than at the other galley slaves and went up to them in pity. Some features of their disfigured faces seemed to him to have some resemblance to Pangloss and to that hapless Jesuit, the Baron, Mademoiselle Cunégonde's brother. This idea touched and saddened him. He looked at them even more attentively. "Truly," he said to Cacambo, "if I had not seen Doctor Pangloss hanged, and if I had not had the misfortune to kill the Baron, I would think it is they that are rowing in this galley."

At the names "Baron" and "Pangloss" the two convicts uttered a loud cry, sat still on their bench, and dropped their oars. The Levantine captain ran up to them, and the lashes with the bull's pizzle redoubled.

"Stop, stop, my lord," cried Candide, "I will give you as much money as you want."

"What! It's Candide!" said one of the convicts.

"What! It's Candide!" said the other.

"Is it a dream?" said Candide. "Am I really awake? Am I in this galley? Is that My Lord the Baron, whom I killed? Is that Doctor Pangloss, whom I saw hanged?"

"It is indeed, it is indeed," they replied.

"What! Is this that great philosopher?" said Martin.

"Oh! Master Levantine Captain," said Candide, "how much money do you want for the ransom of My Lord of Thunder-ten-tronckh, one of the first barons of the Empire, and for Monsieur Pangloss, the most profound metaphysician of Germany?"

"Dog of a Christian," replied the Levantine captain, "since these two dogs of Christian convicts are barons and metaphysicians, which is no doubt a great dignity in their country, you shall give me fifty thousand sequins for them."

"You shall have them, sir; take me back like a flash to Constantinople, and you shall be paid on the spot. But no, take me to Mademoiselle Cunégonde."

The Levantine captain, at Candide's first offer, had already turned his prow toward the city, and he was making the oarsmen row faster than a bird cleaves the air.

Candide embraced the Baron and Pangloss a hundred times. "And how is it that I did not kill you, my dear Baron? And my dear Pangloss, how is it that you are alive after being hanged? And why are you both in the galleys in Turkey?"

"Is it really true that my dear sister is in this country?" said the Baron.

"Yes," replied Cacambo.

"So I see my dear Candide again," exclaimed Pangloss.

Candide introduced Martin and Cacambo to them. They all embraced, they all talked at once. The galley flew, they were already in the port. They sent for a Jew, to whom Candide sold for fifty thousand sequins a diamond of the value of a hundred thousand, and who swore to him by Abraham that he could not give any more. Candide immediately paid the ransom of the Baron and Pangloss. The latter threw himself at the feet of his liberator and bathed them with tears; the other thanked him with a nod and promised to repay him the money at the first opportunity. "But is it really possible that my sister is in Turkey?" he said.

"Nothing is so possible," retorted Cacambo, "since she is scouring dishes for a prince of Transylvania."

Immediately they sent for two Jews; Candide sold some more diamonds; and they all set out again in another galley to go and deliver Cunégonde.

28 *What Happened to Candide, Cunégonde,*
    Pangloss, Martin, et al.

"Once again, pardon," said Candide to the Baron, "pardon me, Reverend Father, for having given you a great sword thrust through the body."

"Let's say no more about it," said the Baron; "I was a little too hasty, I admit; but since you want to know by what chance you saw me in the galleys, I will tell you. After being cured of my wound by the brother apothecary of the College, I was attacked and carried off by a party of Spaniards; they put me in prison in Buenos Aires at the time when my sister had just left. I asked to return to the Father General in Rome. I was named to go to Constantinople and serve as almoner with My Lord the Ambassador of France. Not a week after I had taken up my duties, I met, toward evening, a very attractive ichoglan.¹ It was very hot; the young man wanted to bathe; I took the opportunity to bathe too. I did not know that it was a capital crime for a Christian to be found stark naked with a young Moslem. A cadi had me given a hundred strokes on the soles of my feet and condemned me to the galleys. I do not think a more horrible injustice has ever been done. But I would certainly like to know why my sister is in the kitchen of a sovereign of Transylvania who is a refugee among the Turks."

"But you, my dear Pangloss," said Candide, "how can it be that I see you again?"

"It is true," said Pangloss, "that you saw me hanged; naturally I was supposed to be burned; but you remember there was a heavy downpour just when they were going to cook me; the storm was so violent that they despaired of lighting the fire; I was hanged because they could do no better; a surgeon bought my body, took me home, and dissected me. First he made a cross-shaped incision in me from the navel to the clavicle. No one could have been worse hanged than I had been. The Holy Inquisition's Executor of High Operations, who was a subdeacon, did indeed burn people marvelously, but he was not accustomed to hanging them; the rope was wet and slipped badly, it became knotted; in short, I was still breathing. The cross-shaped incision made me utter such a loud scream that my surgeon fell over backward and, thinking that he was dissecting the devil, he fled, half-dead from fear, and he fell again on the staircase as he fled. His wife came running from a nearby room at the noise; she saw me stretched out on the table with my cross-shaped incision; she was even more afraid than her husband, fled, and fell over him. When they had recovered a little, I heard the surgeon's wife say to the surgeon: 'My dear, what are you thinking of, dissecting a heretic? Don't you know that the devil is always in those people? I am going quickly to get a priest to exorcise him.'

"I shuddered at these words and collected the little strength I had left to call out: 'Have pity on me!' Finally the Portuguese barber² grew bolder; he sewed up my skin; his wife even took care of me; in two weeks I was on my feet. The barber found me a job and made me lackey to a knight of Malta who was going to Venice; but as this master had no money to pay me, I entered the service of a Venetian merchant and followed him to Constantinople.

"One day I took a notion to enter a mosque; there was no one there but an old imam and a very pretty young devotee who was saying her prayers. Her bosom was fully uncovered; between her breasts she had a beautiful bouquet of tulips, roses, anemones, buttercups, hyacinths, and yellow primroses; she dropped her bouquet; I picked

---

¹ Page to the Sultan.
² The surgeon.

it up, and I replaced it for her with the most respectful eagerness. I was so long in replacing it for her that the imam grew angry, and, seeing that I was a Christian, called for help. I was taken before the cadi, who had me given a hundred strokes on the soles of the feet and sent me to the galleys. I was chained precisely in the same galley and on the same bench as My Lord the Baron. In this galley there were four young men from Marseilles, five Neapolitan priests, and two monks from Corfu, who told us that similar adventures occurred every day. My Lord the Baron claimed that he had suffered a greater injustice than I; for my part I claimed that it was much more permissible to replace a bouquet on a woman's bosom than to be stark naked with an ichoglan. We were arguing unceasingly and receiving twenty strokes a day of the bull's pizzle, when the concatenation of the events of this universe brought you into our galley and you ransomed us."

"Well, my dear Pangloss," said Candide, "when you were hanged, dissected, racked with blows, and rowing in the galleys, did you still think that all was for the very best?"

"I am still of my first opinion," replied Pangloss; "for after all I am a philosopher, it is not fitting for me to recant, for Leibniz cannot be wrong, and besides, pre-established harmony is the finest thing in the world, like the plenum and subtle matter."

29 How Candide Found Cunégonde and the Old Woman Again

While Candide, the Baron, Pangloss, Martin, and Cacambo were relating their adventures, reasoning on the contingent or noncontingent events of this universe, arguing about effects and causes, moral and physical evil, free will and necessity, and the consolations that may be experienced when one is in the galleys in Turkey, they landed on the shore of Propontis at the house of the prince of Transylvania. The first objects that met their eyes were Cunégonde and the old woman, who were spreading out towels on lines to dry.

The Baron paled at this sight. The tender lover Candide, on seeing his fair Cunégonde dark-skinned, eyes bloodshot, flat-bosomed, cheeks wrinkled, arms red and rough, recoiled three steps in horror, and then advanced out of good manners. She embraced Candide and her brother; they embraced the old woman; Candide ransomed them both.

There was a little farm in the neighborhood; the old woman proposed to Candide that he buy it while waiting for the entire group to enjoy a better destiny. Cunégonde did not know that she had grown ugly, no one had told her so; she reminded Candide of his promises in so positive a tone that the good Candide did not refuse her. So he notified the Baron that he was going to marry his sister.

"I shall never endure," said the Baron, "such baseness on her part and such insolence on yours; no one shall ever reproach me with that infamy; my sister's children would not be able to enter the chapters[1] of Germany. No, never shall my sister marry anyone but a baron of the Empire."

Cunégonde threw herself at his feet and bathed them with tears; he was inflexible.

"You maddest of madmen," said Candide, "I rescued you from the galleys, I paid your ransom, I paid your sister's too; she was washing dishes here, she is ugly, I am kind enough to make her my wife, and you still presume to oppose it; I would kill you again if I heeded my anger."

"You may kill me again," said the Baron, "but you shall not marry my sister while I am alive."

---

[1] Knightly assemblies.

30 Conclusion

At the bottom of his heart, Candide had no desire to marry Cunégonde. But the Baron's extreme impertinence determined him to clinch the marriage, and Cunégonde urged him on so eagerly that he could not retract. He consulted Pangloss, Martin, and the faithful Cacambo. Pangloss composed a fine memoir by which he proved that the Baron had no rights over his sister, and that according to all the laws of the Empire she could make a left-handed marriage[1] with Candide. Martin's judgment was to throw the Baron in the sea; Cacambo decided that he should be returned to the Levantine captain and put back in the galleys, after which he would be sent by the first ship to the Father General in Rome. The plan was considered very good; the old woman approved it; they said nothing about it to his sister; for a little money the thing was carried out, and they had the pleasure of trapping a Jesuit and punishing the pride of a German Baron.

It was quite natural to imagine that after so many disasters Candide, married to his mistress and living with the philosopher Pangloss, the philosopher Martin, the prudent Cacambo, and the old woman, moreover having brought back so many diamonds from the land of the ancient Incas, would lead the most pleasant life in the world. But he was so cheated by the Jews[2] that he had nothing left but his little farm; his wife, becoming uglier every day, became shrewish and intolerable; the old woman was an invalid and was even more bad-humored than Cunégonde. Cacambo, who worked in the garden and who went and sold vegetables at Constantinople, was worn out

---

[1] A morganatic marriage, giving no equality to the party of lower rank.
[2] Voltaire had suffered financial losses from the bankruptcies of Jewish bankers.

with work and cursed his destiny. Pangloss was in despair at not shining in some university in Germany. As for Martin, he was firmly persuaded that a man is equally badly off anywhere; he took things patiently.

Candide, Martin, and Pangloss sometimes argued about metaphysics and morality. They often saw passing under the windows of the farm boats loaded with effendis, pashas, and cadis who were being sent into exile at Lemnos, Mitylene, and Erzerum. They saw other cadis arriving, other pashas, other effendis, who took the place of the exiles and were exiled in their turn. They saw properly impaled heads on their way to be presented to the Sublime Porte.[3] These sights redoubled their discourses; and when they were not arguing, the boredom was so excessive that one day the old woman dared to say to them:

"I would like to know which is worse—to be raped a hundred times by Negro pirates, have a buttock cut off, run the gantlet among the Bulgarians, be flogged and hanged in an auto-da-fé, be dissected, row in the galleys, in short to undergo all the miseries we have all been through—or to stay here doing nothing?"

"It's a great question," said Candide.

These remarks engendered new reflections, and Martin above all concluded that man was born to live in the convulsions of anxiety or the lethargy of boredom. Candide did not agree, but he asserted nothing. Pangloss admitted that he had always suffered horribly; but having once maintained that everything was wonderful, he still maintained it and believed not a bit of it.

One thing completely confirmed Martin in his detestable principles, made Candide hesitate more than ever, and embarrassed Pangloss: one day they saw coming to their farm Paquette and Friar Giroflée, who were in the utmost misery; they had very quickly gone through their three thousand piasters, had parted, made it up, quarreled, been put in prison, escaped, and finally Friar Giroflée had turned Turk. Paquette continued to ply her trade everywhere, and no longer earned anything at it.

"I had quite foreseen," said Martin to Candide, "that your presents would soon be dissipated and would only make them more miserable. You and Cacambo were once glutted with millions of piasters, and you are no happier than Friar Giroflée and Paquette."

"Aha!" said Pangloss to Paquette, "so heaven brings you back among us here, my poor child! Do you realize that you cost me the end of my nose, an eye, and an ear? Look at you now! Ah! What a world is this!"

This new adventure led them to philosophize more than ever.

In the neighborhood there was a very famous dervish who was

---

[3] Originally, the gate of the Sultan's palace, where justice was once administered; hence, his government.

considered the best philosopher in Turkey; they went to consult him; Pangloss was the spokesman and said to him: "Master, we have come to ask you to tell us why such a strange animal as man was ever created."

"What are you meddling in?" said the dervish. "Is that your business?"

"But, Reverend Father," said Candide, "there is a horrible amount of evil on earth."

"What does it matter," said the dervish, "whether there is evil or good? When His Highness sends a ship to Egypt, is he bothered about whether the mice in the ship are comfortable or not?"

"Then what should we do?" said Pangloss.

"Hold your tongue," said the dervish.

"I flattered myself," said Pangloss, "that you and I would reason a bit together about effects and causes, the best of all possible worlds, the origin of evil, the nature of the soul, and pre-established harmony." At these words the dervish shut the door in their faces.

During this conversation the news had gone round that in Constantinople they had just strangled two viziers of the Divan and the mufti and impaled several of their friends. This catastrophe caused a great stir everywhere for a few hours. Pangloss, Candide, and Martin, returning to the little farm, came upon a good old man enjoying the fresh air by his door under a bower of orange trees. Pangloss, whose curiosity was as great as his love of reasoning, asked him the name of the mufti who had just been strangled.

"I know nothing about it," replied the good man, "and I have never known the name of any mufti or any vizier. I am entirely ignorant of the adventure that you are telling me about; I presume that in general those who meddle with public affairs sometimes perish miserably, and that they deserve it; but I never inquire what is going on in Constantinople; I content myself with sending there for sale the fruits of the garden that I cultivate."

Having said these words, he had the strangers come into his house; his two daughters and his two sons presented them with several kinds of sherbets which they made themselves, Turkish cream flavored with candied citron peel, oranges, lemons, limes, pineapples, pistachios, and Mocha coffee that had not been mixed with the bad coffee from Batavia and the West Indies. After which the two daughters of this good Moslem perfumed the beards of Candide, Pangloss, and Martin.

"You must have a vast and magnificent estate?" said Candide to the Turk.

"I have only twenty acres," replied the Turk; "I cultivate them with my children; work keeps away three great evils: boredom, vice, and need."

As Candide went back to his farm, he reflected deeply on the

Turk's remarks. He said to Pangloss and Martin: "That good old man seems to me to have made himself a life far preferable to that of the six Kings with whom we had the honor of having supper."

"Great eminence," said Pangloss, "is very dangerous, according to the report of all philosophers. For after all Eglon,[4] King of the Moabites, was assassinated by Ehud; Absalom was hanged by his hair and pierced with three darts; King Nadab son of Jeroboam was killed by Baasha, King Elah by Zimri, Ahaziah by Jehu, Athaliah by Jehoiada; Kings Jehoiakim, Jeconiah, and Zedekiah became slaves. You know how Croesus perished, Astyages, Darius, Dionysius of Syracuse, Pyrrhus, Perseus, Hannibal, Jugurtha, Ariovistus, Caesar, Pompey, Nero, Otho, Vitellius, Domitian, Richard II of England, Edward II, Henry VI, Richard III, Mary Stuart, Charles I, the three Henrys of France, the Emperor Henry IV? You know . . ."

"I also know," said Candide, "that we must cultivate our garden."

"You are right," said Pangloss, "for when man was put in the Garden of Eden, he was put there *ut operaretur eum,* to work; which proves that man was not born for rest."

"Let us work without reasoning," said Martin, "it is the only way to make life endurable."

All the little society entered into this laudable plan; each one began to exercise his talents. The little piece of land produced much. True, Cunégonde was very ugly; but she became an excellent pastry cook; Paquette embroidered; the old woman took care of the linen. No one, not even Friar Giroflée, failed to perform some service; he was a very good carpenter, and even became an honorable man; and Pangloss sometimes said to Candide: "All events are linked together in the best of all possible worlds; for after all, if you had not been expelled from a fine castle with great kicks in the backside for love of Mademoiselle Cunégonde, if you had not been subjected to the Inquisition, if you had not traveled about America on foot, if you had not given the Baron a great blow with your sword, if you had not lost all your sheep from the good country of Eldorado, you would not be here eating candied citrons and pistachios."

"That is well said," replied Candide, "but we must cultivate our garden."

---

[4] For this first group of Old Testament rulers, see Judges 3, II Samuel 18, and I and II Kings.

THE BACKGROUND OF *CANDIDE**
George R. Havens

A. THE PHILOSOPHY OF OPTIMISM

Whatever may have been the exact circumstances of the composition of *Candide,* it seems certain that it was written quickly. In 1758 Voltaire was 64 years old. His experience had been long and varied; he had read widely, particularly in connection with the preparation of his universal history known finally as the *Essai sur les mœurs;* he had written in all the important literary *genres* of his time; he had acquired for himself a position of relative independence, safety, and detachment at Les Délices. His intellectual development was complete; his style was formed; Voltaire was at the height of his powers, ready to produce the masterpiece which in its kind has never been surpassed or even equalled. What was the background out of which *Candide,* apparently so spontaneously, came?

ALEXANDER POPE (1688–1744):—Among the philosophical viewpoints dominant in eighteenth-century thought, that known by the misleading name of Optimism[1] held a high place.[xxix] Of this philosophy the English poet, Alexander Pope, was one of the chief exponents and popularizers. While living in England during the years 1726 to 1729, Voltaire had formed some personal acquaintance with Pope and had increased his knowledge of the latter's works. Then, in 1733 and 1734, after Voltaire's return to France, appeared Pope's most famous poem, his *Essay on Man,* still one of the classics of English literature. Voltaire, who read English fluently, received the poem almost immediately upon its appearance, the first two epistles probably as early as May, 1733.[2] Two months later, in a letter to his friend Thieriot, he commented upon the poem in an amusing mingling of French and English: "A propos d'épître, dites à M. Pope que je l'ai très bien reconnu[3] in his *Essay on Man;* 't is certainly his style. Now and then

---

* Reprinted from Voltaire, *Candide, ou l'Optimisme,* ed. George R. Havens (New York: Henry Holt and Co., 1934), pp. xxix–lii, by permission of Holt, Rinehart, and Winston, Inc.

1 See the important article by Arthur O. Lovejoy, "Optimism and Romanticism," *PMLA,* December, 1927.

2 Cf. my article in *Modern Language Notes* (November, 1928), "Voltaire's Marginal Comments upon Pope's *Essay on Man,*" p. 429.

3 ["With respect to the epistle, tell M. Pope that I very easily recognized him in his . . ."]

there is some obscurity; but the whole is charming."[4] Such a contrast of praise and criticism, in varying proportions, remains characteristic of nearly all of Voltaire's comments upon Pope during the rest of his life.

The *Essay on Man* became quickly popular on the continent of Europe and was translated into French and many other languages. In 1738 and 1739, Voltaire paid Pope the homage of imitation by writing his seven *Discours en vers sur l'Homme* which, without often following Pope closely, obviously took their general inspiration from his work. Likewise Voltaire composed in 1752, and in 1756 published, his *Poème sur la Loi naturelle,* which in many ways harmonized with Pope's attitude. By the general public therefore Voltaire in 1756 had come to be regarded, not altogether unfairly on the basis of his published work,[5] as a leading exponent of Optimism in France. Certainly at heart he was far from[xxx] holding such a viewpoint. This is clearly shown by his *Poème sur le Désastre de Lisbonne* of this same year 1756, the Preface of which was aimed directly at clarifying his attitude on Pope. Voltaire here was eager to state that he was by no means a literal follower of philosophical Optimism.

What was the view expressed by Pope in the *Essay on Man?* The reader who will give a little time to the four brief epistles of this poem followed by the *Universal Prayer* so frequently circulated with it will understand better the subject under discussion. A few quotations from the *Essay on Man* will help to make clear the author's thought.

Pope starts with the premise that this world must be a planned world and that God must have chosen the best plan for all nature and life.

> *Of Systems possible, if 'tis confest,*
> *That Wisdom infinite must form the best,*
> *Where all must full or not coherent be,*
> *And all that rises, rise in due degree;*
> *Then, in the scale of reas'ning life, 'tis plain,*
> *There must be, somewhere, such a rank as Man:*
>
> .   .   .   .
>
> *Respecting Man, whatever wrong we call,*
> *May, must be right, as relative to all.*
>
> .   .   .   .
>
> *Then say not Man's imperfect, Heaven in fault;*
> *Say rather, Man's as perfect as he ought:*

---

[4] Moland, XXXIII, 364. [Voltaire, *Œuvres complètes,* ed. Moland (Paris, 1877–1885), 52 vols.]

[5] Note Rousseau's admiration for *Le Poème sur la Loi naturelle* and his attitude toward the meaning of *Zadig* as expressed in the opening pages of his *Lettre sur la Providence* (Hachette), X, 122, 124. See below, pp. xl–xli. Cf. also Morize, p. xxxi.

.   .   .   .

> *Who finds not Providence all good and wise,*
> *Alike in what it gives, and what denies?*

Emphasizing the continuity of all creation, Pope says:

> *Vast chain of Being! which from God began,*
> *Natures ethereal, human, angel, man,*
> *Beast, bird, fish, insect, what no eye can see,*
> *No glass can reach; from Infinite to thee,*
> *From thee to Nothing.—On superior powers*
> *Were we to press, inferior might on ours;*[xxxi]
> *Or in the full creation leave a void,*
> *Where, one step broken, the great scale's destroy'd:*
> *From Nature's chain whatever link you strike,*
> *Tenth, or ten thousandth, breaks the chain alike.*

.   .   .   .

> *All are but parts of one stupendous whole,*
> *Whose body Nature is, and God the soul;*

The last four lines in this quotation summarize excellently the idea of the universe as a *plenum* or whole and state the concept of continuity, or the chain of being, about which so much is heard in the philosophy of Optimism. The First Epistle now closes with these equally characteristic lines:

> *All Nature is but Art, unknown to thee;*
> *All Chance, Direction, which thou canst not see;*
> *All Discord, Harmony not understood;*
> *All partial Evil, universal Good:*
> *And, spite of Pride, in erring Reason's spite,*
> *One truth is clear, WHATEVER IS, IS RIGHT.*

Thus the universe is declared to be essentially harmonious, partial evil (or evil to the individual) contributes to the universal good, and "whatever is, is right" and is in accordance with God's fundamental plan. The principle of continuity and the general good are further developed in Epistle III.

> *See Matter next, with various life endued,*
> *Press to one centre still, the gen'ral Good.*
> *See dying vegetables life sustain,*
> *See life dissolving vegetate again:*
> *All forms that perish other forms supply,*
> *(By turns we catch the vital breath, and die)*
> *Like bubbles on the sea of Matter born,*
> *They rise, they break, and to that sea return.*
> *Nothing is foreign: Parts relate to whole;*
> *One all-extending, all-preserving Soul*
> *Connects each being, greatest with the least;*[xxxii]
> *Made Beast in aid of Man, and Man of Beast:*
> *All served, all serving: nothing stands alone;*
> *The chain holds on, and where it ends, unknown.*

> . . . .
> *God in the nature of each being founds*
> *Its proper bliss, and sets its proper bounds:*
> *But as he framed a Whole, the Whole to bless,*
> *On mutual Wants built mutual Happiness:*
> *So from the first, eternal ORDER ran,*
> *And creature linked to creature, man to man.*

Epistle IV makes individual happiness consist in the general good.

> *Remember, Man, "the Universal Cause*
> *Acts not by partial, but by gen'ral laws";*
> *And makes what Happiness we justly call*
> *Subsist not in the good of one, but all.*
>
> . . . .
> *ORDER is Heaven's first law; and this confest,*
> *Some are, and must be, greater than the rest,*
> *More rich, more wise; but who infers from hence*
> *That such are happier, shocks all common sense.*
> *Heaven to Mankind impartial we confess,*
> *If all are equal in their Happiness:*
>
> . . . .
> *God sends not ill, if rightly understood;*
> *Or partial Ill is universal Good.*

Twice more in this final epistle Pope repeats his characteristic phrase: "Whatever is, is right," thus furnishing the direct source for the recurring ironical "tout est bien"[6] of *Candide*.

LEIBNITZ[7] (1646–1716):—Not only in Pope must we seek the philosophical background of Voltaire's *Candide*, but also in Leibnitz, who preceded Pope in time and outranked him as an original thinker. So far from being the ridiculous figure suggested by the Pangloss of *Candide*, Gottfried Wilhelm[xxxiii] Leibnitz was a mathematician and a scientist of high order, seeking earnestly the truth in every quarter, a student of all the great philosophers of past and present, a master of universal knowledge in a way truly phenomenal, a man comparable in importance to Descartes, Hobbes, Spinoza, and Newton. He was a physicist also, a co-discoverer with Newton (though independently of him) of differential calculus. Interested in jurisprudence, he was eager to bring about an alliance between the small German states, as well as to bridge the gap between Catholics and Protestants, and between the Reformed and Lutheran churches within Protestantism. As one of the most significant philosophers of his day, who has not been with-

---

6 ["All is well."]

7 The spelling *Leibnitz*, rather than *Leibniz*, has been followed here as better indicating the pronunciation to English-speaking readers.

out influence upon some aspects of modern philosophy, Leibnitz must not be judged merely by Voltaire's witty satire in *Candide*. In fact, Voltaire seems always to have respected Leibnitz the *man* and to have recognized the astounding breadth of his mind, while rejecting his metaphysical system, as he tended to reject all others likewise. "Toute la métaphysique," Voltaire wrote to Frederick the Great of Prussia as early as 1737, "contient deux choses: la première, tout ce que les hommes de bon sens savent; la seconde, ce qu'ils ne sauront jamais."[8]

Leibnitz was inclined to be more constructive than destructive, and since the building of a philosophical system is vastly more difficult and uncertain than finding the defects in those of others, it is not surprising that he laid himself open to attack. His endeavor was to reconcile a mechanistic interpretation of the universe with belief in a God whose ends are just and good. His effort was imperiled by the use of a special terminology too easily susceptible of ridicule and often misunderstood. Moreover, much of his most significant work remained unpublished until long after his death and even after the appearance of *Candide*. Some of it has only become known in recent years. He was unfortunate, too, in that his disciple, Wolff, actually weakened and misrepresented[xxxiv] his philosophy under the guise of clarifying and systematizing it. In spite of this, Leibnitz furnished Kant in many ways with a point of departure for his own philosophical system, was the real founder of German philosophy, and is highly esteemed by the philosophical idealists of the present day.

Leibnitz starts with two main assumptions: (1) God is good; (2) of all the possible worlds which God could have created he must therefore in creating this one have chosen the best. Leibnitz in no way suggests that this world is perfect and free from defects. On the contrary he acknowledges the existence of evil in the world, but reconciles it with belief in the goodness of God by assuming its inevitability and its moral value in the scheme of things. The world "is the expression, not of an indifferent all-powerful Will, but of an all-powerful Will which knows and decrees the best."[9] What is matter? No one even today knows. Leibnitz, in seeking to explain it, posited the existence of an indivisible something beyond the atom which he called the *monad*. All matter is then composed of monads which rise in due gradations from the lowest to the highest. Thus expression is given to the principle of continuity and the chain of being. The highest monad is God himself. Each monad is an entity with a certain degree of what might be called freely consciousness. The body and the mind do not interact, but they function according to a harmony

Leibnitz

---

[8] Moland, XXXIV, 249. ["All metaphysics contains two things: first, all that which men of good sense know; second, that which they will never know."]

[9] Robert Latta, *Leibnitz*, Oxford, 1898, p. 107.

which is pre-established. They act as it were in parallel lines. This is the celebrated "preëstablished harmony" of which Voltaire makes mock in *Candide*. Everything has its cause or, as Leibnitz puts it, its "sufficient reason," another phrase easily distorted for purposes of satire.

With his intense desire for clearness, Voltaire saw in Leibnitz only words, abstruse, heavy words, which might impress the uncritical, but which did not in any real sense explain. He saw in what was alled Optimism a dispiriting and really[xxxv] fatalistic philosophy sed by followers of Pope and Leibnitz in justification of the *status uo*. Making a rapidly moving synthesis of most of the ills which beset mankind, Voltaire set it in sharp contrast to the phrases "the best of possible worlds," "sufficient reason," and "preëstablished harmony." The result was *Candide,* which marked definitely the decline of Leibnitz's influence in France and ruined his prestige with many a reader both of that time and since.

At first only slightly acquainted with the writings of Leibnitz, Voltaire as early as the end of the year 1736[10] was introduced by Frederick the Great to the works of Wolff, the voluminous systematizer of the Leibnitzian philosophy. The mistress of Voltaire, Mme du Châtelet, with whom he was then living at Cirey in eastern France, was much interested in mathematics and physical science. With her usual passionate intensity of application she threw herself into the study of the abstruse system of Leibnitz. She was aided by the German mathematician, Kœnig, who, secured expressly for the purpose, spent some two years at Cirey around 1738 to 1740. At this time, Voltaire writes of himself and Mme du Châtelet: "Notre plus grande attention se tourna longtemps du côté de Leibnitz et de Newton."[11] While he himself preferred Newton, Mme du Châtelet wrote a treatise endeavoring to expound the Leibnitzian philosophy, and Voltaire was forced to take cognizance of the ideas of this German philosopher. He did so without enthusiasm, but he appears to have read some of his works at first hand, not merely refracted through Wolff,[12] and from this time some of the characteristic Leibnitzian phrases, "l'harmonie préétablie," "la raison suffisante,"[13] begin to appear, jocularly or ironically in his correspondence. By 1741 Voltaire is definitely hostile both to Leibnitz and to Wolff. In a letter to M. de Mairan he[xxxvi] writes: "Franchement, Leibnitz n'est venu que pour embrouiller les sciences. Sa raison

---

10 Moland, XXXIV, 196–97.
11 *Ibid.*, I, 8. ["Our greatest attention for a long while turned in the direction of Leibniz and Newton."]
12 Verne M. Pettit, *Voltaire's Opinion of Leibnitz* (unpublished Master's thesis, Ohio State University, 1930), pp. 18, 26, 37, 41, 46 n., 66.
13 ["Preëstablished harmony," "sufficient reason."]

insuffisante, sa continuité, son plein, ses monades, sont des germes de confusion dont M. Wolff a fait éclore méthodiquement quinze volumes in—4°, qui mettront plus que jamais les têtes allemandes dans le goût de lire beaucoup et d'entendre peu."[14] The Leibnitzian terms, "sufficient reason" (labeled *insufficient* by Voltaire), the principle of the continuity of all things, the *plenum* or all-embracing whole of the universe, the *monades,* appear together in this passage, forecasting the effective use to be made of them seventeen years later in *Candide.* In 1744, an ironical letter to the German, Martin Kahle, shows Voltaire's repertory of such terms complete for his purposes. "Au reste, si jamais vous comprenez quelque chose aux *monades, à l'harmonie préétablie;* et ... si vous découvrez aussi comment, tout étant nécessaire, l'homme est *libre,*[15] vous me ferez plaisir de m'en avertir. Quand vous aurez aussi démontré en vers ou autrement pourquoi tant d'hommes s'égorgent dans *le meilleur des mondes possibles,* je vous serai très obligé."[16] Thus the language of Pangloss, "le plus profond métaphysicien d'Allemagne,"[17] is already formed, awaiting only the provocative occasion and the manner of its use.

A great earthquake at Lisbon with its enormous destruction of life and property was to constitute, if not precisely the cause, at least a most important link in what might be called with M. Morize[18] the Leibnitzian *chain* of causes leading up to *Candide.*

B. THE EARTHQUAKE AT LISBON (1755)

On November 1, 1755, occurred at Lisbon a terrible earthquake, which, followed by a tidal wave and the inevitable fire,[xxxvii] destroyed the lives of from 30,000 to 40,000 people and caused property damage estimated at $100,000,000 in modern money. News traveled slowly in those days. It was the 4th of November before a courier could be dispatched from the midst of the disorder and terror.[19] It was two weeks

---

[14] Moland, XXXVI, 50. ["Frankly, Leibniz has only confused the sciences. His insufficient reason, his continuity, his plenum, his monads, are the germs of confusion of which M. Wolff has methodically hatched fifteen volumes in quarto, which will put German heads more than ever in the habit of reading much and understanding little."]

[15] *Nécessaire,* inevitable, (philos.) determined; *libre,* having the gift of Free Will. Thus two irreconcilable principles are presented.

[16] Moland, XXXVI, 309–10. Italics mine. ["Nevertheless, if you ever understand something about *monads, preëstablished harmony;* and ... if you also discover how, all being inevitable, man has *free will,* you will give me pleasure by informing me about it. When you also will have demonstrated in verse or otherwise why so many men cut their own throats in *the best of all possible worlds,* I shall be very obliged to you."]

[17] ["The most profound metaphysician of Germany."]

[18] Morize, pp. vii–viii. [Voltaire, *Candide,* ed. André Morize (Paris, 1913).]

[19] Unpublished letter of Du Pan to Mme Freudenreich, Nov. 23–24, 1755. Bibliothèque de Genève, Mss. Du Pan, V. f. 32 and verso.

later when this courier finally arrived in Paris with the news.[20] It
was November 23 when the first report of the disaster reached Geneva.[21] On the 24th Voltaire mentioned it in his correspondence.[22]
But if the news arrived slowly, it lost none of its effect by the delay.
We moderns are in danger of becoming blasé and callous from the
very rapidity and completeness with which crime and disaster and
accident are heaped upon our breakfast tables every morning in the
daily papers. It was not so in the eighteenth century. The first details
of the disaster have been reported and preserved for us in private
letters whose words still evoke a shudder at the horror of the news.
Ministers preached upon the subject endeavoring to justify the ways
of God to man. The question of Providence was hotly debated in
private discussion.

Voltaire's brief letter to one of the Tronchin brothers at Lyons,
written on November 24, shows his first unpremeditated impressions
which already forecast some parts of *Candide*.

Voilà, monsieur, une physique bien cruelle. On sera bien embarrassé à
deviner comment les lois du mouvement opèrent des désastres si effroyables
dans *le meilleur des mondes possibles;* cent mille fourmis, notre prochain,
écrasées tout d'un coup dans notre fourmilière, et la moitié périssant sans
doute dans des angoisses inexprimables, au milieu des débris dont on ne
peut les tirer, des familles ruinées aux bouts de l'Europe, la fortune de cent
commerçants de votre patrie abîmée dans[xxxviii] les ruines de Lisbonne. Quel
triste jeu de hasard que le jeu de la vie humaine! Que diront les prédicateurs,
surtout si le palais de l'inquisition est resté debout? Je me flatte qu'au moins
les révérends pères inquisiteurs auront été écrasés comme les autres. Cela
devrait apprendre aux hommes à ne point persécuter les hommes; car, tandis
que quelques sacrés coquins brûlent quelques fanatiques, la terre engloutit
les uns et les autres. Je crois que nos montagnes nous sauvent des tremblements de terre.[23]

Here already appears the phrase, *le meilleur des mondes possibles,* soon to be used as the *Leitmotiv* of *Candide*. Here, too, appear

---

20 *Ibid.* Also D'Argenson, *Mémoires*, Paris, 1859–67, IX, 131.

21 Du Pan to Mme Freudenreich.

22 Moland, XXXVIII, 511.

23 *Ibid.* ["Here, sir, is a very cruel physics. One will find it quite difficult to
divine how the laws of motion bring about such frightful disasters in *the best of
all possible worlds;* one hundred thousand ants, our neighbor, crushed all in one
blow in our ant-hill, and half of them perishing no doubt in unspeakable agonies
in the midst of debris from which they could not be pulled, families all over
Europe ruined, the fortune of a hundred merchants of your native land engulfed
in the ruins of Lisbon. What a sad game of chance is the game of human life!
What will the preachers say, especially if the Palace of the Inquisition has remained standing? I hope at least that the reverend fathers inquisitors will have
been crushed like the others. That should teach men never to persecute men, for
while some holy rascals burn some fanatics, the earth swallows them all. I believe
that our mountains save us from earthquakes."]

the earthquake and also the attack upon the Inquisition which figure so prominently in the first part of the novel. Thus some of Voltaire's most important materials are now ready to his hand, accompanied by a decided urge in the direction of using them.

First, however, was published his philosophic poem on the earthquake, *Le Poème sur le désastre de Lisbonne*. It was written almost at once during the early days of December,[24] retouched several times in the direction of prudence at the advice of friends, and issued along with the *Poème sur la Loi naturelle* as one of his "deux petits sermons"[25] during the first part of 1756. In serious mood, protesting in the Preface to the poem against the fatalistic implications of ineradicable evil in the so-called Optimism of Pope and Leibnitz,[26] Voltaire endeavors to steer a delicate course between a too dangerous heresy on the one hand and on the other an orthodoxy unbefitting the poem's none too orthodox author. The irony, the mockery, the ridicule of *Candide* would be out of place here,[xxxix] but Voltaire calls in question the operation of Providence in connection with the problem of Evil from a viewpoint essentially similar. His attitude was at once to draw forth a protest from the man who was soon to become his great rival, Jean-Jacques Rousseau.

C.   JEAN-JACQUES ROUSSEAU (1712–1778)

Eighteen years younger than Voltaire, Jean-Jacques Rousseau at this time had only recently attained fame. His *Discours sur les sciences et les arts*, published in 1750, challenged the popular, if somewhat fatuous, modern tendency to believe that material and moral progress go necessarily hand in hand. It had won for him a prize from the Academy of Dijon and the reputation of *un homme à paradoxes*. A second work, his *Discours sur l'origine de l'inégalité parmi les hommes*, appearing in 1755, attacked social inequality among men. Like modern socialists and communists, Rousseau found the cause of this inequality in the institution of private property. Needless to say, the wealthy occupant of Les Délices did not share Rousseau's views in these two discourses and on August 30, 1755, wittily poked fun at the second in a letter of acknowledgment addressed to the author himself. The relations of the two men still remained, however, friendly.

Nearly a year later, August 18, 1756, Rousseau wrote Voltaire a very long letter acknowledging the receipt of his two poems on *La*

---

[24] See my article, "Voltaire's Pessimistic Revision of the Conclusion of his *Poème sur le Désastre de Lisbonne,*" *Mod. Lang. Notes,* December, 1929, p. 489, n.

[25] Moland, XXXIX, 26. Thus Voltaire hits at the sermons on the same subject by his ministerial friends and acquaintances at Geneva and elsewhere. ["Two little sermons."]

[26] *Ibid.,* IX, 468.

Loi naturelle and on *Le Désastre de Lisbonne,* agreeing with the viewpoint of the former, but refuting at great length the latter. Rousseau defends Pope and Leibnitz as consoling. The origin of moral evil he finds in man's Free Will. For this evil man is therefore responsible. Physical evil Rousseau considers relatively negligible, though much increased by the regrettable luxury and complexity of civilization. Seeming irregularities in nature are to be accounted due to laws still unknown to us. Rousseau suggests that the [xli] familiar phrase "tout est bien"[27] might be worded more accurately "le tout est bien," or "tout est bien pour le tout."[28] Providence is to be thought of as general in its operation rather than particular, but the charge of injustice to the individual in this present life is met by belief in immortality and the rewards and punishments of a future existence. Finally, Rousseau rejects "l'état de doute" as "trop violent pour mon âme,"[29] attacks atheism and intolerance, and asserts his agreement with the theism expressed in Voltaire's previous works.[30] This letter is commonly called Rousseau's *Lettre sur la Providence.*

Promptly on September 12, Voltaire wrote from Les Délices a brief, but courteous, reply to Rousseau in which he excused himself from engaging in a philosophical debate on account of the serious illness of one of his nieces, Mme de Fontaine, as well as because of his own ill health, hoped that Rousseau would return to his native city, Geneva, and closed: "Comptez que de tous ceux qui vous ont lu, personne ne vous estime plus que moi malgré mes mauvaises plaisanteries, et que de tous ceux qui vous verront, personne n'est plus disposé à vous aimer tendrement."[31] It would hardly be possible to be more polite than Voltaire is here, even to the point of half apologizing for the "mauvaises plaisanteries" of his letter of the preceding year directed against the *Discours sur l'inégalité.* Such indeed was Rousseau's own first impression, as he wrote a few days later to Mme d'Epinay: "J'ai reçu hier une lettre obligeante de Voltaire."[32] Such too was Rousseau's attitude four months later on January 25, 1757, in a letter to Dr. Tronchin of Geneva: "J'ai été charmé de la réponse de M. de Voltaire; un homme qui a pu prendre ma lettre comme il a fait mérite le titre de philosophe, et l'on ne peut être plus porté que je le suis à joindre à l'admiration que j'eus toujours pour ses écrits l'estime

---

27 ["All is well."]

28 ["The whole is well" or "all is well for the whole."]

29 ["The state of doubt" as "too violent for my soul."]

30 Rousseau, *Œuvres* (Hachette), X, 122–33.

31 *Ibid.,* 133–34, and Moland, XXXIX, 108–09. ["Consider that of all those who have read your works, no one values you more than I in spite of my wicked jokes, and of all those who will see you, no one is more disposed to love you tenderly."]

32 Rousseau, *Œuvres,* X, 136. ["I received yesterday an obliging letter from Voltaire."]

et l'amitié pour sa[xli] personne."[33] Truly all is for the best in the best possible of worlds as far as the relations of the two men up to this time are concerned.

But in October, 1758,—probably too late to affect the first draft of *Candide*—appeared Rousseau's *Lettre à D'Alembert sur les spectacles*, which attacked the latter's article in the Encyclopedia favoring the establishment of a theater at Geneva. Voltaire himself eagerly desired a theater there and resented Calvinistic restrictions on his favorite literary *genre*. Indeed he was thought to have partly inspired D'Alembert's article on this point. Therefore Voltaire fell within the scope of Rousseau's attack also, and not unnaturally considered him in consequence a sort of renegade now gone over to the enemy and aligned against the Encyclopedia and the philosophic party so dear to Voltaire's heart. Hostility increased between the two men with no continuance of direct relations until finally on June 17, 1760, Rousseau wrote to Voltaire disclaiming responsibility for the unauthorized publication in the middle of 1759 of the so-called *Lettre sur la Providence*. In the final paragraph Rousseau suddenly without warning threw into the Patriarch's face the startling words: "Je ne vous aime point, monsieur ... Je vous hais enfin,"[34] which meant a definite breach never to be closed.

Many years later, when Rousseau wrote the second part of his famous *Confessions*, which were published only after his death, his earlier view of the reception accorded his *Lettre sur la Providence* was changed by the embittered relations between himself and Voltaire. Rousseau dwelt then upon the fact that he had never received a detailed reply to the philosophical arguments developed at such great length. "Depuis lors," he wrote, "Voltaire a publié cette réponse qu'il m'avait promise, mais qu'il ne m'a pas envoyée. Elle n'est autre que le roman de *Candide* dont je ne puis parler, parce que je ne l'ai[xlii] pas lu."[35] Already in 1764 one of Rousseau's friends, the Prince of Wurtemberg, had shown surprise that the *Letter on Providence* had not *prevented* the writing of *Candide*. On March 11 of that year Rousseau repied: "Vous êtes surpris que ma *Lettre sur la Providence* n'ait pas empêché *Candide* de naître? C'est elle, au contraire, qui lui a

---

[33] Rousseau, *Correspondance*, Paris, Colin, III (1925), p. 8. ["I was charmed by the answer from M. de Voltaire; a man who could take my letter as he has done merits the title of philosopher, and one cannot be more disposed than I am to join to the admiration that I always had for his writing esteem and friendship for his person."]

[34] Rousseau, *Œuvres* (Hachette), X, 228. ["I do not like you at all, sir ... In short, I hate you."]

[35] *Ibid.*, VIII, 308. ["Since then, Voltaire has published that answer that he had promised me but which he has not sent me. It is none other than the novel *Candide*, of which I cannot speak because I have not read it."]

donné naissance; *Candide* en est la réponse."³⁶ According to Rousseau, then, *Candide* is primarily a reply to his *Letter on Providence*.

Such a view is an exaggeration. Voltaire's attitude toward the question of Providence had already been made clear in the *Poème sur le désastre de Lisbonne* which had in fact provoked Rousseau's long rejoinder. Rousseau's *Letter on Providence* appears as one more incident, important certainly, but not absolutely essential, in the chain of circumstances connected with the genesis of *Candide*.

Nevertheless certain indications may support Rousseau's view in milder form. While it is true that nothing in *Candide* shows him to be attacked in the same fundamental way as Pope and Leibnitz, we should not forget that every blow leveled at them must likewise hit Rousseau who in his *Letter* had made himself their spokesman and consequently the most important contemporary defender of Optimism. It is noteworthy that the implication of both of Rousseau's statements relative to *Candide* is that he was reflecting an opinion of others as well as himself. Moreover, in his extraordinary letter of rupture in 1760 Rousseau stated that Voltaire had been asked and had refused permission to allow the *Letter on Providence* to be printed. If this is true—and Rousseau could hardly have ventured to write such a statement to Voltaire if it were not—it seems to indicate a certain pique on the part of the latter caused perhaps by the effectiveness of Rousseau's *Letter* and a consequent unwillingness on the part of the Patriarch either to reply or to be left in the embarrassing position of not having replied. Thus Rousseau[xliii] added by his *Letter on Providence* one more reason for Voltaire to attack Optimism, but after his own manner and with his own weapons.

" 'Je me flattais, dit Pangloss, de raisonner un peu avec vous des effets et des causes, du meilleur des mondes possibles, de l'origine du mal, de la nature de l'âme, et de l'harmonie préétablie.' Le Derviche à ces mots leur ferma la porte au nez."³⁷ Whether intentionally or not, this passage in *Candide*—its brusqueness apart—admirably paints the situation between Pangloss-Rousseau and the Derviche-Voltaire, who had refused to be drawn into discussion.

At the close of his *Letter on Providence*, Rousseau had admitted consciousness of his suffering, but had insisted upon the consolations of Optimism. The passage was made the more pointed by a deliberate contrast with Voltaire enjoying wealth and all the external elements of good fortune. Should we perhaps see Voltaire's rejoinder in the final chapter of *Candide*? "Pangloss avouait qu'il avait toujours horriblement souffert; mais ayant soutenu une fois que tout allait à merveilles,

---

36 *Ibid.*, XI, 123–24, and *Correspondance* (Colin), X, 347. ["You are surprised that my Letter on Providence may not have prevented *Candide* from being born? On the contrary, it is the letter that has given it birth; *Candide* is the answer to it."]

37 [See p. 69, paragraph 7, of this book.]

il le soutenait toujours, et n'en croyait rien."[38] The *Discourse on Inequality* probably comes in for attack in the sentence: "Ah! que dirait maître Pangloss, s'il voyait comme la pure nature est faite?",[39] though Voltaire had never had illusions about the supposed joys of primitivism, but constantly—even as early as *Le Mondain* (1736), when Rousseau was unheard of—had preferred the delights of civilized society. Voltaire had annotated his copy of the *Discours sur l'inégalité* with derogatory remarks, the strongest of which was directed against Rousseau's attack upon private property. Though the latter was by no means alone in expressing such views, it is probable that Voltaire's thrust at communism is particularly aimed in his direction. "Hélas, dit Candide, le bon Pangloss m'avait souvent prouvé que[xliv] les biens de la terre sont communs à tous les hommes, que chacun y a un droit égal."[40]

All in all, however, the direct thrusts at Rousseau are neither numerous, violent, nor absolutely certain. They were written, it should be remembered, in 1758 before the relations between the two men became completely embittered, and it is perhaps surprising that Voltaire did not take occasion to insert in his additions to *Candide* of 1761 invective against Rousseau as he did against some of his lesser enemies. Satisfied with the effectiveness of his work as a whole and his mockery of Optimism, Voltaire did not trouble in *Candide* to attack Rousseau more directly. If the latter saw himself hit, he was probably right in appropriating to himself much of the general satire of Optimism and Providence. In this sense, but less exclusively than Rousseau thought, his *Letter on Providence* did no doubt have a certain repercussion upon the composition of *Candide*.

D. "SCARMENTADO" (1756)

Already in 1756 Voltaire had published a brief work only a few pages in length characterized by M. Lanson as a sort of preliminary sketch of *Candide*.[41] This work is known as the *Histoire des Voyages de Scarmentado*. Not only the general framework of the rapid voyage of adventure and disillusion, common to most of Voltaire's *contes philosophiques,* ties *Scarmentado* and *Candide* together, but many of the same countries are visited in both: France, England, Spain, Holland, Turkey, North Africa. The situation of the lady Fatelo between three suitors, Scarmentado, and the Reverend Fathers Poignardini and Aconiti, exactly parallels that of Cunégonde amid the Grand In-

---

38 [See p. 68, paragraph 5, of this book.]
39 [See p. 29, paragraph 8, of this book.]
40 [See p. 16, paragraph 6, of this book.]
41 G. Lanson, *Voltaire* (Grands Ecrivains français), p. 150. Cf. also Morize, p. lii.

quisitor, Don Issachar, and Candide. The execution of Barneveldt shocks Scarmentado[xlv] on his arrival in Holland just as that of Admiral Byng horrifies Candide in England. Notre Dame d'Atocha, Muley-Ismael are referred to in both. The experiences of Scarmentado with the Inquisition resemble strikingly, even to the language used for their narration, those of Candide. Both works mention the *devils* and the *flames* painted on the costumes of the victims of the Auto-da-fé. In *Scarmentado,* there are "des chrétiens qui avaient épousé leurs commères";[42] in *Candide,* as M. Morize indicates,[43] the detail becomes more precise; it is "un Biscayen convaincu d'avoir épousé sa commère."[44] The "cachot très frais"[45] of *Scarmentado* becomes the more piquant expression, "des appartements d'une extrême fraîcheur,"[46] of *Candide.* Of his treatment by the Inquisition, Scarmentado says: "J'en fus quitte pour la discipline,"[47] and Candide is released after being "fessé en cadence."[48] Both works refer to a dispute over "la manière de faire la révérence."[49] Both bring in the African corsairs and their victims. A reference in *Scarmentado* to "une espèce de terre jaune qui par elle-même n'est bonne à rien"[50] is a first hint of the yellow mud and precious pebbles (gold and diamonds) which arouse the covetousness of Candide and Cacambo in El Dorado. The parallels are numerous enough and definite enough to show a real connection in Voltaire's mind between the two works. Thus *Scarmentado* occupies a somewhat special place among the numerous sources of *Candide* to be found in other works of Voltaire himself. It is in effect something of a little *Candide,* much less interesting, very slightly developed, lacking the important thrusts at Optimism and Providence, but constituting nevertheless a sort of embryo of the greater work which was to be.

E.   THE "ESSAI SUR LES MŒURS" (1753–1756)

The *Essai sur les Mœurs,* first known as *L'Histoire universelle,* is Voltaire's ambitious, and for the time remarkably[xlvi] successful, attempt at a synthesis of universal history. With a true spirit of cosmopolitanism he tried to see the history of the human race as a whole and to gather up from it those facts of real significance in the development of humanity. Voltaire saw in history, not primarily the bare

---

42 ["Christians who had married their Godmothers."]
43 Morize, p. 40.
44 ["A Biscayan convicted of having married his Godmother."]
45 ["Very cool dungeon."]
46 ["Apartments of an extreme coolness."]
47 ["I got off with chastisement."]
48 ["Flogged in time."]
49 ["The manner of making a bow."]
50 ["A kind of yellow dirt that by itself is good for nothing."]

narrative of wars and battles, reigns and dynasties, but rather the story of the gradual increase of liberty and comfort, the progress of invention, the slow spread of tolerance, the improvement little by little of conditions of life for the people as a whole. True, it is a record also of the wickedness and folly of mankind. The scourge of war without rhyme or reason constantly takes its terrible toll. Monks and nuns withdrawn into monasteries and convents deprive humanity of the service of large groups of men and women, who might have contributed to agriculture and manufacture. There is much to be put on the debit side of the ledger. Nevertheless there *is* progress and the present after all is better than the past, even though improvement comes on laggard feet. Thus Voltaire viewed history with clairvoyant, yet with hopeful, eyes.

For years Voltaire had been working upon this "philosophic" interpretation of universal history. He had started it at Cirey in order to convince Mme du Châtelet that history was not merely the dull record of dates and battles. After the publication of some fragments serially in the *Mercure de France,* an unauthorized edition suddenly appeared in 1753, much to Voltaire's disgust. He immediately published a third volume in 1754 and followed this in 1756 with a tentatively complete edition whose four volumes were supplemented by a reprinting of *Le Siècle de Louis XIV* (1751) making three volumes more. Other reworkings and additions testified to Voltaire's unremitting zeal in perfecting his work.

Obviously a history of such immense scope required great breadth of reading and this reading came to a head in the years immediately preceding *Candide.* In fact during 1758, the very year when the novel was composed, Voltaire was[xlvii] engaged in preparing for a new edition "les chapitres de la religion mahométane, des possessions françaises et anglaises en Amérique, des anthropophages, des jésuites du Paraguai, des duels, des tournois, du commerce, du concile de Trente, et bien d'autres."[51] This important material on the French and English colonies in America, cannibalism, and particularly on the Jesuit rule in Paraguay was fresh in his mind at this time and quite naturally figured prominently in *Candide.* As M. Morize has pointed out, the abstract generalizations of the *Essai* become concrete persons and incidents in the novel. The Anabaptists of Holland become "un bon anabaptiste, nommé Jacques."[52] The Jesuit officers of Paraguay are personified by "le Révérend Père provincial,"[53] who turns out to be the brother of Cunégonde. The treatment of captured Christians by the Moors furnishes the background for part of the

51 Moland, XXXIX, 353. ["The chapters on the Mohammedan religion, the French and English possessions in America, cannibals, the Jesuits of Paraguay, duels, tournaments, commerce, the Council of Trent, and many others."]

52 ["A good Anabaptist named Jacques."]

53 ["The Reverend Provincial Father."]

narrative of the sufferings of "la vieille."[54] Where in the *Essai* the
author aims for the most part at sober accuracy, in *Candide* he sometimes intentionally heightens the tone for picturesque effect. Thus in
the former the Spanish officers are allowed by the Jesuits a stay of
only three days in Paraguay; in the latter we are told that they must
not remain more than three hours. Some of the changes in *Candide*
are due to the confusing or blending of various sources, some to the
general fact that in a work of fiction the author could cease verification
and invent, change, combine, omit, as he pleased and in accordance
with the effect desired. Throughout *Candide* details too numerous to
mention find their inspiration in reading done for the *Essai*. The novel
was composed when Voltaire was at the summit of his intellectual
development, when his rich memory was particularly well stocked with
historical information, allusions, and anecdotes, and with all the fund
of his own active life and experience. It is no wonder that *Candide*
could be written rapidly. It was a natural and nearly spontaneous
synthesis of a long chain of circumstances which had gone before. In
this chain of circumstance[xlviii] Voltaire's own work, the *Essai sur les
Mœurs,* occupied a very important place and furnished much of the
material out of which his greatest work of fiction was composed.

F.   THE NOVEL OF ADVENTURE AND THE PHILOSOPHIC CONTE

The philosophy of Optimism, Leibnitz, Pope, the earthquake at
Lisbon, Jean-Jacques Rousseau and the discussion over Providence,
Scarmentado, the *Essai sur les Mœurs,* all played prominent parts in
furnishing inspiration or material for *Candide.* All through the novel
numberless incidents can be directly traced to one or another of these
sources. There is still another important influence, however, which determined the very form and framework in which the novel was composed. When Voltaire sat down to write his novel, the main characteristics of his rapidly-moving plot were ready to his hand. He had only
to draw upon the conventionalities of the popular novels of adventure
and thwarted love and treat ironically what his predecessors had written seriously. Thus his satire falls not only upon his philosophical opponents, his numerous personal enemies, and upon human frailty,
ferocity, and wickedness in general, but also upon the unreality and
exaggeration of popular romance throughout the seventeenth and
eighteenth centuries down to the time of the composition of *Candide*
itself.

In the seventeenth century two main tendencies in the French
novels of the time early revealed themselves, corresponding to the two
ever-divergent characteristics of the human mind in all ages, the
idealistic and the realistic. Thus the pastoral romance of Honoré
d'Urfé, *L'Astrée* (1607–1627), under the guise of shepherds and

---

54 ["The old woman."]

shepherdesses, represented the *préciosité,* the high-flown sentiments, and the somewhat affected language which as ideals at least were supplanting in aristocratic circles the blunt grossness of the troubled period of civil war immediately preceding. Like the love-sick hero Céladon separated from his beloved Astrée, Candide too[xlix] after leaving El Dorado will carve the name of his absent sweetheart Cunégonde on the bark of trees, but in the former case the author is serious, in the latter satirical. Gomberville in *Polexandre* (1619–1637), La Calprenède in *Cassandre* (1642–1645) and in *Cléopâtre* (1647), Mlle de Scudéry in *Ibrahim ou l'illustre Bassa* (1641), *Artamène ou le grand Cyrus* (1649–1653), and *Clélie* (1654–1660) with its famous "Carte du Tendre," abandon the pastoral for the heroic-gallant novel of marvelous adventure and unrealistic courtship in lands equally foreign to author and reader. Shipwrecks, kidnappings by rival suitors, the incursions of corsairs and pirates, recognition scenes in which long-separated characters are suddenly and unexpectedly reunited, furnish the regular stock in trade of these and many later novelists. These very same elements reappear satirically in *Candide.* Such in brief was the idealistic novel of the seventeenth century. It was early satirized in realistic *bourgeois* novels like Sorel's *Francion* (1622) and *Le Berger extravagant* (1627–1628), Scarron's *Roman comique* (1651–1657), and Furetière's *Roman bourgeois* (1665). The critic Boileau in a brief, witty dialogue, *Les Héros de roman,* composed in 1665, but not printed until 1688, likewise effectively poked fun at the same excesses. In attitude at least, if not in manner, Voltaire in *Candide* continues this tradition of matter-of-fact common sense and *terre à terre* realism. Perhaps even Cervantes's *Don Quijote* (1605–1615), of which Voltaire had in his library the Spanish original as well as a French translation, was not entirely without influence in this connection, but, if so, it constituted only one more impulse in the direction he was naturally inclined to follow.

In the eighteenth century the novels of D'Urfé, Gomberville, La Calprenède, and Mlle de Scudéry continued to be popular. They were not killed off by the satire of Sorel, Scarron, Furetière, or Boileau. All but Gomberville were represented in the library of Voltaire himself. Of D'Urfé's *Astrée* Lenglet du Fresnoy, a contemporary authority, wrote in 1734: "Sa réputation se soutient toujours depuis plus d'un[1] siècle."[55] Other novelists continued the tradition of exaggerated fiction and adventure. Although the Abbé Prévost is today remembered for the classic simplicity of his *Manon Lescaut* (1731), his contemporaries thought especially of the now nearly forgotten *Mémoires et Aventures d'un homme de qualité* (1728–1731), of *Cléveland, fils naturel de Cromwell* (1731–1739), of *Le Doyen de Killerine* (1736–1740), or of *L'Histoire d'une Grecque moderne* (1740), filled with "torrents of

---

55 Gordon de Percel [Lenglet du Fresnoy], *De l'usage des romans,* Amsterdam, 1734, II, p. 43. ["His reputation still holds up for more than a century now."]

tears," swooning heroines, unexpected recognition scenes, somber narratives of violent death by the duelist's sword, journeys from country to country, even on occasion amongst the "communistic" savages of America who in this communism somewhat resemble the inhabitants of El Dorado in *Candide*. Other novelists less well known than Prévost mixed similar ingredients and enjoyed wide popularity. No wonder Voltaire in his *Siècle de Louis XIV* (1751) decried "tous ces romans dont la France a été et est encore inondée" and called them "des productions d'esprits faibles qui écrivent avec facilité des choses indignes d'être lues par les esprits solides."[56] This is of course an excessive statement which takes no account of the occasional work of genius already in process of raising the novel in France to a major *genre*, but it was true of a great mass of popular productions and explains the plot of *Candide* and one whole side of its satire. Voltaire too wanted to try his hand at laughing the romantic novel of adventure out of court.

Still another tradition lay behind him. Many novels of travel had been used as vehicles for ideas. It was safer in an age of censorship to present under the guise of fiction criticism of contemporary society or admiration for the idealized manners and customs of primitive peoples of far-off lands. All sorts of extraordinary and imaginary voyages, as well as occasional real voyages, fulfilled this function as *romans*[II] *philosophiques*. Foigny's *La terre australe connue* or *Les Aventures de Jacques Sadeur* (1676), Tissot de Patot's *Voyages et Aventures de Jacques Massé* (1710), and Denis Vairasse's *Histoire des Sévarambes* (1677–1679) are three of the most important. Even the *Relations of* Jesuit missionaries furnished similar material. Garcilaso de la Vega's *Histoire des Yncas, Roys du Peru,* had appeared in French translation in 1633 and was several times reprinted during the eighteenth century. These works along with Sir Walter Raleigh's *Discoverie of Guiana,* first published at the end of the sixteenth century, but available in a French translation of 1722, are especially significant here as the main sources of the details of Voltaire's Utopia which as the mythical El Dorado furnished a foil to the realistic horrors of the rest of Candide's world. Add to these such works as Fénelon's *Télémaque* (1699), Montesquieu's *Lettres persanes* (1721), Le Sage's picaresque *Gil Blas* (1715–1735), to which *Candide* bears interesting resemblances, and numerous *contes philosophiques,* now forgotten but indicative of the great popularity of this rising *genre,* and we can more easily understand why Voltaire even in his old age should feel that here was a vehicle for his ideas too important to neglect. Furnishing a marvelous synthesis both of his own ideas and of what had gone before him, Voltaire did not so much create, he surpassed.[III]

---

56 Moland, XIV, 142. ["All these novels with which France has been and still is inundated" . . . "the productions of weak minds that write with facility things unworthy to be read by strong minds."]

PART TWO

COMMENTS ON *CANDIDE* AS A WORK OF ART

"THE BEST COMIC FOOL"*
Nicolas-Claude Thieriot

Oh most cherished *Candide,* most excellent author and inventor of quips and jests! Your book is snatched from hand to hand. It so delights the heart that those who usually laugh with tight lips are forced to laugh with open mouths . . . Why, you have every right to call yourself the best old comic fool that ever was seen on this earth, where you will live a hundred years, more like Lucian, Rabelais, and Swift than all three put together.

"GAIETY AND BAD TASTE"†
Friedrich M. Grimm

Gaiety is one of the rarest qualities to be found in wits. We had not read anything diverting in literature for a long time: M. de Voltaire has just now cheered us up with a little novel entitled *Candide, or Optimism,* translated from the German of Dr. Ralph. One should not judge this production with severity; it would not hold up under serious criticism. There is in *Candide* neither order, nor plan, nor wisdom,[85] nor those fortunate strokes of the pencil that one meets in some English novels of the same type; you will find there, on the contrary, many things of bad taste, others of vulgarity, indecent talk, and filth without any disguise to make them bearable; however, the gaiety, the fluency—which never desert M. de Voltaire, who banishes from his most frivolous as well as his most thoughtful works that pretentiousness that spoils everything—of the bolts and flashes of wit that fly from him every instant make the reading of *Candide* most amusing.[86]

---

* From Nicolas-Claude Thieriot, letter to Voltaire, dated February 23, 1759. Quoted in Norman L. Torrey, *The Spirit of Voltaire* (New York: Columbia University Press, 1938), p. 167. By permission of Norman L. Torrey.

† From Friedrich M. Grimm, letter dated March 1, 1759, in *Correspondance Littéraire, Philosophique et Critique par Grimm, Diderot, Raynal, Meister, Etc.* (Paris: Garnier Frères, 1878), IV, 85–86.

"GLOOM AND DISCONTENT"*
Edward Young

Why close a life so justly fam'd
    With such bold trash as this?
This for renown? yes, such as makes
    Obscurity a bliss:

Your trash, with mine, at open war,
    Is obstinately bent,[271]
Like wits below, to sow your tares
    Of gloom and discontent:

With so much sunshine at command,
    Why light with darkness mix?
Why dash with pain our pleasure? why
    Your Helicon with Styx?

Your works in our divided minds
    Repugnant passions raise,
Confound us with a double stroke,
    We shudder whilst we praise;

A curious web, as finely wrought
    As genius can inspire,
From a black bag of poison spun,
    With horror we admire.[272]

    . . . . .

Sound heads salvation's helmet seek,
    Resplendent are its rays,[273]
Let that suffice; it needs no plume,
    Of sublunary praise.

May this enable couch'd Voltaire
    To see that—"All is right,"
His eye, by flash of wit struck blind,
    Restoring to its sight;

If so, all's well: who much have err'd,
    That much have been forgiven;
I speak with joy, with joy he'll hear,
    "Voltaires are, now, in heaven."[274]

---

* From Edward Young, "Resignation," in *The Poetical Works of Edward Young* (Boston: Little, Brown & Co., 1859), II, 235–304. Young wrote "Resignation" in 1762, addressing Voltaire directly about *Candide* in the lines quoted here—lines 149–168 and 201–212 of Part II of the poem.

CANDIDE AND RASSELAS*
James Boswell

Voltaire's Candide, written to refute the system of Optimism, which it has accomplished with brilliant success, is wonderfully similar in its plan and conduct to Johnson's *Rasselas;* insomuch, that I have heard Johnson say, that if they had not been published so closely one after the other that there was not time for imitation, it would have been in vain to deny that the scheme of that which came latest was taken from the other. Though the proposition illustrated by both these works was the same, namely, that in our present state there is more evil than good, the intention of the writers was very different. Voltaire, I am afraid, meant only by wanton profaneness to obtain a sportive victory over religion, and to discredit the belief of a superintending Providence: Johnson meant, by shewing the unsatisfactory nature of things temporal, to direct the hopes of man to things eternal.[342]

"THAT SCOFFING PHILOSOPHY"†
Madame de Staël

Voltaire so well perceived the influence that metaphysics exercise over the general bias of the mind, that he wrote *Candide,* to combat Leibnitz. He took up a curious whim against final causes, optimism, free-will; in short, against all the philosophical opinions that exalt the dignity of man; and he composed *Candide,* that work of a diabolical gayety; for it appears to be written by a being of a different nature from ourselves, insensible to our condition, well pleased with our sufferings, and laughing like a demon or an ape at the miseries of that human species with which he has nothing in common.

The greatest poet of the age, the author of *Alzire, Tancrède, Merope, Zaïre,* and *Brutus,* showed himself in this work ignorant[143] of all the great moral truths which he had so worthily celebrated.

When Voltaire as a tragic author felt and thought in the character of another, he was admirable; but when he remains wholly himself, he is a jester and a cynic. The same versatility which enabled him to adopt the part of the personages whom he wished to represent, only too well inspired the language which in certain moments, was suited to Voltaire.

---

* From James Boswell, *The Life of Samuel Johnson, LL.D.,* ed. George Birkbeck Hill (New York: Macmillan and Co., 1887). The book was originally published in 1791.

† From Madame de Staël (The Baroness de Staël-Holstein, Anne Louise Germaine), *Germany,* ed. O. W. Wight (Boston: Houghton, Mifflin and Co., 1859), II, 143–144. The book, originally written in French and called *De l'Allemagne,* was first published in 1810.

Candide brings into action that scoffing philosophy, so indulgent in appearance, in reality so ferocious; it presents human nature under the most lamentable point of view, and offers us, in the room of every consolation, the sardonic grin, which frees us from all compassion for others, by making us renounce it for ourselves.[144]

"THIS DULL PRODUCT OF A SCOFFER'S PEN"*
William Wordsworth

    The book, which in my hand
Had opened of itself (for it was swoln
With searching damp, and seemingly had lain
To the injurious elements exposed
From week to week,) I found to be a work
In the French tongue, a Novel of Voltaire,
       His famous Optimist.

         . . . . .

. . . this dull product of a scoffer's pen,
Impure conceits discharging from a heart
Hardened by impious pride![429]

"A MASTERPIECE OF WIT"†
William Hazlitt

    . . . *Candide* is a masterpiece of wit. It has been called 'the dull product of a scoffer's pen'; it is indeed the 'product of a scoffer's pen';

---

* From William Wordsworth, "The Excursion" (II, 438–444, 484–486), in *The Complete Poetical Works of William Wordsworth*, ed. A. J. George (Boston: Houghton Mifflin Co., 1932), pp. 403–524. Wordsworth wrote the poem between 1795 and 1814.

    † From William Hazlitt, *Lectures on the English Poets* ("On Swift, Young, Gray, Collins, etc."), in *The Collected Works of William Hazlitt*, ed. A. R. Waller and Arnold Glover (London: J. M. Dent and Co., 1902), V, 114. First published in 1818 and 1819.

but after reading the Excursion, few people will think it *dull*. It is in the most perfect keeping, and without any appearance of effort. Every sentence tells, and the whole reads like one sentence. There is something sublime in Martin's sceptical indifference to moral good and evil. It is the repose of the grave. It is better to suffer this living death, than a living martyrdom. 'Nothing can touch him further.' The moral of *Candide* (such as it is) is the same as that of *Rasselas*: the execution is different. Voltaire says, 'A great book is a great evil.' Dr. Johnson would have laboured this short apophthegm into a voluminous common-place.

"MERE LOGICAL PLEASANTRY"*
Thomas Carlyle

In his other prose works, in his Novels, and innumerable Essays and fugitive pieces, the same clearness of order, the same rapid precision of view, again forms a distinguishing merit. His *Zadigs* and *Baboucs* and *Candides,* which, considered as products of imagination perhaps rank higher with foreigners than any of his professedly poetical performances, are instinct with this sort of intellectual life: the sharpest glances, though from an oblique point of sight, into at least the surface of human life, into the old familiar world of business; which truly, from his oblique station, looks oblique enough, and yields store of ridiculous combinations. The Wit, manifested chiefly in these and the like performances, but ever flowing, unless purposely restrained, in boundless abundance from Voltaire's mind, has been often and duly celebrated. It lay deep-rooted in his nature; the inevitable produce of such an understanding with such a character, and was from the first likely, as it actually proved in the latter period of his life, to become the main dialect in which he spoke and even thought. Doing all justice to the inexhaustible readiness, the quick force, the polished acuteness of Voltaire's Wit, we may remark, at the same time, that it was nowise the highest species of employment for such a[166] mind as his; that, indeed, it ranks essentially among the lowest species even of Ridicule. It is at all times mere logical pleasantry; a gaiety of the head, not of the heart; there is scarcely a twinkling of Humour in the whole of his numberless sallies.[167]

* From Thomas Carlyle, "Voltaire," in *Critical and Miscellaneous Essays* (London: Chapman and Hall, Ltd., 1869), pp. 166–167. "Voltaire" was originally published in the *Foreign Review* in 1829.

"A MOST EXTRAORDINARY PERFORMANCE"*
Henry Brougham

The best of the Romances are 'Zadig,' one beautiful chapter of which is taken from the more beautiful 'Hermit' of our Parnell; the 'Ingenu;' and, above all, 'Candide.' Some are disposed to place this last at the head of all his works; and even Dr. Johnson, with all his extreme prejudices against a Frenchman, an unbeliever, and a leveller, never spoke of it without unstinted admiration, professing that had he seen it, he should not have written 'Rasselas.' It is indeed a most extraordinary performance; and while it has such a charm that its repeated perusal never wearies, we are left in doubt whether most to admire the plain sound sense, above all cant, of some parts, or the rich fancy of others; the singular felicity of the design for the purposes it is intended to serve, or the natural yet striking graces of the execution. The lightness of the touch with which all the effects are produced —the constant affluence of the most playful wit—the humour wherever it is wanted, abundant, and never overdone—the truth and accuracy of each blow that falls, always on the head of the right nail—the quickness and yet the ease of the transitions—the lucid clearness[91] of the language, pure, simple, entirely natural—the perfect conciseness of diction as well as brevity of composition, so that there is not a line, or even a word, that seems ever to be superfluous, and a single phrase, sometimes a single word, nay a point, produces the whole effect intended; these are qualities that we shall in vain look for in any other work of the same description, perhaps in any other work of fancy. That there is caricature throughout, no one denies; but the design is to caricature, and the doctrines ridiculed are themselves a gross and intolerable exaggeration. That there occur here and there irreverent expressions is equally true; but that there is anything irreligious in the ridicule of a doctrine which is in itself directly at variance with all religion, at least with all the hopes of a future state, the most valuable portion of every religious system, may most confidently be denied. We have already seen Voltaire's sober and enlightened view of this subject in his moral poems, and those views agree with the opinions of the most pious Christians, as well as the most enlightened philosophers, who, unable to doubt the existence of evil in this world, or to account-for it in consistency with the Divine goodness, await with patient resignation the light which will dawn upon them in another state of being, and by which all these difficulties will be explained.[92]

---

* From Henry Brougham, *Lives of Men of Letters of the Time of George III* (London: Richard Griffin and Co., 1856), pp. 91–92.

"FRESH AND UNFLAGGING SPONTANEITY"*
John Morley

In dazzling and irresistible caricature Voltaire has no equal. There is no deep humor, as in *Don Quixote*, or *Tristram Shandy*, which Voltaire did not care for, or Richter's *Siebenkäs*, which he would not have cared for any more than de Staël did. He was too purely intellectual, too argumentative, too geometrical, and cared too much for illustrating a principle. But in *Candide, Zadig, L'Ingénu*, wit is as high as mere wit can go. They are better than *Hudibras*, because the motive is broader and more intellectual. Rapidity of play, infallible accuracy of stroke, perfect copiousness, and above all a fresh and unflagging spontaneity, combine with a surprising invention, to give these stories a singular quality, of which we most effectively observe the real brilliance by comparing them with the too numerous imitations that their success has unhappily invited since.

"CLARITY, SIMPLICITY, AND WIT"†
G. Lytton Strachey

Voltaire's philosophical views were curious. While he entirely discarded the miraculous from his system, he nevertheless believed in a Deity—a supreme First Cause of all the phenomena of the universe. Yet, when he looked round upon the world as it was, the evil and the misery in it were what seized his attention and appalled his mind. The optimism of so many of his contemporaries appeared to him a shallow crude doctrine unrelated to the facts of existence, and it was to give expression to this view that he composed the most famous of all his works—*Candide*. This book, outwardly a romance of the most flippant kind, contains in reality the essence of Voltaire's maturest reflections upon human life. It is a singular fact that a book which must often have been read simply for the[163] sake of its wit and its impro-

---

* From John Morley, *Voltaire* (London: Macmillan & Co. Ltd., 1893), p. 146. First published in 1872. By permission of Macmillan & Co. Ltd., London.

† From *Landmarks in French Literature* by G. Lytton Strachey (New York: Henry Holt and Co., 1912), pp. 163–165. Reprinted by permission of Holt, Rinehart and Winston, Inc., and Ernest Benn Limited, London.

priety, should nevertheless be one of the bitterest and most melancholy
that was ever written. But it is a safe rule to make, that Voltaire's
meaning is deep in proportion to the lightness of his writing—that it
is when he is most in earnest that he grins most. And, in *Candide*, the
brilliance and the seriousness alike reach their climax. The book is
a catalogue of all the woes, all the misfortunes, all the degradations,
and all the horrors that can afflict humanity; and throughout it Voltaire's grin is never for a moment relaxed. As catastrophe follows
catastrophe, and disaster succeeds disaster, not only does he laugh
himself consumedly, but he makes his reader laugh no less; and it is
only when the book is finished that the true meaning of it is borne
in upon the mind. Then it is that the scintillating pages begin to
exercise their grim unforgettable effect; and the pettiness and misery
of man seem to borrow a new intensity from the relentless laughter
of Voltaire.

But perhaps the most wonderful thing about *Candide* is that it
contains, after all, something more than mere pessimism—it contains
a positive doctrine as well. Voltaire's common sense withers the
Ideal; but it remains common sense. "Il faut cultiver notre jardin" is
his final word—one of the very few pieces of practical wisdom ever
uttered by a philosopher.[164]

Voltaire's style reaches the summit of its perfection in *Candide*;
but it is perfect in all that he wrote. His prose is the final embodiment
of the most characteristic qualities of the French genius. If all that
that great nation had ever done or thought were abolished from the
world, except a single sentence of Voltaire's, the essence of their
achievement would have survived. His writing brings to a culmination
the tradition that Pascal had inaugurated in his *Lettres Provinciales*:
clarity, simplicity, and wit—these supreme qualities it possesses in an
unequalled degree. But these qualities, pushed to an extreme, have
also their disadvantages. Voltaire's style is narrow; it is like a rapier—
all point; with such neatness, such lightness, the sweeping blade of
Pascal has become an impossibility. Compared to the measured march
of Bossuet's sentences, Voltaire's sprightly periods remind one almost
of a pirouette. But the pirouette is Voltaire's—executed with all the
grace, all the ease, all the latent strength of a consummate dancer; it
would be folly to complain; yet it was clear that a reaction was bound
to follow—and a salutary reaction. Signs of it were already visible in
the colour and passion of Diderot's writing; but it was not until the
nineteenth century that the great change came.[165]

VOLTAIRE'S USE OF IRONY*
William H. Barber

Many of the characteristic features of Voltaire's style in *Candide* will by now have become apparent, for they reflect aspects of the book which we have already discussed. The whole conception of the tale as a compact adventure story in which, after the manner of the picaresque novel but in much smaller compass, the central figures are hurried along through a rapid series of encounters, necessarily commits the author to a pungent brevity of manner. The many minor characters must be hit off in a phrase, situations must be presented in a sentence or two, journeys accomplished, intervals of time passed over, without the reader's losing that sense of furious pace which is essential, yet without his feeling that the sketch is too hasty to have life. Such demands were not uncongenial to Voltaire, whose natural manner was the epigrammatic rather than the rhetorical, and whose creative powers were not richly imaginative. And his success in meeting them is considerable. A typical passage is that in which he describes the adventures of Candide and Cacambo when, after leaving the Oreillons, they try to make for Cayenne:

Il n'était pas facile d'aller à la Cayenne; ils savaient bien à-peu-près de quel côté il fallait marcher; mais des montagnes, des fleuves, des précipices, des brigands, des sauvages, étaient partout de terribles obstacles. Leurs chevaux moururent de fatigue; leurs provisions furent consumées: ils se nourrirent un mois entier de fruits sauvages, et se trouvèrent enfin auprès d'une petite rivière bordée de cocotiers, qui soutinrent leur vie et leurs espérances [chap. 17].[1]

Weeks of hardship and manifold dangers are here brought to life for the reader in a paragraph, by a continual emphasis upon detail which is all the more evocative for being conveyed in a word—'des précipices, des brigands, des sauvages'—and by a discreet, but repeated insistence upon the travellers' reactions—'il n'était pas facile ...', 'de terribles obstacles', 'soutinrent leur vie et leurs espérances'. And all this is a necessary preparation for the climax of the hazardous river voyage to Eldorado and the contrasting scenes of comfort and safety which follow it.[35]

Again, the element of parody which, we have seen, is of the essence of the tale, finds reflection in the style. It occasions, for one thing, such caricatures of the conventional rhetorical outbursts of lovers as the one already quoted: 'à quoi me servira de prolonger mes misérables jours, puisque je dois les traîner loin d'elle dans les remords et dans

* From William H. Barber, *Voltaire: Candide* (London: Edward Arnold, Ltd., 1960), pp. 35–40. Reprinted by permission of the publisher.
[1] [See p. 30, paragraph 7; p. 31, paragraph 1, of this book.]

le désespoir?' (chap. 16).[2] But it also permits a degree of caricature which reaches the level of fantasy. The disease-ridden Pangloss whom Candide finds in Holland makes his appearance at first anonymously, as 'un gueux', and he is a figure of, deliberately, nightmarish repulsiveness—'tout couvert de pustules, les yeux morts, le bout du nez rongé, la bouche de travers, les dents noires, et parlant de la gorge, tourmenté d'une toux violente, et crachant une dent à chaque effort' (chap. 3).[3] Voltaire, indeed, insists upon the unreality of this vision by calling him 'le fantôme' in the next paragraph, immediately before shocking Candide, and the reader, with the revelation of the beggar's identity. This is fantasy of description which is parallel to the narrative fantasy of the resurrection of Pangloss and the Baron at the end of the tale.

The aspect of style in *Candide* which is most characteristic, however, and worth more attention than critics have commonly given it, is Voltaire's use of irony. Here, too, the manner of writing is organically related to the matter, for the central theme of *Candide*, the doctrine of optimism and its critique through the disillusionment of Candide, is one which, so to speak, spontaneously generates the ironical. Optimism, or at least the optimism of Pangloss, is essentially here a dogma, an article of faith which insists upon interpreting in a good sense, as ultimately beneficial, every event in human experience, however negative, degrading, or painful. Its natural tendency in expression is consequently towards euphemism. But neither author nor reader, nor ultimately Candide himself, shares this optimistic faith. Hence what is presented to us in the voice of optimism inevitably acquires the tone of irony: we interpret it as meaning the opposite of what it says, and the events of the story confirm for us, and convince Candide, that this is the correct interpretation. In this way, Voltaire effectively satirizes the optimists by transforming their[36] affirmations of dogmatic faith into ironic comments on a grim reality. The reader finds himself continually echoing the words of Candide himself in a moment of disillusionment: 'Si c'est ici le meilleur des mondes possibles, que sont donc les autres?'[4]

It is not only optimistic dogma, however, which creates such effects in *Candide*. Other satirical themes are also presented as generating irony. The barbaric primitiveness of life in Westphalia is revealed to the reader, not by any direct judgment, but through the confident pride of the inhabitants, who in their ignorance believe they live in 'le paradis terrestre'. And in the brilliant opening chapter of the book this is combined with our introduction to Pangloss and his optimism; Voltaire ironically adopts the tone of both, so that naïveté and dogmatism together give us a picture full of superlatives and at the same

---

2 [See p. 28, paragraph 4, of this book.]
3 [See p. 6, paragraph 6, of this book.]
4 [See p. 11, paragraph 5, of this book.]

time wholly deflatory in its effect. 'Monsieur le baron était un des plus puissants seigneurs de la Westphalie, car son château avait une porte et des fenêtres.' Pangloss 'prouvait admirablement qu'il n'y a pas d'effet sans cause, et que dans ce meilleur des mondes possibles, le château de monseigneur le baron était le plus beau des châteaux, et madame la meilleure des baronnes possibles'.[5] And by the same means the mock tragedy of Candide's expulsion from Thunder-ten-tronckh is enhanced: 'tout fut consterné dans le plus beau et le plus agréable des châteaux possibles'.[6]

War, too, is a satirical theme which can be presented ironically. Here also a gap exists between euphemism and reality, between the picture of war which rulers find it useful to sponsor—gay uniforms, cheerful music, and the splendour of heroism—and the grim and cruel facts. The recruiting officers who enlist Candide into the Bulgarian army themselves use the flattering convention of military heroism ironically, as a bait, when they talk of fortune and glory; but the irony is at first lost upon the still innocent Candide—it is only a little later that, shocked by his first taste of the harsh life of the recruit, he begins to suspect the fraud: 'Candide tout stupéfait ne démêlait pas encore trop bien comment il était un héros' (chap. 2).[7] It is in the battle-scene which opens the following chapter,[37] however, that Voltaire most fully exploits the ironical possibilities of the subject. His description begins in conventional tones of martial splendour, which are carefully thrown into discord by the last word of the second sentence: 'Rien n'était si beau, si leste, si brillant, si bien ordonné que les deux armées. Les trompettes, les fifres, les haut-bois, les tambours, les canons formaient une harmonie telle qu'il n'y en eut jamais en enfer.'[8] Then, the jargon of optimism is employed to lend ironical support to the conventionally euphemistic phrasing of the casualty report:

> Les canons renversèrent d'abord à-peu-près six mille hommes de chaque côté; ensuite la mousquetterie ôta du meilleur des mondes environ neuf à dix mille coquins qui en infectaient la surface. La baïonnette fut aussi la raison suffisante de la mort de quelques milliers d'hommes. Le tout pouvait bien se monter à une trentaine de mille âmes.[9]

It is only after this, when Candide is fleeing from 'cette boucherie heroïque'[10] while the *Te Deum* is being sung in both camps, that the realities of the situation, the dead and dying in the villages sacked 'selon les lois du droit public',[11] are described in savage detail; and

[5] [See p. 1, paragraph 2; p. 2, paragraph 2, of this book.]
[6] [See p. 3, paragraph 1, of this book.]
[7] [See p. 4, paragraph 9, of this book.]
[8] [See p. 5, paragraph 1, of this book.]
[9] [See p. 5, paragraph 1, of this book.]
[10] [See p. 5, paragraph 1, of this book.]
[11] [See p. 5, paragraph 2, of this book.]

the full force of the irony is brought home to the reader.

Similar opportunities for irony are also offered by the Portuguese Inquisition, in the contrast between the supposedly beneficent purposes of the Holy Office, the redemption of heretics and the protection of divine truth, and the cruelty of its actual practices. The agents of the Inquisition treat Pangloss with extreme courtesy as they extract evidence of his heretical views:

'Apparemment que monsieur ne croit pas au péché originel; car si tout est au mieux, il n'y a donc eu ni chute ni punition.'—'Je demande très humblement pardon à votre excellence,' répondit Pangloss encore plus poliment, 'car la chute de l'homme et la malédiction entraient nécessairement dans le meilleur des mondes possibles.'—'Monsieur ne croit donc pas à la liberté?' dit le familier.—'Votre excellence m'excusera,' dit Pangloss ... [chap. 5].[12]

And this courtly tone is retained by Voltaire when he comes to describe[38] the dungeons in which Pangloss and Candide are imprisoned: 'tous deux furent menés séparément dans des appartements d'une extrême fraîcheur, dans lesquels on n'était jamais incommodé du soleil' (chap. 6).[13] Similarly, the aesthetic qualities and entertainment value of the auto-da-fé are ironically emphasized: the victims 'entendirent une sermon très pathétique, suivi d'une belle musique en faux-bourdon. Candide fut fessé en cadence pendant qu'on chantait' (chap. 6).[14] Cunégonde was invited as a spectator: 'Je fus très bien placée; on servit aux dames des rafraîchissements entre la messe et l'exécution' (chap. 8).[15] And by the end of the ceremony Candide is in a position to compare, from experience, the value of the different benefits it has conferred upon him: 'Il s'en retournait se soutenant à peine, prêché, fessé, absous et béni.'[16]

Irony, then, is here much more than one among many possible satirical devices. It forms an essential part of the whole conception of *Candide*, because the book is above all an attack on systems of thought and attitudes of mind which divorce men from reality and reason, which substitute words for facts and prefer habit to reflection. Such systems and attitudes conceal truth behind a mask; they can be most effectively discredited by setting the truth beside the mask and allowing the spectator to judge for himself. The rosy dogma of the optimists, the euphemistic clichés of Church and State, are thus emptied of their positive content and transformed into ironic statements, and the reader is encouraged by this spectacle to reject all such pronouncements whenever they are not supported by his own experience and his own reasoning. 'Il faut cultiver notre jardin' is a motto for self-reliance in thought as well as action.

---

12 [See p. 10, paragraphs 6–9, of this book.]
13 [See p. 11, paragraph 2, of this book.]
14 [See p. 11, paragraph 3, of this book.]
15 [See p. 14, paragraph 2, of this book.]
16 [See p. 11, paragraph 6, of this book.]

Candide thus emerges as a work of art of considerable complexity. Parody, satire, intellectual debate, all contribute their share of the material; each has its own complexity, and each amuses and interests in its own way. The range is vast, within such a small compass: not merely in subject-matter, but also in tone—from bawdy jokes at the expense of La Vieille to compassionate horror at human suffering in war and earthquake, from ironic bitterness to the almost rhapsodical utopianism of[39] Eldorado. Yet for the most part these diverse elements are organically related to each other: the literary framework of parody encourages in the reader a critical alertness which is also essential for his appreciation of the central intellectual theme; the central theme itself, the disillusionment of Candide, is such that the secondary satirical themes can all take their place as agents in the process; while the distinguishing features of the style, the pungent rapidity of manner, the contrasts of scene and incident, the pervading irony, all arise naturally and inevitably from the nature of the material itself. Such organic unity is not solely the result of literary craftsmanship, however, important as that is: it has its roots much deeper in Voltaire's personality. Not merely is *Candide* a vehicle, among many others, for Voltaire's compassion for human suffering and anger at human cruelty, intolerance and stupidity; it is above all an expression of perhaps the profoundest force in his nature, the need for activity, for coming to grips with reality and leaving his own mark upon it. It was precisely this need which the static philosophy of 'optimism', unwilling to face facts and destructive of all hope, seemed most to deny; and it is understandable that in reacting against it Voltaire should marshal all the creative and critical powers at his command, and produce a masterpiece.[40]

THE NATURE OF EVIL*
Radoslav A. Tsanoff

Voltaire's earlier attitude towards the problem of evil was similar to that of Bolingbroke and Pope. Convinced of God's existence and of God's infinite perfection, he regarded criticism of God's world as inadmissible. The strongest argument for God he found in the admirable order of nature:[146] "The Heavens declare the glory of God."[1] In the hands of Voltaire this teleological argument was a double-edged sword: what the heavens declared to him regarding God or what meaning he attached to his glory would depend on what his inquiring eyes saw in heaven and especially on earth. So long as his view of life was in the main contented, the evils in life would present no insuperable difficulties to his belief in God. Man of course has his defects and vices, imperfections of his finite nature.[2]

Voltaire is not overwhelmed either by our vices or by our woes; they are part of the universal order, and in that order man is the happiest and the most perfect of beings. Indeed in his critique of Pascal, Voltaire expressed grateful acquiescence in things as they are, grateful surprise that they are no worse. "You are surprised that God has made man so limited, so ignorant, and so little happy; why are you not surprised that God has not made him more limited, more ignorant, more unhappy?"[3] He was pleased to note Pope's agreement with him in this sentiment; before them both Leibniz had recorded the same complacent astonishment. Toning down evil as he did, Voltaire in any case found it no grave embarrassment in his theodicy. Sometimes he agrees with Bolingbroke (or Bolingbroke with him): we may not and we need not think of the eternal, infinite Almighty God as good and just in our human sense of these terms. Goodness and justice are purely human in connotation and inapplicable to Deity: "It is quite as absurd to speak of God as just or unjust in this sense, as to speak of God as blue or square."[4] The anthropocentric view of nature and the

---

* Reprinted from Radoslav A. Tsanoff, *The Nature of Evil* (New York: The Macmillan Co., 1931), pp. 146–151, by permission of Radoslav A. Tsanoff.

1 [*Mélanges*], *Œuvres complètes*, ed. Moland, Vol. XXII, p. 405.
2 *Deuxième discours de la liberté*, *Œuvres*, Vol. IX, pp. 390 f.
8 *Remarques sur les Pensées de Pascal*, *Œuvres*, Vol. XXII, p. 44.
4 *Traité de métaphysique*, 1734, *Œuvres*, Vol. XXII, p. 201.

anthropomorphic view of God are equally naïve: in the cosmic machinery each part has its place, but no part is unique, hub and center. A mind like Voltaire's could not permanently neglect a moral estimate of God, but his reasoning on the subject is halting: even we imperfect men pursue[147] goodness and justice, then surely perfect Deity is bound to be good and just despite the apparent injustice and evils in this world.

This view of God and nature was insecure: a radical change in Voltaire's estimate of man's lot in nature was certain to change Voltaire's attitude towards God. Actually, in Voltaire's experience, man, God, and nature seemed to conspire to wreck his optimism. The age of which Voltaire was the outstanding spokesman was an age committed to the Universal Harmony, an age of trust in human character and human intelligence, yet Voltaire's own life was a long struggle with injustice, stupidity, bigotry, and cruelty. He did get the best of it in the clash of wits with the Lords of the Earth, but when the Rohans sent their lackeys to beat him up and had him locked in the Bastille, had him banished from Paris, he had no recourse. The Great Frederick might call him to Berlin and profess to treat him as a friend and equal, but after all to the royal cynic, Voltaire was just an orange to suck.

The cruelties of ecclesiastic bigotry embittered him against all organized religion, and he undertook to crush the infamous sanctity which in the name of God shackled the human mind and turned man against man in bloody wars. "So many frauds, so many errors, so many disgusting absurdities. ... Our religion ... is unquestionably divine, since seventeen centuries of imposture and imbecility have not destroyed it."[5] Pouring contempt and ridicule on God's prelates did not deepen Voltaire's piety. The manifold reaction against his earlier optimism came to a head in 1755, and in his poem on the disastrous Lisbon earthquake he shocked Europe with his violent disdain of theodicies and ideas of Divine Providence. The bitter irony of the novel *Candide ou l'optimisme* reveals a scepticism of a decidedly pessimistic cast, which is familiar also to the readers of the *Dictionnaire philosophique*.[148] The best of all possible worlds had been subjected to a sneering scrutiny and docile optimism pierced all the way through.

The whole discussion is now put on a humanistic plane. The vast harmony of the universe, which in ways thinkable or unthinkable transfigures our evils into elements of perfection, does not meet Voltaire's demands; nor the view that goodness and justice as we understand them are not to be ascribed to God and that God's perfection is untarnished by any evil or injustice with which our life may be beset.

5 *Essai sur les moeurs*, Chap. IX; *Œuvres*, Vol. XI, p. 235; transl. in John Morley, *Voltaire*, p. 322.

It is precisely the question of God's alleged goodness which concerns Voltaire, and in insisting on it, he distinguishes himself sharply from the complacent rationalists of the Enlightenment. Do the facts of life justify belief in a benevolent Divine Providence, and if they do not, what standing ground is left for despairing but unyielding humanity?

How is placid theodicy to dispose of a Lisbon disaster? Is Lisbon engulfed because of its sins? But then why not Paris and London as well? Or, if the earthquake is a mere event in the order of nature, is it beyond the reach of Divine Goodness to prevent, or has it been preferred by Eternal Wisdom as the least evil of all possible alternatives? Would the universe have been worse for sparing Lisbon this disaster? Is God testing Lisbon's virtue in his fiery furnace? Or is He the impassive spectator of his anguished creation? Or is matter, crude and resistant to Divine Perfection, the source and medium of our woes? These are all blind alleys and lead us to shuddering confusion. Voltaire exclaims: "Alas, I am like a doctor; I know nothing."

Thus we are left groping in the twilight of despair; the book of destiny is closed to us. We are atoms tormented but thinking, measuring the heavens and piercing the infinite, but ignorant of our own station and of our own lot. To pretend to wisdom is tragic folly; we can neither affirm nor[149] deny the presence of the blessed Providence which we do not perceive. Voltaire abandons Plato and rejects Epicurus; Bayle is wiser in his doubt than they with their professed knowledge; Bayle, "the advocate-general of the philosophers," is great enough and wise enough not to have a system.

This dark scepticism is not of the tragically pious variety as Pascal's; it is deliberately and sneeringly aggressive. In this wretched world one of Voltaire's undoubted joys, during the latter part of his life, was flaying optimists to disclose their unsound substance. His irony is blighting. What do you mean by your formula that "all is well in this world"? Ordered it is in accordance with moving forces and necessary laws; but can you mean that it is a happy world, that all is well with you, with me, that no one suffers? "Here is an odd general good, composed of gallstones, gout, and all sorts of crimes, sufferings, death, and damnation." So Shaftesbury, Bolingbroke, and Pope speak of the universal order, and universal it is: "flies are born to be devoured by spiders, who are in turn devoured by swallows, and swallows by shrikes, and shrikes by eagles, and eagles are born to be killed by men, who in turn live to kill each other and to be consumed by worms or by devils, at least in thousand cases to one." The novel *Candide* is an elaborate satire on this best of all possible worlds. Far be it from poor Candide to doubt the 'metaphysico-theologo-cosmolonigology' of the great Pangloss, but his own experiences leave him sorely perplexed again and again. "If this is the best of possible worlds, what must the others be like!" But he never gives up hope; fleeing from Portugal and bound for Paraguay, he remarks: "Now we are going to another world, ... it is in that one, no doubt, that all is well." And all *is* well: in Eldorado! But, outside of Eldorado, even Candide in the course of time becomes weary of Pangloss' philosophizing: [150] "That is well said,—but we should cultivate our garden."

This in fact was Voltaire's solution, in so far as he had any solution. Renouncing theodicy and entangled in the gray webs of doubt, he never lost his faith in civilization: this at least was at hand and reliable,—cultivating our garden. "Let us work without reasoning; ... this is the only way of making life endurable." One can live through Monday by this gospel alone; whether intelligent man can thus live through the week of life is an open question, which we cannot quite ignore. But it was not with this question that Rousseau confronted Voltaire; rather with the bold assertion that Voltaire had made a cosmic tragedy of evils which for the most part man had brought on himself, and that precisely by becoming civilized. So the issue was sharply drawn. [151]

THE LISBON EARTHQUAKE*
Thomas D. Kendrick

OPTIMISM ATTACKED

Now we pass from Portuguese to French literature,[1] to Voltaire and to Rousseau, beginning at once with Voltaire's poem on the Lisbon earthquake, which he wrote very soon after hearing the news of the disaster.[2] In his preface to it he says that its purpose was to ex-

* From Thomas D. Kendrick, *The Lisbon Earthquake* (London: Methuen & Co., 1956), pp. 119–135, 138–141. Reprinted by permission of Methuen & Co., Ltd.

1 On the subject of French thought concerning the Lisbon earthquake see B. Rohrer, *Das Erdbeben von Lissabon in der frauzösischen Literatur des achtzehnten Jahrhunderts.* Heidelberg, 1933; also W. H. Barber, *Leibniz in France: from Arnauld to Voltaire.* Oxford, 1955. I am sorry I did not read this important book before I wrote the chapter that follows. I am, however, indebted to Mr. Theodore Besterman's *Voltaire et le désastre de Lisbonne: ou la mort de l'Optimisme,* which the author was kind enough to show me in advance of its delivery and publication in the *Travaux* of the Institut et Musée Voltaire.

2 The main idea expressed in the poem was in his mind by 24 November 1755; cf. his letter to Robert Tronchin of that date. *Lettres inédites aux Tronchin.* Geneva, 1950, I, CIX. The first version of the poem had been written by 7 December.

pose the folly of the popular optimism derived from Pope's *Essay on Man* (1733–4), an optimism that he calls the *tout est bien*[3] philosophy. If, he asks, when Lisbon, Mequinez, Tetuan, and so many other towns were destroyed with multitudes of their inhabitants in November 1755, the philosophers had said to the wretched survivors, 'Whatever happens is for the best; the heirs of the dead will benefit financially; the building-trade will enjoy a boom; animals will grow fat on meals provided by the corpses trapped in the debris; an earthquake is a necessary effect of a necessary cause; private misfortune must not be overrated; an individual who is unlucky is contributing to the general good.'—would not such a speech be as cruel as the earthquake itself was destructive? We cannot turn our backs on the suffering this calamity has caused and pretend it is all some kind of benefit in disguise. We must admit there is evil, positive and inexcusable evil, in the world, and *that* in short, said Voltaire, was the message of his poem. Let men henceforth think of ruined Lisbon and stop deluding themselves with the silly cliché *tout est bien;* the truth is otherwise. *Le mal est sur la terre.*[4]

Today we wonder that it should ever have been necessary to conduct such an argument, but when Voltaire wrote his poem the popular philosophy of optimism, the *tout est bien* kind to[119] which he referred, had forgotten, or rather had chosen to ignore, the formidable significance of the problem presented to man by the existence of moral and physical evil. Evil was something that could be left in the background, unattended, a disagreeable and grating, but all the same necessary, part of the machinery that worked the world. This kind of optimism was not a variety of thought confined to readers of the learned periodicals, to scholars acquainted with Leibniz's *Théodicée* and *Monadologie,* and to the intelligencia who discussed Pope's *Essay on Man;* it was a force generally inspiring a contentment with the world as men then found it, a universal mood that had become, as Professor Basil Willey has said, 'in essence an apologia for the status quo'.[5] It was not even mainly an aristocratic mood, a kind of extravagant Versailles carelessness, but a popular creed. Almost every generalization about eighteenth-century thought can be strongly contradicted, but there is good reason for saying that most men at the time of the Lisbon earthquake were comfortably sure that the world was a good place in which everything that happened was on a long view likely to be 'for the best', and so they lived their lives as happily as they could, very little troubled by any responsibility for the alleviation of collective unhappiness.

---

[3] [All is well.]
[4] [Evil is on the earth.]
[5] *The Eighteenth Century Background.* London, 1953, p. 48. On this subject cf. p. 22 *ante.*

It is true enough that Voltaire first of all attacked this optimism in the form in which he found it in Pope's poem, for the famous passage at the end of the First Epistle beginning 'Cease then, nor ORDER Imperfection name', condensed into a conspicuous bull's-eye precisely the sentiments to which he objected; and later he made Leibniz the butt of his novel *Candide*. But he was not conducting an academic argument, and it is certainly true that the Lisbon earthquake controversy in France did not depend upon a thorough re-examination of the theodicy of Gottfried Wilhelm Leibniz (1646–1716), which was imperfectly understood in that country and disliked by the Church as fatalistic. Voltaire really did not know much about what Leibniz had actually said, but with some justification he took the clichés of the Leibnizian theodicy as symptomatic of popular optimism and poured upon them in *Candide* his own brilliant variety of destructive scorn.[6] [120]

The importance of Voltaire's part in the moralizing over the Lisbon earthquake is that he had something to say to which a large audience would pay attention; for he was addressing contemporary European society on a general matter of conscience, knowing that the news of the earthquake was likely to have made his hearers in an unexpected measure vulnerable. Long before the earthquake took place, he had himself lost faith in this general optimism, and he felt that this calamity provided an incontestable and grisly proof that he was right in rejecting the *tout est bien* doctrine. He believed that

---

[6] Leibniz said that God, perfect in love, wisdom, and power, after considering all the logically possible worlds, created the world in which there was the greatest excess of good over evil. God had therefore decided that a world containing no evil would not have been so good a world as this world, which does contain evil. Once this world was created and evil of various kinds admitted into it, God cannot logically intervene to prevent evil from fulfilling its appointed role, because to do this would imply that God had not chosen the best possible world. The theory of the pre-established harmony, which is the subject of much jesting in *Candide,* is a consequence of the theory of the monads which had forced Leibniz to the conclusion that at the time of the creation once and for all God had ordered everything that was ever going to happen (*Theodicy* 9). Therefore, we can be sure that a world in which there were no such things as disastrous earthquakes would not be so good a world as one in which they do occur. Leibniz, however, did not rate earthquakes very high as evil things. 'One Caligula alone, one Nero, has caused more evil than an earthquake,' he said (*Theodicy* 26). What we have to remember is that if we could understand the universal harmony, we should see that what we describe as a completely evil thing is a proper part of the plan most worthy of being chosen; in a word, we should ourselves understand that what God has done is the best (*Dissertation* 44). Leibniz, however, would not have said that the Lisbon earthquake was a disguised blessing, for he admitted that what was 'best' in the infinite wisdom of God may seem to us to be only painful and wasteful act of destruction, however much we may try to see some good in it; nor would he have said that the earthquake was a suddenly contrived punishment of the Lisbon people. Yet we are led to grace by the ways of nature (*Monadology* 88), and the mechanism of the physical world, determined at the creation, works in harmony with the course of its moral government, also determined at the creation.

everyone would now have to admit that man dare not hope for a
safe life in this world under the benevolent protection of a providence that could be counted on to reward virtuous behaviour. Man
was weak and helpless, ignorant of his destiny, and exposed to
terrible dangers, as all must now see; the optimism of the age must
be replaced by something that is not much more than an apprehensive
hope that providence will lead us through our dangerous world to
a happier state. *Un jour tout sera bien*[7] should be the new limit of
optimistic thought.

The *Poème sur le désastre de Lisbonne* is addressed directly to
men in this mood, and, once in circulation, it was widely read and discussed, for it was the comment of one of the wisest men in Europe on
a disaster that had shocked western civilization more than any other
event since the fall of Rome in the fifth century. As the poem was
written so soon after the earthquake, Voltaire inevitably made some
use of the earliest reports about the calamity; but he did not need
gruesome overstatements to make the effect he wanted, and he knew
quite well that the first accounts of the earthquake that reached
Switzerland would need revision. 'It is said that half the town is still
standing,' he wrote on 16 December. 'There is a tendency to exag-
gerate both good tidings and bad tidings on their first announcement.'[8]
His poem obtained its hearing, because it dealt directly with the
perplexity filling the minds of his readers, and because it is movingly

---

Later, commenting on the Lisbon earthquake, Voltaire said that
its effect was to make men introspective, by which he meant apprehensive about their mortality and ultimate destiny, and that wise
observation should always be the first answer to the[121] question—in
what way did the Lisbon earthquake influence European thought?
Dreadful doubts and fears chilled the hearts of men when they considered what the Lisbon earthquake must really have been like to
those who died in it and to those who lived through it. No doubt, in
their full intensity these doubts and fears were short-lived, and in
many cases of the most superficial kind; but Voltaire knew that, and
he regretted the way in which the world turned quickly again to its
pleasures, trying to forget the earthquake as soon as possible, in the
excitements of dancing, the theatre, and the lottery. Yet the tre-
mendous shock that the news had caused could not be completely
absorbed by such feeble defences. Men were frightened. They asked
what really was the part they had to play in God's scheme for the
universe; what really was the nature of the providence under whose
protection they thought they lived; what, in fact, was their relation
to God?

---

[7] [One day all will be well.]
[8] Voltaire gives a revised reference to the Lisbon earthquake in the *Précis
du siècle de Louis XV*, Moland, XV, 335–6.

inspired by sorrow for the people of Lisbon. Condorcet, his biographer, said that though Voltaire was over sixty when he wrote this poem, his soul, deeply stirred by the suffering of humanity, had all the zest and all the fire of youth. Voltaire's melancholy is indeed strongly expressed, and it is all the more powerful a force because he has so little comfort to offer humanity in place of the brittle optimism he was now determined to destroy.[122]

The poem is addressed to the deluded *philosophes* who tell everybody that all is for the best. They are told to look at tragic shattered Lisbon and its smoking ruins, and to think of the excruciating fate of the hundred thousand victims of the earthquake. Hearing their cries, seeing them being burnt alive or suffering other unspeakable tortures, are the philosophers going to tell us that all this is part of the good providence of a benevolent God. Are we going to be told of these pitiful heaps of corpses that they are the bodies of sinners who are justly the victims of God's anger because of their crimes?

> Quel crime, quelle faute ont commis ces enfants
> Sur le sein maternel écrasés et sanglants?
> Lisbonne, qui n'est plus, eut-elle plus de vices
> Que Londres, que Paris, plongés dans les délices?
> Lisbonne est abîmée, et l'on danse a Paris.[9]

The fine philosophers, comfortably far away from all this suffering, would talk very differently if such a disaster had befallen their own towns; then we should hear them crying out at the horrors that had afflicted them, and then they would recognize that a great earthquake brings nothing but miserable evil on man. *Le bien fut pour Dieu seul.*[10]

> Croyez-moi, quand la terre entr'ouvre ses abîmes,
> Ma plainte est innocente et mes cris légitimes.[11]

Are you going to tell me that pride is deceiving me, that pride makes me rebel against suffering?

---

[9] [And can you then impute a sinful deed
To babes who on their mothers' bosoms bleed?
Was then more vice in fallen Lisbon found,
Than Paris, where voluptuous joys abound?
Was less debauchery to London known,
Where opulence luxurious holds her throne?
Earth Lisbon swallows; the light sons of France
Protract the feast, or lead the sprightly dance.
(Translations of passages from *The Lisbon Earthquake* throughout are from *The Works of Voltaire*, trans. and ed. Tobias Smollett and others (Paris: E. R. Du Mont, 1901), XXXVI, 5–18.)]

[10] From a variant passage in a Geneva edition of 1756. [Good was for God alone.]

[11] [When the earth gapes my body to entomb,
I justly may complain of such a doom.]

Allez interroger les rivages du Tage;
Fouillez dans les débris de ce sanglant ravage;
Demandez aux mourants, dans ce séjour d'effroi,
Si c'est l'orgueil qui crie: 'O Dieu, secourez-moi!'[12]
O Ciel, ayez pitié de l'humaine misère!'[13]

We are told that all is for the best and that everything that
happens must happen, but would the universe really be a worse place
if it had not been found necessary to destroy Lisbon? Could not an
omniscient and omnipotent God achieve His[123] purpose otherwise?
If there must be earthquakes why could not the ghastly things happen
in the middle of the desert?

Je respecte mon Dieu, mais j'aime l'univers.[14]

Will the wretched victims die consoled when you tell them that
the earthquake happened for the general good? that Lisbon will be
rebuilt? that it will become populous again? that northern Europe
will become rich as a result of their losses? that all evil things that
happen to us are according to the 'general law' good things? that these
poor people in their death-agonies and the worms that are about to
devour them are alike playing their proper part in God's master plan?
What horrible talk!

Voltaire will have nothing more to do with the dreadful doctrine
of unchangeable laws of necessity. He believes God is free, just, and
merciful, so why do we have to suffer as we do? It is all very well to
launch the furies of Heaven against rocks and trees; they do not feel.
But man is alive and sensitive. He cannot help crying out in his
misery. A pot, liable to be broken, does not ask the potter why it was
made such a poor, coarse, brittle thing; for the potter did not give it
a heart or feeling. Man will not be satisfied by being told that his
misfortune is for somebody else's good.

De mon corps tout sanglant mille insectes vont naître;
Quand la mort met le comble aux maux que j'ai soufferts,
Le beau soulagement d'être mangé des vers![15]

It is easy to say that one suffering man is negligible in relation
to God's whole design for the universe, but all living creatures seem

---

12 In the final version, 'O Ciel, secourez-moi.' ["O Heaven, help me."]
13 [The awful truth on Tagus' banks explore,
   Rummage the ruins on that bloody shore,
   Wretches interred alive in direful grave
   Ask if pride cries, "Good Heaven, thy creatures save."
   If 'tis presumption that makes mortals cry,
   "Heav'n, on our sufferings cast a pitying eye."]
14 [God my respect, my love weak mortals claim.]
15 [To numerous insects shall my corpse give birth,
   When once it mixes with its mother earth:
   Small comfort 'tis that when Death's ruthless power
   Closes my life, worms shall my flesh devour.]

to be condemned to existence in a ferocious world of pain and mutual slaughter. How can anyone say with conviction *tout est bien?* The world around us denies it, and the secret terrors of the philosophers must have told them a hundred times that it is not true.

> Elements, animaux, humains, tout est en guerre,
> Il le faut avouer, le *mal* est sur la terre:[16]

And where has this evil come from? Can it possibly proceed from the author of all good things? One cannot stomach the idea that a benevolent God, loving His people and prodigally bestowing His benefits upon them, at the same time pours down every[124] possible misfortune on their wretched heads. We listen to all the confusing and contradictory theodicies, and while we are arguing Lisbon crashes into smoking dust, and the shock of a great earthquake shatters towns all the way from the Tagus to Cadiz.

Voltaire shows that no theory resting on optimism and a belief in a kind and loving God can explain why mankind should have been afflicted with such sorrow and suffering as the earthquake caused. He turns upon Leibniz. How does he explain the presence of all this misery in his 'best of all possible worlds'? How does he account for the fact that the innocent suffer equally with the guilty? And now the poem moves to its terrible conclusion. We know nothing; nature has no message for us; God does not speak:

> On a besoin d'un Dieu qui parle au genre humain.
> Il n'appartient qu'à lui d'expliquer son ouvrage,
> De consoler le faible, et d'éclairer le sage.[17]

Men are weak, grovelling, ignorant creatures, their bodies made for decay and their minds for grief. They know nothing of their origin or purpose or destiny:

> Atomes tourmentés sur cet amas de boue,
> Que la mort engloutit, et dont le sort se joue,
> Mais atomes pensants, atomes dont les yeux,
> Guidés par la pensée, ont mesuré les cieux;
> Au sein de l'infini, nous élançons notre être,
> Sans pouvoir un moment nous voir et nous connaître.[18]

---

[16] [Men, beasts, and elements know no repose
From dire contention; earth's the seat of woes:]
[17] [God should His will to human kind explain.
He only can illume the human soul,
Instruct the wise man, and the weak console.]
[18] [Atoms tormented on this earthly ball,
The sport of fate, by death soon swallowed all,
But thinking atoms, who with piercing eyes
Have measured the whole circuit of the skies;
We rise in thought up to the heavenly throne,
But our own nature still remains unknown.]

Que faut-il, o Mortels! Mortels, il faut souffrir,
Se soumettre en silence, adorer, et mourir.[19]

Before it was printed Voltaire was curious to know what the effect of his poem would be when it was read in hostile or suspicious or easily offended religious circles. Of the first draft he had suggested in a light-hearted letter of 19 December 1755 to his most trusted old friend the Comte d'Argental that these verses were really only suitable for private circulation among the *philosophes*;[20] he did not want to be thought *mauvais théologien*,[21] and he was prepared to take some trouble to alter his poem so that it should not offend the heresy-hunters or the timid thinkers. Later on, in April 1756, he wrote of this poem and of the deistic[125] *La Loi Naturelle*, published with it, to another very old friend, Cideville, 'I had to make my way of thinking clear; it is not that either of a superstitious person or of an atheist. I am inclined to think that respectable folk will share my view.' With the Lisbon earthquake poem, the main trouble was the ending. Bertrand, the pastor of the French Church at Berne, had told him that the pessimism of the last lines was hurtful and too violently expressed. Voltaire met the objections by introducing 'to hope' in the concluding lines:

Mortels, il faut souffrir,
Se soumettre, adorer, espérer, et mourir.[22]

That was in February 1756, and his friends did not think it adequate; so, as he did not want his 'sermon' to shock orthodox theologians too violently, he composed a new ending to it about the time the first printed edition of the original version appeared in Geneva, that is in March 1756. In this second and, so to speak, definitive version of the *Poème sur le désastre de Lisbonne* the last two lines are omitted, and the poem is continued with the observation that there is a great and often painful chase after happiness in progress in this world; we can at least say we are sometimes able temporarily to forget our sorrows, and there is always the blessing of being able to hope.

Un jour tout sera bien, voilà notre espérance,
Tout est bien aujourd'hui, voilà l'illusion.
Les sages me trompaient, et Dieu seul a raison.[23]

---

[19] [What must be done, O Mortals! Mortals, we must suffer,/ Submit in silence, adore, and die.]

[20] MS. Louis Clarke. '...ils (ces vers tragiques) pourront exercer votre philosofie, et cette de votre Société. Je les crois aussi sages quel est possible, et de nature cependant a n'être qu'en vos mains.' ["... they (these tragic verses) can exercise your philosophy and that of your Society. I believe them to be as wise as possible and of such a nature that they should be only in your hands."]

[21] [An evil theologian.]

[22] [Mortals, we must suffer,/ Submit, adore, hope, and die.]

[23] [All may be well; that hope can man sustain,
All now is well; 'tis an illusion vain.
The sages held me forth delusive light,
Divine instructions only can be right.]

I shall not blame Providence, said Voltaire. I myself used to write in a light, happy vein, but:

> D'autres temps, d'autres moeurs: instruit par la vieillesse,
> Des humains égarés partageant la faiblesse,
> Dans une épaisse nuit cherchant à m'éclairer,
> Je ne sais que souffrir, et non pas murmurer.[24]

Once upon a time a Caliph, dying, addressed this prayer to the God he worshipped:

> 'Je t'apporte, ô seul roi, seul être illimité,
> Tout ce que tu n'as pas dans ton immensité,
> Les défauts, les regrets, les maux, et l'ignorance,'
> Mais il pouvait encore ajouter *l'espérance*.[25][126]

There exists a copy corrected in Voltaire's hand that turns the last line into a question, as if Voltaire felt that his concessions to orthodox thought had gone a little too far.[26]

The early history of the poem and its first effects on French readers can be illustrated by reference to one or two other poems on the earthquake of about the same date. In the first place, almost anything might be expected of Voltaire, and in fact the circulation of his poem in Paris was preceded there by the appearance of some verses, believed to be by him, which were really written by his young friend the Marquis de Ximenez, an outspoken free-thinker whose poem caused much offence. Ximenez was not prepared to say with Voltaire *Je respecte mon Dieu,* and his main point was that the much-advertised piety of the Portuguese had proved useless as a protection against an implacable and inexplicable God who had suddenly determined to obliterate Lisbon. He asked of what use were the armies of monks, the bloody labours of the Inquisition, the stores of relics, and the endless offerings made to thousands of saints? They were all now proved to be worthless as a means of propitiating God. Heretic England was now laughing at the devotions of the Roman Church. The pirates of Algiers could now plunder Portugal happily; Heaven was on *their* side. O Providence, if sometimes in despair we lose faith in you:

> C'est quand le bras qui frappe la vertu,
> N'a pas au moins commencé par le crime.[27]

---

[24] [But times change manners; taught by age and care
    Whilst I mistaken mortals' weakness share,
    The light of truth I seek in this dark state,
    And without murmuring submit to fate.]

[25] ["Being supreme, whose greatness knows no bound,
    I bring thee all that can't in Thee be found;
    Defects and sorrows, ignorance and woe."
    Hope he omitted, man's sole bliss below.]

[26] Mais pouvait-il encore ajouter l'espérance? [But was he yet able to add hope?] See George R. Havens: *Modern Language Notes,* XLIV, 1929, p. 489 ff.

[27] [It is when the arm that strikes virtue/ Has not at least begun with crime.]

One of the consequences of the great earthquake that had caused much distress in French literary society was the death of the young Racine, son of the poet Louis Racine, and grandson of Jean Racine, the dramatist. This unfortunate youth was drowned in the seismic wave that poured over the slender isthmus between the city of Cadiz and the mainland, with the result that his wretched father, broken-hearted, went into complete retirement. Several poets attempted to console him with offerings of verse, and one of these pieces, by Jean Jacques Lefranc, Marquis de Pompignan, was published in the *Journal Encyclopédique* next to the poem of the impious Marquis de Ximenez as a wholesome corrective. This presents us with the opposite point of view, the complacent attitude to disaster that Voltaire wished to disturb and shame.[127]

In fifteen verses this simple serious man, who so hated the *philosophes* that he described their work in this poem as *recherches pleines d'imposture* and *essais pusillanimes*,[28] who, after his inaugural address to the Académie Français in 1760 was so ridiculed, chiefly by Voltaire, that he was forced into retirement, this godly man summarized ineptly but with Christian bluntness the pious resignation that most of all irritated his opponents. Young Racine is at peace in Heaven. We on earth grieve, but at the same time we know that the innocent are required to suffer while in this world, and we do not complain because Christians are sure that the sufferers will be recompensed in their future life. Presumptuous *philosophes* who depend on scientific explanations of calamities like the Lisbon earthquake have no such consolation; they try to shut God out of their minds and to forget that an earthquake may be the result of His anger. We, on the other hand, have our faith, a faith that can overcome the very worst griefs. Let us expect nothing as certain in this life but the inevitable hour of death, death that is to be followed by eternal happiness or eternal damnation.

Voltaire's *Poème sur le désastre de Lisbonne* was printed in a censored form in the *Journal Encyclopédique* for April 1756, with an introductory note explaining that since the flame of his genius sometimes led him to stray beyond the limits that a good Christian ought to observe, a few short passages likely to cause offence had been omitted, their place being marked by asterisks. Immediately after this comes a *Réponse à Mr De V. . . . ou Défense de l'Axiome, Tout est bien,* a poem by an anonymous author who thought that, though one may grieve over the fate of Lisbon, it was blasphemous presumption to question God's goodness because of the earthquake, thus condemning as an evil thing an event that God Himself had decided should take place. A slave has no right to question a slave-master. God commands, and man must obey in total submission, receiving the gifts of providence with gratitude and divine punishment in meek

---

28 [Pursuits full of imposture and faint-hearted endeavors.]

and unprotesting shame. One of these gifts is hope. Even the earth-quake victim's pitiful cry 'O God, help me' expresses a hope that mercifully lessens the agony of death in an earthquake. The truth is that we fear death too much, said this poet, in company with other writers who were shocked by Voltaire's pessimism.

We come to the heart of the controversy with Rousseau's[128] letter to Voltaire of 18 August 1756.[29] Rousseau was then forty-three, known as a musician and as the author of a famous essay, *Discours sur les arts et sciences*, in which he had delighted civilized France by prov-ing the superiority of the savage state; but his most celebrated works had not yet been published. He had no open quarrel with Voltaire, who had arranged for the little volume containing *La Loi Naturelle* and the poem on the earthquake to be sent to him; probably Rousseau was already envious of Voltaire's fame and had smarted under his witty criticism of the *Discours*; but the letter is not a display of polemical fireworks set off merely to irritate the great man; on the contrary, it is a sincere expression of something Rousseau felt he had got to say, and he began by saying that he entirely approved of *La Loi Naturelle*. It was the earthquake poem that had upset him.

Rousseau rejected Voltaire's gloomy picture of man's unhappy fate on earth. He said that the optimism attacked in the poem had helped him to endure the very things supposed to be unendurable. Man must be patient, recognizing evil as a necessary consequence of his own nature and of the nature of the universe. A benevolent God desired to preserve man from evil, and of all the possible systems whereby His creation might be ordered, He had chosen the one that contained the least evil and the most good. Put bluntly, said Rousseau, the reason why God had not done better for mankind was that He could not do better. Voltaire, on the other hand, argues that an omnipotent God could have prevented evil from tarnishing His creation, and the fact that He did not do so means that the only dis-coverable reason for our existence on earth is that we are here in order to suffer and to die. That view Rousseau could not accept. He maintained that moral evil originated in man himself, and that, even though physical evil is a necessary part of the creation, the majority of physical evils are man's own fault. This did not dispose of Vol-taire's argument; indeed, Voltaire agreed that man was responsible for much of the evil in the world;[30] but Rousseau wanted to put the case in its most extreme form.

---

29 *Lettre de J. J. Rousseau citoyen de Genève à Monsieur de Voltaire.* First published 1759.

30 In a letter to Pastor Allamand of Bex of 16 December 1755, referring to the Lisbon earthquake, Voltaire said, 'Je plains comme vous les portugais; mais les hommes se font encore plus de mal sur leur petite taupinière que ne leur en fait la nature. Nos guerres égorgent plus d'hommes que les tremblements de terre n'en engloutissent.' ["As you do, I pity the Portuguese, but men do to themselves even more evil on their little mole-hill than nature does to them. Our wars slaughter more men than earthquakes swallow up."]

Consider Lisbon, for example. It was not Nature that had[129] congregated 20,000 houses of six or seven stories on that particular site. If the inhabitants of the city had not chosen to crowd themselves together in dangerous buildings, the damage would have been much less. Had they dwelt properly distributed and in smaller houses they could have escaped easily at the first shock and have been far from the danger-centre by the next day; but they stayed obstinately on the spot, worrying about their money and their possessions, and many were killed in consequence.

Everyone would agree with Voltaire in wishing the earthquake had taken place in the middle of a desert rather than at Lisbon. There *are* earthquakes in deserts, but we do not hear much about them as they do no harm to the precious town-dwellers, and merely frighten a few savages who are sensible enough to live scattered over a large area and do not have to fear falling roofs and burning houses. What does Voltaire really mean? Are the town-dwellers' requirements to alter the laws of nature? Man cannot talk in this way. We cannot so arrange matters that to prevent an earthquake at a certain place, we have only got to go and set up a town there!

Rousseau's general case in favour of the *tout est bien* school of thought depends on the usual arguments. It is not always a misfortune to be killed suddenly. Providence is a universal supervision of God's creation and is not concerned with what happens to an individual creature during his brief appearance on earth. And so on. The important part of the letter is Rousseau's perception of the fundamental difference between the kind of man who is a pessimist, and the kind of man who is an optimist, in regard to the circumstances of our mortal life. Voltaire is accused of thinking that few people would wish to be reborn to live again the same kind of life they have already lived. He got that idea from Erasmus, said Rousseau, and he went on to ask whom Voltaire had actually consulted on this point? Bored, stupid, frightened rich people? Or his fellow writers, a sedentary, unhealthy, unhappy lot of men? He ought to have consulted an honest *bourgeois,* a good craftsman, or one of his Swiss peasants. Rousseau said there was probably not one single highlander of the 'haut Valais' who was tired of his simple existence and would not exchange Paradise for the chance to be reborn time after time so that he could go on living his accustomed uneventful life for ever and ever.[130]

In a famous passage at the end of the letter Rousseau presents the problem as the personal difference between himself and Voltaire:

Je ne puis m'empêcher, Monsieur, de remarquer à ce propos une opposition bien singulière entre vous et moi dans le sujet de cette lettre. Rassasié de gloire et désabusé des vaines grandeurs vous viviez libre au sein de l'abondance, bien sûr de l'immortalité vous philosophez paisiblement sur la nature de l'ame, et si le corps ou le coeur souffre vous avez Tronchain pour Médecin et pour Ami; vous ne trouvez pourtant que mal sur la terre; et moi, homme obscur, pauvre, et tourmenté d'un mal sans remède, je médite avec plaisir dans ma retraite, et je trouve que tout est bien.[31]

And how is this difference to be explained? The answer is to be found in the word *hope* with which Voltaire ended his poem. His variety of hope is vague and dubious, and without anything better than that, worldly happiness and prosperity, such as he enjoys, is worth nothing; therefore he is a pessimist. But Rousseau possesses hope of another kind, strong and certain, a hope that illumines and beautifies everything in his life. He can tolerate no doubt on the subject of the immortality of the soul and the heavenly recompense that he will receive for his suffering on earth. God is kind. *Tout est bien.* Rousseau was absolutely sure.

We see now that the arguments about God's providence that were the result of the Lisbon earthquake are in detail not very important. As Rousseau had said earlier in this same letter, for the pious providence is always right and for the *philosophes* it is always wrong. Men have a conviction one way or the other, and this conviction cannot be altered for one party by pointing to the unjust death of innocent people, or for the other party by observing that premature death saves its victims from a gruesome death-bed agony in old age and sends them to Heaven unembarrassed by a load of sins that they would have committed had they lived. Therefore, we need not examine in full the small pros and cons of this unavailing dispute; but we cannot leave the matter without noting one or two more expressions of opinion. And, finally, there is *Candide*.

First there is Immanuel Kant, aged thirty-one, at the beginning of his great career and still closely adhering to the optimistic philosophy of Leibniz. When the news of the Lisbon earthquake[131] reached Konigsberg the townsfolk, as was generally the case in Germany, were exceedingly alarmed and also full of sympathy for the Portuguese; but young Kant seems to have been first of all more interested in the event as a scientific problem than as a tragedy that had destroyed a city and led to great loss of life. He published three short papers on the subject in 1756, reviewing theories of the causes of earthquakes and recording all the attendant phenomena of the 1755 shock, the widespread nature of which had strongly impressed him. He even includes a note on the beneficial aspect of earthquakes. Just as we complain of ill-

---

31 [I cannot prevent myself, Monsieur, from noticing, by the way, a very singular contrast between you and me concerning the subject of this letter. Sated with glory and undeceived by empty grandeur, so that you may live in the bosom of abundance; quite certain of immortality, you philosophize peacefully on the nature of the soul, and if your body or your heart suffers, you have Tronchin for your doctor and your friend; yet you find only evil on the earth; and I, a man who is obscure, poor, and tormented by an incurable illness, I meditate with pleasure in my retreat, and I find that all is well.]

timed or excessive rain, forgetting that rain feeds the springs necessary
in our economy, so we denounce earthquakes, refusing to consider
whether they too may not bring us good things. Are they, in the first
place, really as bad as we make out? We lament the dead; but all men
must die. We grieve over the loss of property; but property is not
everlasting. Our cities of high houses will inevitably be destroyed if
we build them in places like Lisbon. Earthquakes are a part of nature;
and instead of expecting nature to suit our convenience we must
accommodate ourselves to nature. On the credit side let us remember
that the subterranean fire that is the cause of earthquakes also gives
us hot springs and baths; it has also formed the valuable mineral ores
in the rock; vegetation benefits by the release of subterranean sub-
stances; the escaping sulphur fumes have a welcome sanitary effect. It
is possible the world itself would not really be a warm enough place
to support life properly without this subterranean fire. It may occasionally do great damage, but it seems very likely that we could not
get on without it, and we ought to be grateful for it.

　　Finally, Kant added a short note about earthquakes in relation
to God's government of the world. In this, his pre-critical and Leibnizian period, he could offer only small comfort, pointing out that at
least we are not the helpless victims of a dangerous natural order that
may irresponsibly destroy us at any time, because the course of our
lives in prosperity and adversity has been determined by God. However, his modest postscript is historically interesting. In his later life
he rejected any theodicy dependent on our reasoning about God's
purpose, since he maintained that human reason was powerless in
this respect, and even in this early footnote to a natural history paper
he condemned[132] the interpretation of the Lisbon earthquake as the
punishment of a sinful town, not because such an interpretation was
uncharitable, but because it was a shocking act of impertinence to
offer any opinion at all on such a subject. We cannot possibly know
why God allowed this earthquake to happen. We must remember that
man is not the only object of divine care; God in his inscrutable wisdom presides over the whole gigantic content of nature, and it may be
necessary that the ordering of the universe should include events un-
favourable to man. But at this point Kant makes an important observation. In practice, he says, we are not left in any uncertainty. We
know what we must think and what we must do. We know that this
disaster teaches us that we were not created for life in the present
world only and that we cannot expect our longing for happiness to
be fully satisfied here; we know also that it is now more than ever our
business to love our neighbours and do all that we can to make this
world a pleasant place. This is the germ of Kant's subsequent view
that the only possible theodicy is a practical act of faith in divine
justice. If our reason can assure us that there is a God, and that he is
good, then our lives must be lived in absolute loyalty to him, however grievous the misfortunes of ourselves or our fellow men.

Another young man who wrote on this subject was Louis de Beausobre (1730–83), son of a Protestant theologian who had taken refuge in Berlin and won the favour of Frederick the Great. He had been sent to Paris for his education, and there he wrote a book called *Essai sur le Bonheur,* which was published in 1758. In this he fought a fine battle on behalf of the *tout est bien* school of thought. He said there was far too much crying out about the horrors of a great disaster like the Lisbon earthquake; in fact, he thought the *frivoles déclamateurs,*[32] wailing about the tragedy in Portugal, were probably not so grieved as they pretended to be, and that there was a great deal of exaggeration and insincerity. Men forget the blessings and happiness of normal life when they are suddenly shocked by a great disaster; they think only of grief and suffering, and say God's providence has failed them. What does it all amount to? asked Louis de Beausobre. The earthquake victims are dead; but death is not a greater evil when it strikes many people simultaneously than when it removes them one by one at intervals, so why should death suddenly be deemed[133] so awful when it is accompanied by the quaking of the earth? Why is it specially sad to die in a disaster? And what is so terrible about a disaster like this earthquake? A lot of riches are lost; but man can get on without them. Overthrown cities can be rebuilt. A great calamity is just a multiplication of the ordinary calamities that may happen to anyone without causing any general alarm. Suffering simultaneously with others does not make suffering worse, and all that can really be said about an earthquake as an evil thing is that it causes a greater total amount of grief on one occasion than a single accident. At which we may be sorry; but, after all, plagues, war, famine, and earthquakes are divine punishments on mankind, and we cannot expect them to be pleasant.

If this young gentleman was thinking of Voltaire when he referred to the *frivoles déclamateurs* and believed he had scored a point or two against the *Poème sur le désastre de Lisbonne,* he was very quickly made aware of his mistake, for in the following year (1759) *Candide* was published, and the whole *tout est bien* philosophy was thereby blown to pieces in company with poor Louis de Beausobre's book and everything else of the kind to the accompaniment of the derisive laughter of literary Europe. Voltaire had not changed his mind. He disliked more and more the common version of Leibniz's theodicy now that the earthquake had shown its obvious untenability, and he knew there was confusion of thought on this subject since he himself had been classed as an optimist, having once said that he considered it proved that there was more good than bad in the world.[33] He now knew that there was much evil, unfair, undeserved, cruel evil,

---

32 [Frivolous ranters.]
33 Cf. d'Alès de Corbet, P.A., Vicomte. *De l'origine du Mal.* Paris, 1758, p. 50.

for man in this world, and in the autumn and winter of 1758 the thoughts that had been developing in his mind over many years blossomed suddenly into the brilliant little novel that on publication instantly made every glib optimist look a fool. It is the end of the controversy. 'After *Candide,* there was no more to be said; the case was finished, and the case was lost.'[34]

Candide is, as we have said, directed against Leibniz rather than Pope, for Pangloss, the philosopher, is a German primed[134] with a complete apparatus of clichés and jargon derived from Leibniz's *Théodicée;* but the general target of all this rapid-fire raillery is the uncritical popular mixture of his optimism and Pope's, and the inadequacy of providential protection.[35] The novel is so simple in structure that its point could hardly be missed by the most careless reader. Poor Candide, always hankering after the equally unfortunate heroine, Cunégonde, progresses hopefully and trustingly and rapidly through a world packed with every imaginable misery for him, including excruciating physical hardships and cruelly delusive periods of respite. From time to time Dr. Pangloss, who has his own special ration of hardship to endure, appears as his companion and comforter, always ready to justify every new horror befalling the characters in the book as a necessary event in the pre-established harmony of the universe.[135] . . .

The sufferers in this novel are a very tough lot. Pangloss, taken down when he was only half dead, recovers consciousness when he is being dissected, and Cunégonde, believed to have been disemboweled by the Bulgars in her ancestral home, turns up in Lisbon having suffered nothing worse than a cut in the groin and frequent raping. At the end of the book, when at last all their trials and disappointments

---

34 Paul Hazard: *European Thought in the 18th Century,* trans. J. Lewis May. London, 1954, p. 322. Hazard adds, 'Not that optimism suddenly disappeared completely; a doctrine lives on for a long time, even when wounded, even when its soul has fled.'

35 David Hume wrote on 12 April 1759 to Adam Smith, 'Voltaire has lately published a small work called *Candide ou L'optimisme.* It is full of sprightliness and impiety, and is indeed a Satyre upon Providence, under Pretext of criticizing the Leibnitian System.' *New Letters,* ed. Klibansky and Mossner. Oxford, 1954. William Warburton's judgement on this novel is also interesting: 'The real design of *Candide* is to recommend naturalism (i.e. natural religion): the professed design is to ridicule the *optimisme* not of Pope, but of Leibniz, which is founded professedly in fate, and makes a sect in Germany . . . you will wonder perhaps, the translation was made at my recommendation.' Warburton-Hurd Letters. 8 July 1759, No. CXXX. It is a tribute to this novel that two English translations, one by William Rider, were published in London in 1759. For the background to *Candide,* see the introduction by André Morize to the edition published by the *Société des textes français modernes.* Paris (Hachette), 1913; also introductions by Richard Aldington in *Candide and other Romances* (Broadway Translations), London, 1927; by H. N. Brailsford in *Candide and Other Tales,* London, 1937 (Everyman's Library, No. 936), a volume that contains Smollett's translation revised by James Thornton; by O. R. Taylor in *Candide* (Blackwell's French Texts), Oxford, 1942; and by John Butt to his translation in *Penguin Classics,* first published in 1947.

are over, a little party finished up on a small farm near Constantinople. The chief characters assembled are Candide; Cunégonde, now a scraggy old shrew; her ancient attendant, the Pope's daughter, who had a buttock cut off and eaten by Turkish soldiers; Martin, a pessimistic old scholar picked up in America; and Pangloss, now become a revolting pimply syphilitic.

But Pangloss is still an unchanged *tout est bien* optimist. Candide asked him, 'When you were hanged, dissected, beaten black and blue, and when you were rowing in that galley, did you always think that everything in this world is for the best?' 'I have not changed my mind at all,' Pangloss answered, 'I am a philosopher, and it would not be proper for me to do so; besides Leibniz could not have been wrong.' Candide, however, had been thinking things over. He had come very bravely through his sufferings; he had never really lost heart or given up hope; but he had found that the commonly accepted worldly ways of being happy did not bring happiness. He is impressed, however, by the example of a happy and sensible Turk who kept clear of politics and all worldly affairs, knowing Constantinople only as a good market for the produce of his tiny estate. 'Work without worrying,' the pessimistic Martin had said; 'it is the only way to make life endurable.' So the little group set to work to develop their[138] own small farm. Occasionally Pangloss would remark, 'There is a chain of events in the best of possible worlds. For if you had not been chased out of the Baron's castle with a kick on the bottom for making love to Miss Cunégonde; if you had not been caught by the Inquisition; if you had not wandered about America on foot; if you had not run your sword through Miss Cunégonde's brother, and lost the gold you got in Eldorado, you would not be here munching preserved fruit and pistachio nuts.' 'That may be quite true,' Candide would reply. 'Nevertheless, we have got to work in our garden.'[36]

So the novel ends on this quiet note. In spite of all the evil on earth, hope does still remain, the unquenchable hope of humanity for sufficiency and contentment. One facile kind of optimism is dead, but Voltaire knows that there is another humble, tough, and resilient human optimism that no adversity can completely extinguish. It is, admittedly, a vulnerable attitude of mind; but, at least, it is always there. The prospect for mankind is not hopelessly dark, provided that we all perform our immediate duties quietly and efficiently, and undisturbed by ambition.

It is said of the Lisbon earthquake that it brought an age to an end, and in the sense that the characteristic popular optimism of the first half of the eighteenth century did not long survive the disaster,

---

36 On this famous passage, see the notes to [Letter 185 (Henry St. John, first viscount Bolingbroke, to Voltaire), in *Voltaire's Correspondence*, ed. Theodore Besterman (Geneva: Institut et Musée Voltaire, 1953), I, 248.]

this saying is as true as any such generalization can be about so self-contradictory and complicated a subject as eighteenth-century thought. After the earthquake pessimism became a more familiar and understandable mood, while the undefeatably hopeful minds occupied themselves more and more with the idea of perfectibility, a gradual progress by man under God's providence towards a full happiness and perfection. In effecting this change, the influence of *Candide* played a significant part; indeed, what the tragedy of the Lisbon earthquake had only partly achieved by the resulting emotions of horror and pity, a novel turned into a significant revolution of thought.

A young French poet gives an example of the changed outlook. When the Lisbon earthquake happened, Ponce-Denis Écouchard Le Brun, already a budding literary figure of some promise, was twenty-six. As soon as the news reached Paris he wrote a poem on the disaster that was published almost immediately, a prettily[139] conventional piece about the folly of pride. Lisbon was over-proud; now Lisbon, Queen of the Seas, is no more; puny, foolish mankind must reflect that it is God who rules the world. Then came the further news of the death of young Racine, and deeply grieved at the loss of this beloved friend, Le Brun wrote a second poem, gloomily describing the physical causes of earthquakes and the terrible effects the forces of nature can produce. God seems to be always changing the face of the world and the life upon it; He oppresses in this way sea and land and all mankind; He mocks our credulous happiness; there is ultimately no escape from the forces He has unleashed against us. Smyrna, Pompeii, Herculaneum, Lima, and now Lisbon! We are all in peril.

The world is a hard place for us poor mortals. What have they really done to deserve such miseries? Dear Racine, cries Le Brun, if my complaints can reach you in the shades, let my love for you make up for the cruel injustice of fate.

In 1761, in the middle of the Seven Years War, Le Brun, who was newly married and had a good post and no private reasons at that time for being excessively gloomy, wrote an 'Ode to the Sun on the Misfortunes of the Earth since the Lisbon earthquake in 1755.' 'O Sun,' he asked, 'have you ever looked upon such awful horrors as those now afflicting mankind?' The earthquake at this moment seemed almost a minor disaster, for man himself had begun to join with nature in wrecking the world. There had been an attempt to assassinate King Louis XV in 1757, and also an attempt on the life of King José of Portugal in 1758, even while poor Lisbon still lay in ruins. 'O Sun! When you looked down almost into Hell through the earthquake-chasms did you not see the evil spirits escaping?' Three times in this century the Turks have terrified Europe, and Europe itself is ablaze with war; from the Dneiper and the Vistula to the Thames and the Seine the rivers are crowded with assembling fleets. And consider the New World! Tyrannical Europe has inflicted every possible misery on America, and the greed of white men has destroyed the happiness of the native peoples. England is at war with us in North America; there are bloody battles in the territory where our gallant Jumonville was killed eight years ago. War destroys all the blessings that the sun gives, and gold brings equal disaster; it is because of a shameless lust for gold that African slaves are poured into Mexico.[140]

> Ah! périsse la mémoire
> De nos lamentables jours!
> Grand Dieu! quelle ombre assez noire
> En peut absorber le cours!
> Siècle infame! siècle atroce!
> Ou l'impiété féroce
> Du ciel usurpa les droits![37]

The poet hopes that the sun will lead mankind to a happy existence in the Fortunate Islands, very pleasantly imagined; but we need not follow him further. It is enough to know that in the space of about six years the age of optimism had in Le Brun's opinion degenerated into the Dark Ages. The eighteenth century: *siècle infame, siècle atroce.*[141]

---

[37] [Ah, that the memory of our lamentable days might perish! Great God! What shadow black enough can obscure the length of them! Infamous century! Atrocious century! When fierce impiety encroached upon the rights of heaven!]

VOLTAIRE AND *CANDIDE**
Ira O. Wade

CONCLUSION

The *Journal encyclopédique*[1] was far from favorable in its review of *Candide*. Indeed, it was so severe that Voltaire felt constrained to take its editors to task for what he deemed their ineptitude. Their article, however, certainly merits attention, since it contains the type of ambiguous evaluation characteristic of all criticism of *Candide* down to the present day:

---

* From Ira O. Wade, *Voltaire and Candide* (Princeton: Princeton University Press, 1959), pp. 311–322. Reprinted by permission of the publisher. Copyright 1959, Princeton University Press.
[1] March 15, 1759, p. 103.

Comment juger ce roman? Ceux qu'il aura amusés, seroient révoltés
d'une critique sérieuse, ceux qui l'auront lû d'un œil sévère, nous feroient
un crime de notre indulgence. Les partisans de Leibnitz au lieu d'y voir une
réfutation de l'optimisme, n'y verront d'un bout à l'autre qu'une plaisanterie
qui fait beaucoup rire, et ne prouve rien; ses adversaires soutiendront que
la réfutation est complète, parce que le système de Leibnitz n'étant qu'un
roman, on ne peut le combattre avec avantage que par un autre roman.
Ceux qui chercheront uniquement la peinture des mœurs et des usages du
siècle, en trouveront les traits trop licencieux et trop peu variés. C'est enfin
une débauche d'esprit à laquelle il manque pour plaire généralement, un
peu de décence, et plus de circonspection. Nous désirerions que l'auteur eût
parlé avec plus de respect de tout ce qui regarde la religion et ses ministres,
qu'il n'eût point adopté la misérable fable du Paraguai qui n'a ici rien de
neuf, ni de piquant,...[2]

Thus the author of the article assumed that if the conte were intended
to refute Leibnitz, its success would be doubtful, and even if it were
effective as a refutation, it could not be considered a work of art because of its indecencies and exaggerations. In general, the *Journal*'s
criticism gives the impression that *Candide* can neither be taken seriously nor dismissed lightly.

Voltaire found present in his period this same peculiar ambiguity noted by the *Journal encyclopédique* in its review. At the time
he was writing the conte, he commented again and again that Paris
"qui chante et qui danse"[3] had abandoned its frivolous air for the
serious air of the English. Instead of being "singes" performing
"singeries,"[4] which was perfectly normal and natural, Parisians had
become "ours,"[5] debating and prattling about serious things. One
gathers from his comment that he deplored the[311] change, and in
fact he does so in his *Correspondence,* but in Chapter XXII of the
novel itself, he condemns Paris "qui chante et qui danse," Paris of the
"singeries." His attitude toward this situation is not the important
thing, however; the author's attitude never is, in a work of art. What
is really significant is that the conte has absorbed the ambiguity both
of its time and of its author. *Candide* is the product of those "qui

---

[2] [How to judge this novel? Those whom it will have amused will be re-
volted by a serious criticism; those who will have read it with a severe eye will
consider our forbearance a crime. The partisans of Leibniz, instead of seeing there
a refutation of optimism, will see, from beginning to end, only a joke which produces much laughter and proves nothing; his opponents will maintain that the
refutation is complete, because the system of Leibniz, being only a fiction, can be
combated advantageously only with another fiction. Those who will look only for
a description of the morality and customs of the century will find in it strokes
that are too licentious and too little varied. It is, in short, a debauch of wit that
lacks a bit of decency and much circumspection in order to please generally. We
should wish that the author had spoken with more respect about everything having
to do with religion and its clergy, and that he had not included the miserable
story of Paraguay, which has here nothing new nor lively,...]

[3] ["Which sings and dances."]

[4] ["Apes" performing "apish tricks."]

[5] ["Bears."]

danse et qui chantent," the "singes" and their "singeries," but also of the "ours" who take themselves seriously. And it is difficult to know which is the real, authentic *Candide.*

Grimm's review in the *Correspondance littéraire,* less favorable still, did precisely what the author of the *Journal encyclopédique* article deemed impossible. Renouncing any attempt to treat the work seriously, Grimm insisted that the only way to handle it was to take it lightly. After finding the second half superior to the first, after condemning the chapter on Paris, after denying the conte every serious literary and philosophical quality, he found only Voltaire's gaiety to praise:

> La gaieté est une des qualités les plus rares chez les beaux esprits. Il y avait longtemps que nous n'avions rien lu de réjouissant en littérature; M. de Voltaire vient de nous égayer par un petit roman intitulé: *Candide ou l'optimisme,* traduit de l'allemand de M. le docteur Ralph. Il ne faut pas juger cette production avec sévérité; elle ne soutiendrait pas une critique sérieuse. Il n'y a dans *Candide* ni ordonnance, ni plan, ni sagesse, ni de ces coups de pinceau heureux qu'on rencontre dans quelques romans anglais de même genre; vous y trouverez en revanche beaucoup de choses de mauvais goût, d'autres de mauvais ton, des polissonneries et des ordures qui n'ont point ce voile de gaze qui les rend supportables; cependant la gaieté, la facilité, qui n'abandonnent jamais Mr. de Voltaire qui bannit de ses ouvrages les plus frivoles, comme les plus médités cet air de prétention qui gâte tout, des traits et des saillies qui lui échappent à tout moment, rendent la lecture de *Candide* fort amusante.[6]

Thus *Candide* became for Grimm what Voltaire often called it: "une plaisanterie."[7]

Mme de Staël, on the other hand, takes a position the very opposite of Grimm's. She admits willingly that the book abounds in laughter, but considers it in no way a "plaisanterie," for this[312] laughter contains something inhumanly diabolical. She concedes that *Candide* basically was directed against Leibnitz, but stresses that it was directed against the fundamental propositions which preoccupy mankind, especially those philosophical opinions which enhance the spirit of man. Nothing could be more serious:

> Voltaire sentait si bien l'influence que les systèmes métaphysiques exercent sur la tendance générale des esprits, que c'est pour combattre Leibnitz qu'il a composé *Candide.* Il prit une humeur singulière contre les opinions philosophiques qui relèvent la dignité de l'homme; et il fit *Candide,* cet ouvrage d'une gaîté infernale: car il semble écrit par un être d'une autre nature que nous, indifférent à notre sort, content de nos souffrances, et riant comme un démon, ou comme un singe, des misères de cette espèce humaine avec laquelle il n'a rien de commun.[8]

---

6 [See p. 89 of this book.]

7 ["A joke."]

8 [See p. 91 of this book, the first paragraph of the quotation from Madame de Staël.]

While Grimm stresses the conte's gaiety, and Mme de Staël its seriousness, Linguet in his *Examen des ouvrages de M. de Voltaire* (Bruxelles, 1788) notes its dual character, that is to say, the glee with which Voltaire destroys the philosophy of optimism by graphically describing the tragic miseries of humanity:

> *Candide* présente le fonds le plus triste déguisé sous les accessoires les plus plaisans, mais de cette plaisanterie philosophique qui est particulière à Mr. de Voltaire, et qui, je le répète, aurait, ce semble, dû en faire un excellent comique. Il tourne complètement en ridicule le système du *tout est bien*, soutenu par tant de philosophes, et fait éclater mille fois de rire, en nous remettant à chaque instant sous les yeux, et avec un pinceau très énergique, toutes les infortunes qui accablent la société. (p. 170)[9]

Without being too dogmatic, we can confidently assert that these four opinions, though based on the same fundamental ambiguous assumptions, are widely divergent and represent the cardinal points of all *Candide* critics. There are those who, like the author of the *Journal encyclopédique,* feel that the work can be taken neither seriously nor lightly, those who maintain with Grimm that it must be treated only lightly, those who aver with Mme de Staël that it can be taken only seriously, and finally those who like Linguet, find that it must be taken seriously and lightly at the same time.

This double quality of gaiety and seriousness, so characteristic[313] of Voltaire and of his time, is apparent at every turn throughout the conte, but it is not a simple matter to grasp the deep ambiguity of its personality. When the reader is ready to revolt in horror, a sudden reflection, a quick turn in events, an unexpected quip, or the mere insertion of a remark brings him back to normal. When he is inclined to levity, an incident, an observation, or an injustice brings him back to consider the deadly earnest attack which is being made on all aspects of life.

The difficulty in harmonizing these two attitudes in the reader's understanding has led to divers partial interpretations of *Candide,* practically all of them valid in their way but each woefully deficient in itself. If the book is to be taken lightly, how lightly? Can it be dismissed as the "crème fouettée de l'Europe,"[10] or is it a "bonne plaisanterie," with a "fonds le plus triste"?[11] Does Candide, like Figaro, rail at everything to keep himself from weeping? Is it, as

---

9 [*Candide* presents the saddest subject disguised by the most humorous devices of that philosophical joking that is peculiar to M. de Voltaire and which, I repeat, should make of it, it seems, an excellent comedy. It turns completely into ridicule the *all is well* philosophy upheld by so many philosophers and causes us to burst into laughter a thousand times, yet all the while putting before our eyes with a very energetic pencil all the misfortunes that overwhelm society.]

10 ["Whipped cream of Europe."]

11 ["Good joke," with the "saddest subject."]

Montaigne once said of Rabelais, "simplement plaisant" on the surface, but "triste" underneath? There is a similar progression in the opposite attitude. How far does Voltaire go in his satire? Does he, for instance, merely castigate the social conditions of his time, as Boileau or Horace had done before him, or does he satirize the fundamental conditions of life, like a Homer or a Racine, or does he push his revolt to the point of satirizing the Creator of life? These are difficult, almost irreverent, questions. The answers must always be yes, although every yes is contradicted by another yes, or a yes and no by another yes and no. Far from being a structure of "clear and distinct ideas," *Candide* is confusion confounded. But it is the confusion of a universe clearly and distinctly controlled. Whatever happens may be terribly and devastatingly irrational, but once it has been sifted through Voltaire's intelligence, it has been ordered by the keenest sort of criticism into a created form which does not differ from the form of life itself. *Candide* embraces everything that had occurred in the life of Voltaire as well as everything that had occurred in the eighteenth century. It is astounding in its comprehensiveness, and quite as remarkable in other aspects: the rhythmical arrangement of the above-mentioned phenomena, the careful selection and presentation, the exact apportionment, and the very orderly expression.[314]

That is the reason why every judgment of *Candide* is bound to be partial, one-sided, contradictory, and vague, just like every judgment we make of life or of our individual lives. Since every man is a "Démocrite" and a "Héraclite," he must be "Jean-qui-pleure" and "Jean-qui-rit."[12] But every man must be these two characters at the same time: he is neither optimist nor pessimist, rebellious nor submissive, free nor enslaved, formed nor unformed, real nor unreal. He must make a reality of these necessary contradictions.

The four opinions expressed above, while representing the four cardinal positions in *Candide* criticism, in no way exhaust the range of partial interpretations given the work. I pass over Voltaire's own sly remark that it was written to convert Socinians, as well as the superficial, but amusing, epigram current at the time of its appearance:

> Candide est un petit vault rien
> Qui n'a ni pudeur, ni cervelle,
> A son air on reconnaît bien
> Qu'il est frère de la Pucelle.
>
> Son vieux papa pour rajeunir
> Donnerait une grosse somme.
> Sa jeunesse va revenir
> Il fait des œuvres d'un jeune homme.
>
> Tout n'est pas bien, lisez l'écrit;
> La preuve en est à chaque page,

---

12 ["John who weeps" and "John who laughs."]

Vous verrez même en cet ouvrage
Que tout est mal comme il le dit.[13]

Of more importance is the qualification printed in the *Nouvelles ec-clésiastiques*:[14] "Mauvais roman, plein d'ordures, peut-être le plus impie, le plus pernicieux ouvrage qui soit jamais sorti de la plume de Mr. de Voltaire,"[15] or the opinion attributed to the Patriarch by the unknown author of the *Confession de Voltaire*:[16] "Il résulte de la lecture de *Candide* que la terre est un cloaque d'horreur et d'abominations (with a quotation from *Job* 10:22: Terram miseriae et tenebrarum ubi nullus ordo, sed sempiternus horror inhabitat);[315] j'en ai composé plus d'un chapitre dans des accès de migraine . . ."[17] or the more drastic qualification of Jules Janin in *Le Dernier volume des œuvres de Voltaire*:[18]

Le livre fut beaucoup lu dans le beau monde, où il ne fut pas compris. On ne trouva que des avantures romanesques là où Voltaire dans sa logique de démon avait voulu railler Dieu.[19]

After so many categorical statements, made with appropriately French nuance, it may seem idle to seek a clearer view of *Candide*'s reality. It is quite possible to agree that the work is a "vaurien,"[20] or obscene, or perhaps the most impious ever written by Voltaire, or that its portrayal of the earth is abomination and horror incarnate. One might even go so far as to agree with Janin that "Voltaire avait voulu railler Dieu." But to understand that the work is at the same time a

---

13 [Candide is a little worthless fellow
 Who has neither modesty, nor brains,
 By his manner one easily recognizes
 That he is the brother of la Pucelle.

 In order to grow young again, his old papa
 Would give a large sum.
 To regain his youth
 He does the deeds of a young man.

 All is not well, read what has been written;
 The proof of it is on each page,
 You will see even in this work
 That all is bad, just as he says.]
14 September 3, 1760, p. 158.
15 ["A bad novel, full of filth, perhaps the most impious, the most pernicious work that may have ever come from the pen of M. de Voltaire."]
16 Geneva, 1762, p. 39.
17 ["It follows from the reading of *Candide* that the earth is a sewer of horror and abominations (with a quotation from Job 10:22: A land of darkness, as darkness itself; and of the shadow of death, without any order, and where the light is as darkness); I have composed more than one chapter of it during headache attacks . . ."]
18 Paris, 1861, p. 103.
19 [The book was read very much in the fashionable world, where it was not understood. Readers found only romantic adventures there where Voltaire in his fiendish logic had wished to mock God.]
20 ["Good for nothing."]

revolt and a submission, an attack and a defense, a joy and a suffering, a destruction and a creation requires more than ordinary insight, patience, and serenity. There is, indeed, the temptation to dismiss it as only one thing, as too simple, too superficial.

What is dangerous in *Candide* is not its simplicity, but its duplicity. *Candide* is always deceptively two. Its unremitting ambiguity leads inevitably to a puzzling clandestinity, and the reader, beset with difficulties in forming a well-considered opinion, settles for trite commonplaces. The work actually encourages him in this. Let us take as an example the oft-repeated remark that Voltaire attacked Leibnitz. Though true, this statement adds nothing to the comprehension of *Candide*'s reality.

It would be useful, nevertheless, to understand the relationship between *Candide* and Leibnitz. Undeniably, Voltaire satirized Leibnitzian terminology in his conte but ample testimony has been adduced to show that he never rejected Leibnitzianism: he rejected some things in it—the theory of monads, for example—but he readily accepted other ideas such as the principle of sufficient reason. We have already shown that he needed Leibnitz's principles, just as they were needed by the eighteenth century at large. It is a particularly carefree criticism that envisages the development of ideas as a matter of acceptance or rejection. Voltaire[316] was certainly more realistic in his attitude. What he satirized was the terminology; not the philosophy, but what in that philosophy was now contributing to making life sterile. Moreover, at the moment he was writing *Candide,* he stated explicitly that people had ceased paying attention to what Leibnitz said. Soon after, when a new edition of Leibnitz's works was published, he complimented the editor. The truth of the matter is that Voltaire, like his time, had to integrate Descartes, Pascal, Leibnitz, Spinoza, Malebranche, Locke, and Newton in order to create an Enlightenment philosophy. Leibnitz was as important to that philosophy as any of the others, and fully as useful. It is probable that in 1750 he had played his role and in that sense had ceased to claim people's attention. But even this assessment is subject to caution.

This dilemma has led certain critics to insist that what Voltaire is attacking is not a philosopher, but a philosophy. Ever since the article of March 15, 1759, in the *Journal encyclopédique,* some critics have insisted that Voltaire definitely aimed his attack not against Leibnitz or Pope, but against a system of philosophy to which Leibnitz, Pope, and many others had contributed and which we now call optimism. Since he himself entitled his work *Candide, ou l'optimisme,* it would be extremely difficult to deny that he directed his satire at this way of looking at life. To conclude, however, with Linguet, that "il tourne complètement en ridicule le système du tout est bien,"[21] or,

---

21 ["It turns completely into ridicule the all is well philosophy."]

with Lanson, that "le but est de démolir l'optimisme,"[22] is misplacing
the emphasis. It would not take a very skillful lawyer to prove that
Voltaire's treatment of optimism is quite as optimistic as the treatment of the optimists themselves, that he says no more for or against
it than Leibnitz, Pope, King, and hundreds of others. Voltaire is assailing all feeling of complacency which nullifies and stultifies human
effort in a universe requiring a maximum of human effort to realize
itself—he is assailing, in a word, all restraints upon the creative spirit
of man.

It must be admitted that his attitude toward optimism is difficult to trace because of the ambiguity of his position. He was con-
genitally opposed to any attitude which complacently asseverated that
"tout est bien," mainly because such a belief limited human effort.
But he was quite as opposed to any attitude which[317] despairingly
asserted that "tout est mal,"[23] chiefly because such a standpoint also
limited human effort. But other considerations were important, too.
Voltaire knew that "tout n'est pas bien"[24] because there are numerous
concrete cases of evil, and he knew also that "tout n'est pas mal"[25]
because there are many concrete cases of good. Throughout the conte,
he draws a constant parallel between the wretchedness of others and
his own happiness, and he continually wavers between the achieve-
ments of his time and its follies. He weighs facts as scrupulously as
Montaigne weighed truth: the facts prove two things, two exasperat-
ingly contradictory things. Cacambo's friendship and loyalty make
him "un très bon homme,"[26] while Vanderdendur's duplicity makes
him "un homme très dur,"[27] but both are realities, just as the
"duretés"[28] of the "homme noir"[29] and the kindness of the "bon
Jaques"[30] are realities. There is thus in Candide a compensatory
quality, common to all Voltaire's works and to the eighteenth century
in general, that is, that good is counterbalanced by evil. This is no
new attitude: it is evident throughout his works from the Epître à
Uranie to Candide. Le Monde comme il va, Micromégas, Zadig hold
steadily to this idea.

It is not the view, however, that is important, but the conclusion
to be drawn from it. Should one conclude for optimism, or surrender
to pessimism? Should one be content with weighing impassively

---

22 ["The purpose is to demolish optimism."]
23 ["All is bad."]
24 ["All is not good."]
25 ["All is not bad."]
26 ["A very good man."]
27 ["A very hard man."]
28 ["Hardness."]
29 ["Black man."]
30 ["Good Jaques."]

this against that, refusing to take sides, enjoying fully his own happiness? This skeptical conclusion, characteristic of the Renaissance in general and of Montaigne in particular, did not find favor with Voltaire, although he, like most Frenchmen, was strongly attracted to it. The ambiguity of Candide's garden, and of its actual prototype at Les Délices and Ferney, was occasioned in fact by this skeptical conclusion. But Voltaire's skepticism, which is as positive as Montaigne's, is no proof against his cynicism. It was impossible to "jouir largement de son être"[31] in 1758 after the fiasco at Berlin, the Lisbon Earthquake, and the Seven Years War. It was possible, perhaps, to criticize, blame, satirize, laugh mockingly, always with indifference, in this completely mad world. Voltaire attempted to adopt this attitude also but found it quite unsatisfactory.[318]

Candide is thus in its inner substance not *wholly* optimistic, or pessimistic, or skeptical, or cynical: it is *all* of these things at the same time. Since every created thing resembles its creator and the moment of its creation, it is precisely what Voltaire and his time were: optimistic, pessimistic, skeptical, and cynical, a veritable "moment de la crise."[32] Facts had produced ideas, it is true, but ideas had not yet produced ideals, and no one knew what *to do.*

There are, of course, several ways of meeting this situation. First, there is resignation: Christian or even philosophical resignation, both unacceptable to Voltaire. Having rejected Christianity, dogma and all, he could find no solace in an attitude leading to consequences that he could not accept, and having long since adopted libertine Epicureanism, he saw no sense in any form of stoicism, Christian or pagan.

Second, there is the way of attack, for if conditions are intolerable, they can be denounced. It is as easy to ridicule distasteful facts, offensive people, disagreeable incidents, and unfair judgments as to satirize an unacceptable view of the universe. Voltaire responded freely and fully to this temptation: the list of things and persons he assails is practically endless: kings, religious intolerance, the Inquisition; Fréron, Vanduren, Trublet; war, inequality, injustice; disease, earthquake, tidal waves; petty thievery, rape, social pride; Jesuits, Jansenists, slavery. In this mass and single attack there is a complete upheaval of the social order; in the political area we find deep criticism of monarchy, the policing of the state, the lack of freedom and equality before the law. In the realm of religion there are powerful accusations against persecution, intolerance, useless dogma, and hierarchical institution. In the moral order, dishonesty, sham, false pride, prostitution, rape, all the petty inhumanities of man against man are viciously assailed. In the natural order, disease, cataclysms,

---

31 ["To be fully in possession of his being."]
32 ["Moment of crisis."]

malformations are damned with an irreverence barely short of blasphemy. And yet, though *Candide* attacks, it does not ultimately destroy. The reason for this is very simple: life is full of miseries, but it also has its pleasures. It is perhaps true that few people would like to relive it, but also true that few voluntarily renounce it. Voltaire was certainly not one to abdicate.[319]

Nevertheless, as the crisis developed, he was torn between cynical renunciation and the urge to create. He was completely aware that the forces restraining this urge were powerful enough to eliminate not only the desire but the person desiring. Experience had taught him the stupidities of man, the horrors of war, the power of kings, and the eccentricities of nature. Any one of these could easily suppress him and his urge to create. He was thus literally reduced to living by his wits, like J. F. Rameau and Figaro, and living by his wits meant very literally indeed the application of wit to all [these] stupid phenomena. The world had become a paradox and Voltaire responded with a revolt.

It is imperative to understand the nature of this revolt, since the whole eighteenth century and subsequent centuries have derived from it. Voltaire's response was born of both anger and despair. He was "fâché"[33] with kings, "fâché" with earthquakes, "fâché" with God. Agamemnon, the great Earthshaker and Zeus had "let him down," just as they had seemed to abandon Achilles in a far distant moment. The two urns which stand at the feet of Zeus poured forth both good and evil upon the old Patriarch and he, in his frustration, became deeply unhappy, the more so since events transcended all understanding by the human mind:

> Notre triste raison, faible, aveugle, égarée,
> Si des yeux de Dieu même elle n'est éclairée,
> Ne comprendra jamais quel pouvoir infernal
> Aux célestes bienfaits a mêlé tant de mal. ...[34]

Voltaire's attitude toward Providence must be considered very carefully if we are to grasp the meaning of *Candide*. It is perhaps well to ask ourselves what role Rousseau's letter played in the composition of the conte. While it is extremely unlikely that the *Lettre sur la Providence* provoked *Candide,* as Rousseau would have us believe, it is nevertheless true that Rousseau's defense of Providence touched Voltaire in his sensitive spot. The conclusion of *Zadig,* it will be recalled, had definitely been a defense of Providence, along more rational, Popian lines than Rousseau's later defense. The problem is therefore posed as to Voltaire's subsequent attitude.

---

33 ["On bad terms."]
34 [Our sad reason, weak, blind, misguided,
    Even if it is able to see with the eyes of God himself,
    It will never understand what infernal power
    Has mingled so much evil with heavenly favors. ...]

If, to be specific, Voltaire felt that Pope's arguments no longer[320] "justified the ways of God to man," and Leibnitz's were equally deficient, did he think that he had better ones, or that he could find better ones elsewhere? In other words, was his quarrel with the optimists whose arguments could not justify God's ways or with God whose ways could not be rationally justified? And did he assail the philosophers with fiendish glee because he did not know how to attack Providence which was really responsible for evil? Why did he not heed Rousseau's letter as the Duke de Wurtemburg thought he should have done? Why was it rather an incitement to *Candide,* just as Rousseau thought? These are strange and almost irreverent questions, and totally unanswerable in any critical way, but necessary in divining Voltaire's state of mind. It is undoubtedly true that his act was not a critique but a revolt, a titanic revolt brought about by a breakdown in the power of critique. Having reached the place where understanding was irrational, Voltaire had no other resource than to attack overtly those who thought they understood, and who gave good rational reasons for their comprehension. Simply put, he could only attack the irrationality, the ambiguity of the universe by annihilating rationally all rationality. In that respect his wit is a spiritual, not a rational, instrument for assailing the ambiguity, the clandestinity of a universe which refuses to make itself known.

This state of things explains why one never knows in reading *Candide* whether to laugh with Voltaire or at him, whether to laugh with the philosophers or at them, whether indeed to laugh with or at Providence; whether, in fact, to laugh at all. In uncertainty and despair there is much ground for hesitation, uneasiness, bitterness, frustration. Taken seriously, the moment of *Candide* is a tragic affair. But should it be taken seriously? Mme d'Epinay in her characterization of Voltaire states that when he has become most serious he immediately starts making fun of himself and everybody else. This reaction seems to hold true for *Candide.* Certainly no one takes himself too seriously in *Candide.* When the moment of revolt becomes too intense, each person resorts to his wit to save the situation. Thus wit is not only a means of revolt, it is at the same time an instrument for the release of intolerable pressures and better still, it serves as a release for the inner forces of man; it is a force, too, a creative effort, an urge to[321] be. Standing face to face with the power of annihilation, impotent to solve either the rationality or the irrationality of things, witness to an impossibly ludicrous cosmic tragedy, *Candide* proclaims loudly, not that

> The play is the tragedy Man
> And its hero, the Conqueror Worm

but that the play is puny, insignificant, unregenerate man, and its hero an unconquerable, defiant, eternal wit.[322]

THE NATURE DOCTRINE OF VOLTAIRE*

George R. Havens

The importance of the appeal to Nature in the eighteenth century is well known, but the subject as a whole is so vast that it still awaits its historian. The present article aims to present in brief space the results of a study of this particular topic in the works of Voltaire. It is evident at once that in Voltaire the nature doctrine has less importance than it does in Diderot or in Rousseau or in a host of lesser writers, but this is not to say that it is negligible. On the contrary, it is much more influential in his thinking than one might at first be inclined to suspect, and it leads him to express ideas which one does not ordinarily associate with his name. Yet it is not at all surprising, on second thought, that Voltaire in this respect, as in others, should share the mental attitude of predecessors and contemporaries. Rabelais and Montaigne had appealed to nature. Fénelon had drawn for the readers of *Télémaque* an idyllic picture of Bétique and its inhabitants. Montesquieu's Troglodytes in the *Lettres persanes* make one think, not only of Rousseau, but of El Dorado in Voltaire's *Candide*. Then there was the Epicurean school of the Temple, with which Voltaire was in close contact when he was a youth of eighteen or twenty. In that group were men like Chaulieu and La Fare,[1] who were imbued with a natural religion, which appears in Voltaire as early as 1716 and never disappears from his thought.

So far as possible this study will be chronological. We shall find that nature references in Voltaire's works are during the first half of his career sporadic, if we consider them in proportion to the immense bulk of his writings. Nevertheless, they indicate the trend of his thought, which in later years tends to concentrate, so far as this doctrine is concerned, along two or three main lines.

In 1716, when Voltaire was twenty-two years old, he wrote an *Epître à Madame de G * * *,* in which is expressed clearly the idea that the law of nature is the law of God.[852]

---

* Reprinted from *PMLA*, XL (December 1925), 852–862, by permission of George R. Havens and *PMLA*.
1 Cf. especially *Poésies inédites du Marquis de la Fare*, pub. par Gustave L. Van Roosbroeck, Paris, 1924, pp. 7, 9, 10, 11, 18, 19, 36–37.

> La loi de la nature est sa première loi;
> Elle seule autrefois conduisit nos ancêtres;
> Elle parle plus haut que la voix de vos prêtres,
> Pour vous, pour vos plaisirs, pour l'amour, et pour moi.[2]

But we should be careful not to attach much philosophical importance to these verses, for in them Voltaire is engaged merely in gracefully urging his suit and in breaking down the lady's scruples by an appeal to the so-called law of nature. The author is more in earnest in the following passage from the *Henriade*. Voltaire says of God:

> Partout il nous instruit, partout il parle à nous;
> Il grave en tous les cœurs la loi de la nature,
> Seule à jamais la même, et seule toujours pure.[3]

This law is constant, universal, free from artificial accretions, and by it alone, Voltaire tells us in a variant,[4] the heathen are judged by God. To this law even the unorthodox Spinoza was obedient.

> Spinosa fut toujours fidèle
> A la loi pure et naturelle
> Du Dieu qu'il avait combattu.[5]

Of still more interest is a variant to the *Ode sur la paix de 1736*, which implies that man was born for goodness rather than for evil.

> Notre cœur n'est point né sauvage:
> Grands dieux! si l'homme est votre image,
> Il n'était fait que pour aimer.[6]

Here, as elsewhere, Voltaire is expressing his opposition to war, but he is already by implication attacking the idea that man is by nature evil, a belief which he combats with still more emphasis in his last years.

---

[2] Voltaire, *Œuvres* (Moland ed.), X, 232.
[The law of nature is his first law;
 It alone formerly guided our ancestors;
 It speaks louder than the voice of our priests,
 For you, for your pleasures, for love, and for me.]
[3] *Ibid.*, VIII, 172.
[Everywhere he teaches us, everywhere he speaks to us;
 He engraves on all hearts the law of nature,
 Alone, forever the same, and alone, always pure.]
[4] *Ibid.*, VIII, 191–92.
[5] *Ibid.*, VIII, 428.
[Spinoza was always faithful
 To the pure and natural law
 Of the God whom he had combatted.]
[6] *Ibid.*, VIII, 438. Cf. second variant on the same page. Cf. also the *Avant-Propos sur la Henriade par le Roi de Prusse* (1739) (pub. 1756), VIII, 27: "La nature ne nous forma point assurément," etc.
[Our heart is not born savage:
 Great gods; if man is your image,
 He is made only for loving.]

At the beginning of the *Discours sur l'homme* in 1738 is expressed the basic natural equality of mankind,[7] and in his Ode[853] on *La Félicité des temps* in 1746, Voltaire, the partisan of progress, brushes aside statements that mankind has degenerated,[8] for nature is inexhaustible in her possibilities.

> Loin ce discours lâche et vulgaire,
> Que toujours l'homme dégénère,
> Que tout s'épuise et tout finit:
> La nature est inépuisable,
> Et le Travail infatigable
> Est un dieu qui la rajeunit.[9]

The utterances of Voltaire on this subject thus far cited have been in verse. We come now to a passage in prose in which the author explains more definitely what he means by natural religion. In the *Eléments de la philosophie de Newton* of 1738,[10] Voltaire writes:

> J'entends par religion naturelle les principes de morale communs au genre humain. ... La religion naturelle n'est autre chose que cette loi qu'on connaît dans tout l'univers: *Fais ce que tu voudrais qu'on te fît.* ... Qu'on me trouve un pays, une compagnie de dix personnes sur la terre, où l'on n'estime pas ce qui sera utile au bien commun: et alors je conviendrai qu'il n'y a point de règle naturelle. Cette règle varie à l'infini sans doute; mais qu'en conclure, sinon qu'elle existe? ... Newton pensait donc que cette disposition que nous avons tous à vivre en société est le fondement de la loi naturelle, que le christianisme perfectionne.[11]

Thus natural religion is based upon a sort of lowest common de-

---

[7] *Ibid.*, IX, 379. Cf. again Frederick's preface to the *Henriade*, VIII, 27, and also *Corr.* XXXVII, 145, the verse, "Et tout est égal en ce monde."

[8] Voltaire may have in mind, not only contemporary pre-Rousseauistic statements, but also such passages as are to be found in Lucretius regarding the gradual wearing-out of nature and of life in general.

[9] Voltaire, *Œuvres*, VIII, 459. Cf. *Ibid.*, XIX, 330-31.
[Away with this base and vulgar talk
 That man always degenerates,
 That everything wears out and everything ends:

 Nature is inexhaustible,
 And indefatigable Work
 Is a god who rejuvenates her.]

[10] The text as it stands is certainly not later than 1748; it first appeared in 1738.

[11] Voltaire, *Œuvres*, XXII, 419, 420-21. For this absoluteness of morality, cf. Renan's dictum, "le bien, c'est le bien; le mal, c'est le mal" (*Essais de morale et de critique*, Lévy, 7e éd., p. ii). [I understand natural religion to be the principles of the common morality of mankind. ... Natural religion is nothing more than that law which we perceive throughout the universe: *Do that which you would want others to do to you.* ... If you can find me a country, a society of ten persons on the earth, where the members do not value that which will be beneficial to the common good: then I shall admit that there is not a natural rule. This rule varies infinitely no doubt, but to infer from that anything except that it exists? ... Newton thought therefore that this tendency that we all have for living in society is the basis of natural law, which Christianity improves.]

nominator of human morality, which is summarized in the Golden Rule, a principle to which, here in its affirmative form, elsewhere often stated negatively after the fashion of Confucius, Voltaire frequently returns as representative of the essence of morality and religion. The common welfare is the universal criterion by which morality is determined. This standard of morality is no doubt infinitely variable, it exists nevertheless. Mankind has a disposition to live in society, which makes some[854] sort of natural morality necessary. Voltaire here in advance takes a position regarding society opposite to that of Rousseau. Later, as one would expect, he definitely combats in this respect the attitude of his great rival.

It will be remembered that the poem of 1752 now called *Poème sur la loi naturelle* was first entitled *Poème sur la religion naturelle*. This title caused trouble; it was too bold for the orthodox and was therefore changed. But Voltaire of course was none the less still speaking of natural religion. In the Preface of 1756 he declared: "Qu'on appelle la raison et les remords comme on voudra, ils existent, et ils sont les fondements de la loi naturelle."[12] Voltaire has been speaking of the wild girl of Châlons, who as the type of the primitive, uncultivated mind was inspired by nature with remorse for having killed her companion. Upon this natural remorse, not upon *amour-propre*, says Voltaire, natural morality is based. Similarly in the poem itself the thought is repeated that this moral law is uniform and universal, inspired by God and nature, and preserved by the qualms of conscience.[13]

We come now to the famous letter to Rousseau in which Voltaire in 1755 acknowledged receipt of the *Discours sur l'inégalité*. This letter is a marvelously clever *badinage*, by which Rousseau's Discourse is most effectively ridiculed, if not precisely refuted. Voltaire says that he cannot seek out primitive simplicity among the *sauvages du Canada*, "parce que la guerre est portée dans ces pays-là, et que les exemples de nos nations ont rendu les sauvages presque aussi méchants que nous."[14] This is jesting, of course, but none the less it indicates Voltaire's matter-of-fact opinion that the "state of nature" leaves much to be desired in comparison with civilization. Later Voltaire several times returns to the subject and reiterates the same opinion seriously. In this connection one recalls also Chapter XVI of *Candide*. Candide and his companion, Cacambo, are about to be roasted and eaten by the savages called Oreillons.

---

[12] Voltaire, *op. cit.*, IX, 440. ["No matter what people call reason or remorse, they exist, and they are the foundations of natural law."]

[13] *Ibid.*, IX, 444–45. Cf. J.-J. Rousseau, "Conscience! conscience! instinct divin, immortelle et céleste voix," etc. (*Emile*, Hachette, II, 262).

[14] Voltaire, *Œuvres*, XXXVIII, 447. ["Because war is waged in that country, and because the examples of our nations have made the savages almost as wicked as we."]

Candide, apercevant la chaudière et les broches, s'écria: "Nous allons certainement être rôtis ou bouillis. Ah! que dirait maître Pangloss, s'il voyait[855] comme la pure nature est faite? Tout est bien: soit, mais j'avoue qu'il est bien cruel d'avoir perdu Mlle Cunégonde et d'être mis à la broche par des Oreillons." ... "Messieurs," dit Cacambo, "vous comptez donc manger aujourd'hui un jésuite? c'est très-bien fait; rien n'est plus juste que de traiter ainsi ses ennemis. En effet le droit naturel nous enseigne à tuer notre prochain, et c'est ainsi qu'on en agit dans toute la terre."

But when the Oreillons learn that Candide is not a Jesuit, they reverse their decision forthwith, and Candide exclaims:

"Mais, après tout, la pure nature est bonne, puisque ces gens-ci, au lieu de me manger, m'ont fait mille honnêtetés dès qu'ils ont su que je n'étais pas jésuite."[15]

In this chapter Voltaire's mockery is distributed over the Jesuits, the state of nature, and that *droit naturel* which exists only in theory without being followed in practice even by civilization. The implication is that the Oreillons are not better, but neither are they more ferocious than so-called civilized peoples.

But what of El Dorado to which Candide shortly comes? At first sight this looks like a glorification of primitive simplicity very much in the manner of Fénelon in *Télémaque* and Montesquieu with his Troglodytes. But there is a very considerable difference. Luxury, instead of simplicity, is all about. The children play with gold, emeralds, and rubies, all unheeding. Candide and Cacambo enter a house magnificent as a palace in Europe. It is an inn. There is pleasing music. They sit down at the table.

On servit quatre potages garnis chacun de deux perroquets, un contour bouilli qui pesait deux cents livres, deux singes rôtis d'un goût excellent, trois cents colibris dans un plat, et six cents oiseaux-mouches dans un autre; des ragoûts exquis, des pâtisseries délicieuses; le tout dans des plats d'une espèce de cristal de roche. Les garçons et les filles de l'hôtellerie versaient plusieurs liqueurs faites de cannes de sucre.[16]

After this exotic but magnificent repast, the host apologizes:

"Vous avez fait mauvaise chère ici, parce que c'est un pauvre village; mais partout ailleurs vous serez reçus comme vous méritez de l'être."[17][856]

And this was an inn maintained at government expense "pour la commodité du commerce" and for the accommodation of "des marchands et des voituriers, tous d'une politesse extrême!" The two travelers next visit one of the old and wise men of the village.

Ils entrèrent dans une maison fort simple, car la porte n'était que

---

15 *Ibid.*, XXI, 171, 172. [See p. 29, paragraphs 8, 11; p. 30, paragraph 3, of this book.]

16 *Ibid.*, XXI, 174. On the sources of Voltaire's details on El Dorado, see the authoritative critical edition of *Candide* by André Morize (Hachette, 1913). [See p. 32, paragraph 3, of this book.]

17 *Ibid.*, XXI, 174-175. [See p. 32, paragraph 6, of this book.]

d'argent, et les lambris des appartements n'étaient que d'or. ... L'anti-chambre n'était à la vérité incrustée que de rubis et d'émeraudes; mais l'ordre dans lequel tout était arrangé réparait bien cette extrême simplicité.[18]

The people have preserved their innocence and happiness. They believe in natural religion, worship one God. Their prayers are of adoration, not of petition. There are no priests. Voltaire's El Dorado is a mingling of such idyllic imaginings as those of Fénelon and of Montesquieu with a very strong dose of Voltaire's own *Mondain*, which shows so real an appreciation of "ce siècle de fer" and of the "superflu chose très-nécessaire."[19] There is nothing in this El Dorado to suggest the state of nature. It is a jesting utopia, in which only religion is simplified. Admiration of primitivism is not part of Voltaire's nature doctrine.

This last conclusion is definitely confirmed by the *Essai sur les Mœurs*. Voltaire is refuting Rousseau.

On a écrit que cet état [d'hommes vivant en brutes] est le véritable état de l'homme, et que nous n'avons fait que dégénérer misérablement depuis que nous l'avons quitté. Je ne crois pas que cette vie solitaire, attribuée à nos pères, soit dans la nature humaine.[20]

Voltaire argues that social life has been in accordance with the nature of man from the beginning, since it grows directly out of the family relationships.

L'homme, en général, a toujours été ce qu'il est. ... Il a toujours eu le même instinct, qui le porte à s'aimer dans soi-même, dans la compagne de son plaisir, dans ses enfants, dans ses petits-fils, dans les œuvres de ses mains.[21]

In the *Dictionnaire philosophique* Voltaire wrote similarly:

Quelques mauvais plaisants ont abusé de leur esprit jusqu'au point de hasarder le paradoxe étonnant que l'homme est originairement fait pour vivre seul comme un loup cervier, et que c'est la société qui a dépravé la nature. ...[857] Loin que le besoin de la société ait dégradé l'homme, c'est l'éloignement de la société qui le dégrade.[22]

This last statement suggests comparison with Diderot's assertion in his *Fils naturel*, which so angered Rousseau in his solitude at the

---

18 *Ibid.*, XXI, 175. [See p. 33, paragraph 1, of this book.]

19 *Ibid.*, X, 84. ["This iron century" and of the "unnecessary thing very necessary."]

20 *Ibid.*, XI, 19–20. [It has been written that this state (of men living as beasts) is the true state of man, and we have done nothing but degenerate miserably since we left it. I do not believe that this solitary life, attributed to our forefathers, may be part of human nature.]

21 *Ibid.*, XI, 21. [Man, in general, has always been what he is. ... He has always had the same instinct, which inclines him to be vain about himself, the woman of his pleasure, his children, his grandsons, and the work of his hands.]

22 *Ibid.*, XIX, 378–79. [Some mischievous wags have misused their wit even to the point of suggesting the astonishing paradox that man was originally made to live alone like a lynx, and that it is society which has depraved nature. ... It is far from being true that the need for society has degraded man; it is the removal from society that degrades him.]

Hermitage: "Il n'y a que le méchant qui soit seul."²³ Voltaire's favorable attitude toward society and his hostility to primitivism are clear. It is society, and not solitude, which is natural to man.

But Voltaire is more like Rousseau when he holds that nature supplies an instinct which forms the basis of morality. "Il est donc prouvé que la nature seule nous inspire des idées utiles qui précèdent toutes nos réflexions. Il en est de même dans la morale. Nous avons tous deux sentiments qui sont le fondement de la société; la commisération et la justice."²⁴ Rousseau also had emphasized the importance of pity in his *Discours sur l'inégalité*. "Je parle de la pitié, ... vertu d'autant plus universelle et d'autant plus utile à l'homme, qu'elle précède en lui l'usage de toute réflexion."²⁵

Another Rousseauistic note appears in a dialogue work published by Voltaire in 1768 under the title of *L'ABC*. In it he says: "Je pense que la nature de l'homme n'est pas tout à fait diabolique. Mais pourquoi dit-on que l'homme est toujours porté au mal?"²⁶ A similar and even clearer attack upon the doctrine of the natural perversity of man had already appeared in the *Dictionnaire philosophique*.

On nous crie que la nature humaine est essentiellement perverse, que l'homme est né enfant du diable et méchant. Rien n'est plus malavisé ... Il serait bien plus raisonnable, bien plus beau de dire aux hommes: Vous êtes tous nés bons; voyez combien il serait affreux de corrompre la pureté de votre être. ... L'homme n'est point né méchant; il le devient, comme il devient malade. ... Assemblez tous les enfants de l'univers, vous ne verrez en eux que l'innocence, la douceur et la crainte. ... L'homme n'est donc pas né mauvais; pourquoi plusieurs sont-ils donc infectés de cette peste de la méchanceté? C'est que ceux qui sont à leur tête, étant pris de la maladie, la communiquent au reste des hommes. ... Le premier ambitieux a corrompu[858] la terre.²⁷ ... Vous avez donc tout au plus sur la terre, dans

---

²³ Cf. J.-J. Rousseau, *Confessions* (Hachette), VIII, 327. ["It is only the wicked who would be alone."]

²⁴ Voltaire, *Œuvres*, XI, 22. ["It is therefore proved that nature alone inspires us with beneficial ideas that take precedence over all our thoughts. It is the same with morality. We have both of the feelings which are the basis of society; pity and justice."]

²⁵ J.-J. Rousseau, *Œuvres* (Hachette), I, 98. Cf. *Emile, Œuvres*, II, 193. ["I speak of pity, ... the virtue so much the more universal and so much the more beneficial to man that for him it takes precedence over any other consideration."]

²⁶ Voltaire, *Œuvres*, XXVII, 338. ["I believe that the nature of man is not entirely diabolical. But why is it said that man is always inclined to evil?"]

²⁷ Cf. J.-J. Rousseau, who puts ambition at the climactic point in man's downward course. *Discours sur l'inégalité, Œuvres*, I, 113. [Some cry out that human nature is essentially perverse, that man is born a child of the devil and wicked. Nothing is more ill-advised. ... It would be much more reasonable, much more seemly to say to men: You are all born good; see how frightful it would be to corrupt the purity of your being. ... Man is not born evil, he becomes evil, as he becomes sick. ... Bring together all the children of the universe, you will see

les temps les plus orageux, un homme sur mille qu'on peut appeler méchant, encore ne l'est-il pas toujours.[28]

Here at last Voltaire joins Rousseau to whom he is so often opposed, and curiously enough they are agreed upon the one point where they might have been supposed to be most in disaccord. Just as Rousseau had directed against the doctrine of natural perversity and original sin his idea of natural goodness,[29] so now Voltaire insists: "L'homme n'est point né méchant; il le devient, comme il devient malade." He suggests that we ought to say to mankind: "Vous êtes tous nés bons; voyez combien il serait affreux de corrompre la pureté de votre être." It is hardly probable that Voltaire has been influenced here by Rousseau. To be effective, such influence would have had to act upon Voltaire without his being conscious of it, for he is too definitely opposed to most of Rousseau's characteristic teaching not to react violently against it here also. But the presence of such ideas in this and in other passages[30] of Voltaire's works during this period shows how deeply some phases of Rousseau's doctrine have been called forth by the needs of the age, so that they belong not alone to Rousseau, his precursors, and followers, but even to so different a thinker as Voltaire. The fact shows also how impossible it is to understand Rousseau's theory of "la bonté naturelle" without reference to its opposite against which he was reacting, the doctrine of "la perversité naturelle," to which Voltaire was of course no less opposed and in terms, as we have seen, surprisingly similar. If Rousseau's attitude entitles him to the ridicule of those critics who enjoy holding him up to scorn, then it must be[859] confessed that Voltaire must also in some measure bear the brunt of their mockery.

Voltaire's novel *L'Ingénu* of 1767 has bearing upon the subject of Voltaire's nature doctrine, for "l'ingénu" is Voltaire's portrait of the "bon sauvage." The Huron is without prejudices, because, "son entendement, n'ayant point été courbé par l'erreur, était demeuré

---

in them only innocence, sweetness, and fear. ... Man is therefore not born evil; why then are some of them infected by this plague of wickedness? It is that those whose heads have been seized by the illness give it to other men. ... The first ambitious man has corrupted the earth.]

28 Voltaire, *Œuvres*, XX, 53–56. Cf. the equally vigorous and clear attack under the article *Homme*, XIX, 381. [... You have therefore at the most on the earth, during the stormiest times, one man in a thousand that could be called evil, and even he is not so always.]

29 Cf. George R. Havens, "The Theory of 'Natural Goodness' in Rousseau's *Nouvelle Héloïse*," *Mod. Lang. Notes*, Nov. 1921 (Vol. XXXVI), pp. 385–94, and "The Theory of 'Natural Goodness' in Rousseau's *Confessions*," *ibid.*, May 1923 (Vol. XXXVIII), pp. 257–66. See also three studies of this theory in Rousseau's whole work, in the *Revue d'Histoire litt. de la France* (1924–1925).

30 See various attacks on the "péché originel" in Voltaire, *Œuvres*, IX, 359–60; XVII, 585; XX, 151–156; XXV, 379; XXVI, 341–42; XXVII, 460.

dans toute sa rectitude."[31] So Voltaire after all has his "noble savage," but he is of course not to be taken too seriously. He is very much of a philosophical abstraction, used as a basis to attack the shortcomings of eighteenth century French civilization. Moreover, he is far from the so-called state of nature. What that state was in Voltaire's estimation may be clearly seen from the following passage, under the heading, "De l'homme dans l'état de pure nature":

> Que serait l'homme dans l'état qu'on nomme de *pure nature?* Un animal fort au-dessous des premiers Iroquois qu'on trouva dans le nord de l'Amérique. ... Plus de la moitié de la terre habitable est encore peuplée d'animaux à deux pieds qui vivent dans cet horrible état qui approche de la pure nature, ayant à peine le vivre et le vêtir, jouissant à peine du don de la parole, s'apercevant à peine qu'ils sont malheureux, vivant et mourant sans presque le savoir.[32]

Again we see that Voltaire does not idealize the state of nature.

But the principles of virtue are universally recognized:

> Toute la terre reconnaît donc la necessité de la vertu. D'où vient cette unanimité, sinon de l'intelligence suprême, sinon du grand Demiourgos, qui, ne pouvant empêcher le mal, y a porté ce remède éternel et universel?"[33]

But what is nature, asks the philosopher?

> "Qui es-tu, nature?"—Je suis le grand tout. Je n'en sais pas davantage. ... On m'a donné un nom qui ne me convient pas: on m'appelle *nature,* et je suis tout art.

And the philosopher admits: "Il est vrai. Plus j'y songe, plus je vois que tu n'es que l'art de je ne sais quel grand être bien puissant et bien industrieux, qui se cache et qui te fait paraître."[34] Neither nature nor the God behind it is necessarily infinite in power. As usual, it is from

---

31 *Ibid.*, XXI, 284. Cf. p. 278. Cf. Georges Pellissier, *Voltaire philosophe* (Paris, 1908), 194. ["His understanding, not having been warped at all by error, had remained in all its rectitude."]

32 *Ibid.*, XIX 383–84. [What would man be in the state called pure nature? An animal very much below the first Iroquois found in the North of America. ... More than half of the habitable earth is still peopled by animals on two feet who live in that horrible state which approaches pure nature, having trouble to live and to clothe themselves, enjoying with difficulty the gift of speech, being aware with difficulty that they are unhappy, living and dying almost without knowing it.]

33 *Ibid.*, XXVIII, 462. [All the earth recognizes therefore the necessity of virtue. From whence comes this unanimity, except from the supreme intelligence, except from the great Demiurge, who, not being able to prevent evil, has brought forth this eternal and universal remedy.]

34 *Ibid.*, XX, 115–16. Cf. XXI, 55, 4–55, 578–79. ["Who are you, nature?"— I am the great everything. I know nothing more about it. ... I have been given a name that does not suit me: I am called *nature,* and I am all art.

And the philosopher admits: "It is true. The more I think about it, the more I see that you are nothing but the art of I don't know what great being, very powerful and very industrious, who hides himself and causes you to appear."]

design that Voltaire argues[860] the existence of God. "Tout se correspondant dans ce que je connais de la nature, j'y aperçois un dessein; ce dessein me fait connaître un moteur; ce moteur est sans doute très-puissant, mais la simple philosophie[35] ne m'apprend point que ce grand artisan soit infiniment puissant."[36]

Now the natural law, as we have seen, is based upon the feeling for what is just and unjust. "Il y a une loi naturelle; et elle ne consiste ni à faire le mal d'autrui, ni à s'en réjouir." The other speaker in the dialogue replies: "Vous avez raison, il y a une loi naturelle; mais il est encore plus naturel à bien des gens de l'oublier." Voltaire answers: "Il est naturel aussi d'être borgne, bossu, boiteux, contrefait, malsain; mais on préfère les gens bien faits et bien sains,"[37] a characteristically clever Voltairean answer. Vice is not more natural than deformity or illness.

To conclude, let us try in a few words to sum up Voltaire's thought in regard to this doctrine of nature. We have seen that he early starts with an identification between the law of nature and the law of God. At the beginning he is perhaps only partly serious. The idea appeals to him as making a pretty phrase for his verse. Yet he clings to this belief to the end, and expresses it finally in terms that seem more fully reasoned out and more part of his mental attitude than at the beginning. Natural religion is based upon the Golden Rule, which, since man is naturally sociable, furnishes the only safeguard for society as a whole. El Dorado in *Candide* does not represent a return to natural simplicity. Voltaire's mundane taste for luxury forms a nature idyll quite different from that characteristic of the devotees of Spartan simplicity. The so-called state of nature is not in accordance with man's inherently social nature, which grows out of that basic human institution, the family. Solitude is not man's natural state. The state of nature, so far from being ideal, would be the state of an undeveloped brute. But nature supplies the instinct, the conscience, upon which morality is based. Pity and justice are its fundamental sources. This morality is in the main absolute and universal, with only[861] minor variations in different environments.[38] Man is not born evil. He becomes bad just as he becomes sick. Vice is a disease. Nothing could be more Rousseauistic than this unexpected Voltairean

---

35 Apart from divine revelation.

36 Voltaire, *Œuvres*, L, 75 (*Correspondance*, 1776). [Since all harmonizes in that which I know of nature, I perceive there a design; this design makes me aware of a creator; this creator is without doubt very powerful, but mere philosophy does not at all teach me that this great artisan may be infinitely powerful.]

37 *Ibid.*, XIX, 605–06 (1771). ["There is a natural law; and it consists neither in doing evil to others nor in enjoying oneself." The other speaker in the dialogue replies: "You are right, there is a natural law; but it is still more natural for most people to forget it." Voltaire answers: "It is natural also to be one-eyed, hunch-backed, lame, deformed, sickly; but one prefers whole and healthy people."]

38 Cf. the passage in the *Philosophe ignorant* in which Voltaire on this point disagrees with his favorite philosopher, John Locke. *Œuvres*, XXVI, 85.

opinion. The universal principles of virtue spring from God, who is
not necessarily infinite, but who is the creator of the universe. The
law of nature may be broken, but so also may the laws of health.
Vice is not more natural than deformity or illness.[39] [862]

---

[39] As it has naturally been impossible to cite all passages bearing upon this
subject, reference is here made to those omitted. They are confirmatory of what
has previously been said, but in the main of minor importance. Of special interest
is the passage in which Voltaire, perhaps not altogether seriously, expresses admiration for irregular gardens, "à l'anglaise," X, 307–08.

   Œuvres, VI, 310; VIII, 464–65, 544, 545, 559; XI, 307; XII, 370; XV, 430; XIX,
397 (repeated in XXVIII, 92); XX, 554; XXVII, 351, 570; XXVIII, 98, 100;
XXIX, 456; XXX, 472; XLV, 345.

VOLTAIRE'S *CANDIDE* AND THE PROBLEM
OF SECULARIZATION*
Ludwig W. Kahn

   In *PMLA* for September 1951 (LXVI, 718–733), William F. Bottiglia showed that the famous conclusion of *Candide*, "il faut cultiver
notre jardin," advocates neither a pessimistic withdrawal from the
world nor a rustic life in some actual garden. Instead, Professor Bottiglia adduces convincing support for those critics and scholars,
quoted by him, who interpret the garden allegorically and see in it any
field of realistic, positive, productive, social activity. Perhaps it is not
amiss to extend Professor Bottiglia's argument a little further and to
consider *Candide* and the question of worldly toil within the process
of secularization which reached its crest in the eighteenth century.
   The role of secularization in literature is rather complicated and
comprehensive, and the present writer hopes to present a more detailed
study of it elsewhere. The problem was raised, at least incidentally,
some fifty years ago by the German sociologist Max Weber in his
epoch-making essay, "Die protestantische Ethik und der Geist des
Kapitalismus," now most easily accessible in his *Gesammelte Aufsätze
zur Religionssoziologie* I (Tübingen, 1922). Weber, to state his theory
in a simplified and summary form, attempted to show that Protestantism, and more particularly Calvinism and Puritanism, nurtured the
"Spirit of Capitalism" by their concept of calling and by regarding

---

   * Reprinted from *PMLA,* LXVII (September 1952), 886–888, by permission
of Ludwig W. Kahn and *PMLA.*

mundane economic activity and individual enterprise as the best way of serving God. Weber's startling theory, therefore, is that religious ideas were transferred to everyday life, that not capitalism but the spirit of capitalism is a secularized form of Protestantism, and that although Calvinism and Puritanism did not create the acquisitive society, they did give dignity to labor and justification to acquisition. As an illustration Weber quotes from Richard Baxter's *Christian Directory* (*Gesammelte Aufsätze*, p. 167): "It is for *action* that God maintaineth us and our activities: work is the moral as well as the natural *end of power* ... It is *action* that God is most served and honoured by ..."

Voltaire can hardly be considered a Calvinist or a Puritan, and it is doubtful whether the one-time friend of kings and aristocrats can pass as a representative of the bourgeois spirit which dominated the new commercial classes; and yet *Candide* expresses, as Professor Bottiglia has corroborated, the same exaltation of mundane activity that Weber found in Baxter. Energy and sober industry will, no doubt, bring forth fruit in Candide's garden as they did on Robinson Crusoe's island; and here as there we will perceive the shining glory of man's earthly toil. By the middle of the eighteenth century the secularization has spread to non-Puritan and only doubtfully bourgeois authors like Voltaire, if indeed it did start with the Puritan middle classes; by the middle of the eighteenth century secularization had also become more radical, for now work and activity are no longer valued for the increase they bring to the glory of God but for their own sake. Again, some fifty odd years after *Candide,* we find Goethe's *Faust,* whose significance within the history of progressive secularization is not as a rule adequately recognized by interpreters. Surely, we cannot help thinking of *Faust* when we read the words with which H. N. Brailsford summarizes the[886] philosophy of *Candide* and which Professor Bottiglia quotes in his article, just as Brailsford might well have been thinking of *Faust* when he wrote: "Doubtless 'one's garden,' as Voltaire used the words, is a name for ... any effort, in short, that has a direct social purpose, anything that betters the environment ... Virtue comes to mean something perfectly concrete—the draining of swamps, the building of roads and bridges, the planting of trees." The draining of swamps, the betterment of the environment are precisely Faust's last great enterprise, the crowning achievement of his aspirations—at least, he thinks so at this, his last moment. If Goethe permits Faust to be saved in the end, if that sinner, seducer, and sorcerer is finally admitted into heaven, it surely is not because he is "good" in the traditional, moralistic sense. The Prologue in Heaven offers some help toward interpretation, for there "good" is practically equated with striving, erring, and—we may say—with living a life full of activity:

Es irrt der Mensch so lang er strebt ...
Ein guter Mensch in seinem dunklen Drange
Ist sich des rechten Weges wohl bewusst.[1]   (316,328–329)

The one unforgivable sin is "unbedingte Ruh," is to relax, to flag, to take it easy, to become sluggish (vv. 340 ff.). It is on this premise that Faust concludes his pact with the devil:

Werd' ich beruhigt je mich auf ein Faulbett legen,
So sei es gleich um mich getan! ...
Werd' ich zum Augenblicke sagen:
Verweile doch! du bist so schön!
Dann magst du mich in Fesseln schlagen,
Dann will ich gern zu Grunde gehn![2]

Not unlike his younger contemporary Schopenhauer, Goethe seems to identify "life" and "will": the moment we stop willing, we stop living; and as long as we truly live, we strive and will and cannot wish to hold the moment: a vegetative existence without desires or ambitions is spiritual death. Faust finally dies in the midst of great activity— however shadowy, fraught with sin, and doomed to failure his activity may be. Thus Faust is not saved—as we are told so often by inter- preters—because he aspires to some higher goal outside life, but merely because he lives and acts. The justification of life is life itself, and the justification of activity is activity itself. Life and activity (almost synonymous) have become ends and values per se, not a means for some higher or ulterior purpose (as they had been in Western think- ing ever since Plato and Christianity). In the terminology of St. Augustine, the eighteenth-century poet and philosopher made his home in the earthly cities of men instead of the heavenly City of God.

In the light of this new "religion" of activity, I would like to question those interpretations of *Candide* which maintain that Vol- taire offers in Eldorado an ideal and positive utopian goal. The trou- ble with any "perfect" or "best" world is precisely that it does not leave any room for amelioration or for activity, social or otherwise. Between "one's garden," in the sense established by Professor Bottiglia, and Eldorado there is no possible reconciliation: the former[887] is a sphere of creative activity, the latter a place of idle, sterile life. *Can- dide* is a diatribe against those mistaken philosophers who consider the actual world as incapable of further improvement; such philosophers were wrong in seventeenth-century Germany; they are wrong in eighteenth-century France; could it be that Voltaire considers them

---

[1] [. . . Man/ Must err till he has ceased to struggle .../ ... a good man even in his darkest longings/ Is well aware of the right way.   Translation by Percy Bysshe Shelley.]

[2] [If e'er in indolent repose I'm found,/ Then let my life upon the instant cease! .../ If ever to the passing hour I say:/ "So beautiful thou art, thy flight delay!"/ Then round my soul thy fetters throw—/ Then to perdition let me go! Translation by Anna Swanwick (1849) as revised.]

right in Eldorado? Would their philosophy not always lead to the
same life of passivity? Paradise, Eden, the City of God are places of
rest, not to say of otiosity, because they are perfect. As Faust knew so
well, if all human needs and wants are satisfied—as they are in Eldorado—life is at a standstill. I wish to suggest that the author of
Candide did not differ much from Goethe's opinion in this respect.
There are various reasons why Candide left Eldorado, not least among
them that he wanted to find his beloved Cunégonde; but the fact
remains that Eldorado proved unsatisfactory and could provide
neither an end nor a consummation. It is not merely Candide's unregenerate character or his unfitness for the ideal life, if he says: "Si
nous restons ici, nous n'y serons que comme les autres."[3] Voltaire
makes it quite clear that it is a life without challenge, without litigations, priests, social incentives—a life pleasant, placid, and stagnant
rather than ideal—which proves unattractive for any length of time.
When Candide inquires how people pray to God in Eldorado, the sage
answers: "Nous ne le prions point, nous n'avons rien a lui de-
mander."[4] Can this be an ideal? A world where there is nothing to
pray for is also a world where there is nothing to work for,
nothing to live for. In Eldorado science, too, in its museum-
like "palais des sciences," seems to require no further work for its
already existing perfection. If we are right in assigning to Voltaire a
place in the process of secularization which step by step substitutes
activity and life for religion, Eldorado can hardly be, in the words of
Professor Bottiglia (p. 727), "a philosophic ideal for human aspiration." [888]

---

[3] ["If we stay here, we shall only be like the others."]
[4] ["We do not pray to him; we have nothing to ask him for."]

THEME: ELDORADO*
William F. Bottiglia

Most of the many critics who have discussed Voltaire's Eldorado
maintain that it represents his ideal society and that, as such, it does

* From William F. Bottiglia, *Voltaire's Candide: Analysis of a Classic,* Vol.
VII of *Studies on Voltaire and the Eighteenth Century,* ed. Theodore Besterman
(Les Délices, Geneva: Institut et Musée Voltaire, 1959), ch. v, pp. 113–130. Reprinted by permission of Theodore Besterman. An earlier version of this chapter
appeared as "Eldorado Episode in *Candide*," *PMLA,* LXXIII (Sept. 1958), 339–347.
At the end of this selection will be found a list of the works referred to in brief
form by Bottiglia that are not listed in the bibliography at the end of this book.

not exist (*e.g.*, Lanson, *Voltaire,* p. 151, and *Prose,* p. 184; Toldo, p. 173; Havens: 'Nature doctrine,' p. 857; *Candide,* pp. lii, 125; and *Age of ideas,* p. 201; Bellessort, p. 262; Van Tieghem, i.xx; Torrey, *Spirit,* p. 49; Petit, i.9, and ii.6; Falke, pp. 25–41, passim; Pomeau, *Religion,* p. 306). Most of the few who have discussed its attainability argue that it *can* be realized or approximated, whether by the whole of mankind or by a few sages (*e.g.*, Mornet, *Littérature et pensée,* p. 145, and *Grandes œuvres,* pp. 171, 173; Naves, *Candide,* p. 17; Green, *Contes,* p. xxix). As for the distinctive traits of this perfect State, the critics as a group mention the following: utility blended with charm, luxury with natural simplicity; comfort, good taste, an enlightened public-works policy, peace, happiness, liberty, equality, tolerance, wisdom, justice, deism (all of the foregoing references, plus Flandrin, p. 724, and McGhee, pp. 70–71).

Now, an ideal may be reasonably defined as a standard of perfection supremely desirable but not fully attainable, though more[113] or less approachable. In terms of this definition, reflection on Voltaire's life and intellectual development confirms his emphatic approval of the fifteen distinctively Eldoradan traits listed and his consequent promotion of the ideals which they embody. The key trait is not tolerance as the ground of liberty (Falke, pp. 33, 35, 37–38, 40–41), but deism as the ground of a unanimously cultivated social and practical morality which produces all the other traits. The entire episode displays the deistic ethic in its manifold applications, while the conversation with the old man drives home the deistic view of the relationship between God and man. Since, according to this view, God is the supreme Clockmaker honor-bound by His own laws not to interfere with the functioning of His cosmic chronometer, prayers of petition are ineffectual and even blasphemous. On the other hand hymns of adoration, thanksgiving, submission—in sum, of grateful acceptance—are germane to the utopian condition, constitute its sole cultic observance, and obviate the need for professional priests by automatically conferring priesthood on all (Pellissier, pp. 67–68; Lanson, *Voltaire,* p. 178; Havens, 'Nature doctrine,' p. 857, and *Candide,* p. 126; Torrey, *Spirit,* pp. 227 ff.). The political structure of this model society also proves the centrality of the deistic engagement. Idealizing his preference for a beneficent monarchy (Pellissier, pp. 235 ff.), Voltaire invents a philosopher-king totally committed to deism and governing a nation of deists. It is no wonder, then, that he avoids describing the organization of the State (Falke, pp. 33, 40). In such circumstances it tends to wither away—which is why there are no courts or prisons.

Kahn nonetheless contends that the absence in Eldorado of priests and litigations proves it to be a mock-paradise at variance with the author's dream of perfection (p. 888). Evidence to the contrary is found, not only in *Candide,* but also in the correspondence. The following typical passages are drawn from letters written shortly before *Candide*: 'Mais tout cela importe fort peu à un philosophe qui vit dans la retraitte, et qui n'a ny rois ny parlements ny prêtres. J'en souhaitte autant à tout le genre humain.'[114]—'Libre dans ma retraite auprès de Genève, libre auprès de Lausanne, sans rois, sans intendant, sans jésuites ...'—'Pour moi, dans la retraite où la raison m'attire,/ Je goûte en paix la liberté;/ ... Loin des courtisans dangereux,/ Loin des fanatiques affreux ...'—'Nous avons établi l'empire des plaisirs et les prétres sont oubliez.' (Best. 6681, 6748, 6941, 6970).[1]

Kahn also contends that Eldorado offers a life without challenge, hence sterile; where science, having been perfected, lies stagnant; where prayers of petition are meaningless, so that its inhabitants have nothing to work for or live for; where, in other words, there is no opportunity for amelioration or activity, social or otherwise (pp. 887–888). Voltaire's views on prayer have already been summarized. It should be added that Kahn's analysis tends to blur the distinction between the actual and the ideal: *e.g.*, 'The trouble with any "perfect" or "best" world is precisely that it does not leave any room for amelioration or for activity, social or otherwise' (p. 887); 'Paradise, Eden, the City of God are places of rest, not to say of otiosity, because they are perfect' (p. 888). A standard of perfection cannot by definition be improved beyond itself without ceasing to be a standard of perfection. The Eldoradan society, by its very nature, allows for no amelioration. It does, however, allow for activity, social and otherwise. Eldorado is cultivated 'pour le plaisir comme pour le besoin.'[2] Men and women are seen traveling in sheep-drawn carriages. Children go to school, and receive instruction from professional teachers. Palatial private dwellings have been built and are maintained everywhere in the country. The same is true of inns, which are regularly staffed with hosts, waiters and waitresses, chefs, etc. Musicians are employed for both secular and religious functions. The meals which are served presuppose a highly organized economy, and in fact there is mention of merchants, carters, servants, a special Eldoradan currency, markets, and commerce. The government, it is true, has withered away to the point where courts, prisons, and a military organization do not exist; but it does have a king, court officials, a ceremonial palace guard, and an ambitious[115] public-works program. Theatrical

---

1 ["But all that matters very little to a philosopher who lives in retirement, and who has neither kings, nor courts, nor priests. I wish as much for the whole human race."—"Free in my retreat near Geneva, free near Lausanne, without kings, without a manager, without Jesuits ..."—"For me, in the retreat to which reason attracts me,/ I enjoy liberty in peace;/ ... Far from dangerous courtiers,/ Far from frightful fanatics ..."—"We have established the empire of pleasures, and priests are forgotten."—The abbreviation "Best." refers to *Voltaire's Correspondence*, ed. Theodore Besterman (Geneva: Institut et Musée Voltaire, 1953 etc.), Vols. I–LXIX in progress. The numbers after "Best." refer to individual letters.]

2 ["For pleasure as well as for need."]

spectacles are offered, and the arts are pursued. So are the mathematical and physical sciences; and, in addition to a 'Palais des Sciences,'
Eldorado has a corps of engineers who supervise the public-works
program and manufacture machinery for special purposes. The truth
is that Voltaire has described, not a static, but a dynamic, perfection. If
his ideal society inevitably lacks the challenge of amelioration, it does
provide the challenge of maintenance in perpetuity. Its inhabitants
obviously can have nothing to pray for, but they do have everything
to work for, to live for.

Another aspect of Kahn's analysis also demands scrutiny in connection with the Voltairean conception of the ideal. To support his
thesis of progressive secularization in Western Europe over a period of
several centuries, he develops a parallel between Goethe's *Faust* and
Candide, concluding that both works glorify the 'new "religion" of
activity,' which promotes 'life and activity (almost synonymous), as
'ends and values per se,' not as 'a means for some higher or ulterior
purpose' (pp. 886–887). It is always dangerous to labor such generalizations and such comparisons, particularly so when they involve world
classics more or less autonomously produced by highly individual
geniuses out of unique inspirations amid special circumstances. Insofar
as the parallel in question is suggestive, Brailsford had already drawn
it (p. 164). Insofar as Kahn's intention is to stress Voltaire's this-
worldliness and his unconcern about an afterlife, at least for the
intelligentsia, there can be no objection. But if he means that Voltaire
had no fixed principles or that he lived and acted without regard for
mankind and its future, then objection becomes unavoidable. Torrey
has clearly shown that Voltaire's deism postulates 'basic, fundamental,
universal principles, ... common moral principles which God has
engraved in the hearts of all men, which are true at all times and in all
latitudes' (*Spirit,* pp. 228–29). This belief, as already stated, appears
as early as 1722 in the *Epître à Uranie* and remains unshaken throughout his life (see chapter i above). As for his attitude toward posterity,
it is no accident that[116] the great humanist quotes, in a letter dated 1
October [1757], from La Fontaine's fable, 'Le Vieillard et les trois
jeunes hommes': 'mais planter à cet âge!/ Disaient trois jouvenceaux/
enfans du voisinage;/ Assurément il radotait'[3] (Best. 6710). The old
man's apologia includes a perspective cherished and acted upon by
Voltaire: 'Mes arrière-neveux me devront cet ombrage:/ Eh bien!
défendez-vous au sage/ De se donner des soins pour le plaisir
d'autrui?/ Cela même est un fruit que je goûte aujourd'hui ...'[4] If

---

[3] ["The old man and the three young men": "but to plant at that age!/
Said three young fellows/ children of the neighborhood;/ Surely he was out of
his mind."]

[4] ["My descendants will be obligated to me for this shade: Well, then! Do
you forbid the wise man to take pains for the pleasure of others?/ That in itself
is a fruit which I enjoy today ..."]

Candide derives mature satisfaction from cultivating his garden, it is not 'merely because he lives and acts,' but because he lives and acts in accordance with the fixed principles of the deistic ethic for purposes which extend far beyond his 'petite société' both in space and in time.

This brings us to the problem of humanity's future possibilities. Can it ever fully attain the supremely desirable standard of perfection which Eldoradan society represents? Toldo declares flatly that it cannot (p. 173). Naves suggests that the philosophic minority can (*Candide*, p. 17). Mornet holds that men in general are capable of building an Eldorado 'où l'on soit tolérant, bon et heureux'[5] (*Grandes œuvres*, p. 173). Miss Falke concurs, and supports her argument with a quotation from Voltaire wherein peace based on universal tolerance is envisaged as gradually replacing 'l'infâme,' despite widespread stupidity, through the efforts of the philosophic minority, for 'le petit nombre, qui pense, conduit le grand nombre avec le temps'[6] (p. 35). Green states that a better world, probably resembling Eldorado, *is* possible, provided man revises 'his present scale of values' (*Contes*, p. xxix). Now, it is the function of a vital ideal to serve as a lure so powerful that it seems fully attainable and is in fact approachable; yet, by definition, it must remain forever beyond complete realization. In the passage quoted by Miss Falke, Voltaire is understandably writing under the spell of the lure. He is, moreover, discussing peace based on universal tolerance, not the multifarious components of a model society. In *Candide* he more objectively sets up an ideal State which men may approach, but which they cannot completely realize. The[117] examination of artistic devices which follows shortly will, it is hoped, corroborate this interpretation. As to whether all men or a few can approximate the utopian condition, Eldorado—the ideal—provides felicity for everyone, while Candide's garden—the optimum present reality—provides contentment for a small group. Between these termini and necessarily short of the former, humanity's future possibilities seem indeterminately variable, though the *philosophe's* chances are of course far better than those of the average man.

One such *philosophe* is Voltaire himself, and the correspondence about the time of *Candide* repeatedly suggests that he found Les Délices and Lausanne a present reality bearing some resemblance to Eldorado. In these hermitages (Best. 6878, 6906, 7031, 7052, 7092) or retreats (Best. 6859, 6860, 6866, 6878, 6904, etc.), the former of which deserves its name (Best. 6484, 6998), having renounced the world (Best. 6773, 6866), he lives without priests, litigations, generals, or earthly kings (Best. 6681, 7005): 'bien logé, bien meublé, bien voituré'[7] (Best. 6582); enjoying excellent meals and good company (Best. 6872, 6878, 6924); contentedly absorbed in works of peace—the cultivation of his

---

5 ["Where one may be tolerant, good, and happy."]
6 ["The small number who think lead the large number in course of time."]
7 ["Well housed, well furnished, well conveyed."]

garden and of the arts (Best. 6964, 6965, 6972, 6995). This existence
blending utility with charm has taught him the final wisdom: 'Quand
on est aussi agréablement établi, il ne faut pas changer'[8] (Best. 6837;
Havens, *Candide,* p. 126). The residences he has chosen are the freest,
the calmest, the most beautiful in the world (Best. 6497, 6682, 6998),
and their isolation seems symbolically guaranteed by the mountains,
which, especially at Lausanne, can be seen on the horizon thrusting up
to the very sky (Best. 6859, 6866, 6872, 6878). In this land of fruitful
tranquillity he goes so far as to say: 'je suis si heureux que j'en ai
honte'[9] (Best. 6199), and again: 'on y est presque dégoûté de la félicité
paisible qu'on y goûte'[10] (Best. 7061). The resemblance to Eldorado is
obviously there, yet it must not be exaggerated. The ideal is approached; it is not fully attained. Even in his Swiss 'paradise' Voltaire
finds himself plagued by 'le mal physique'—his poor health (Best. 6135,
6199,[118] 6792); and haunted by both 'le mal physique'—earthquakes
(Best. 6792, 6895, 7031), and 'le mal moral'—the inhumanity of man to
man (Best. 6910, 7061). It is true that at times he gives the impression
of not knowing or caring about the latter (Best. 6529, 6582, 6600, 6866,
6927, etc.); this, however, is merely his way of turning his back on public abominations in a gesture of philosophic disdain. Actually, if he is
ashamed and almost disgusted at being so happy, it is precisely because
he does know and care, because he pities mankind and can neither
sink into indifference nor remain satisfied with setting a distant example. In *Candide* he builds up a synthesis out of these elements. He
attacks social evil, he promotes constructive deism, and he projects his
vision of the perfect State. That vision is in part a product of his intellectual development, but it is also in some measure an idealization
of his experience at Les Délices and Lausanne.

The meaning of the Eldorado episode can be further elucidated
by an inspection of its relationship with other episodes in the tale.
For example, it is not by chance that Candide's ascent to utopia comes
between his perilous adventure among the South-American cannibals
and his grim sojourn in Surinam. Miss McGhee has called attention to
the use of contrast in this arrangement. She finds: that the exotic
splendor of this imaginary kingdom contrasts sharply with 'the
simple landscape of the Oreillons' which precedes; that, 'as a background for the acquisition of Candide's fortune,' it is 'a particularly
effective prelude to his immediate loss of that same fortune'; and that
it provides by antithesis an excellent opportunity 'for present satire
and irony' (pp. 70–71, 116; see also Bellessort, p. 262; Havens, *Candide,* pp. lii, 125–26, and *Age of ideas,* p. 201; Falke, p. 31). It should
be added that these episodes reveal the following significant sequence
of social conditions: the amorality of subcivilization, the moral perfection of supercivilization, and the immorality of civilization. By

---

8 ["When one is so agreeably established, one must not change."]
9 ["I am so happy that I am ashamed of it."]
10 ["One is almost disgusted with the peaceful bliss that one enjoys here."]

juxtaposing the first and the third of these conditions to the second, Voltaire is in effect affirming, for polemical purposes, that they are equal in their abysmal inferiority to the ideal.[119]

Again, in disproof of Grimm's notion that Pangloss should have accompanied his pupil to 'le pays où tout va bien'[11] in order to enjoy the triumph of his philosophy (p. 86), four times while there Candide expresses his preference for Eldorado over the Westphalian 'Paradis terrestre' depicted in the opening chapter. On one of these occasions he refutes Grimm by anticipation: 'si nôtre ami Pangloss avait vû Eldorado, il n'aurait plus dit que le Château de Thunder-ten-trunckh était ce qu'il y avait de mieux sur la Terre ...'[12] (see Falke, p. 38).

Finally, there is the relationship between Eldorado and Candide's garden. The former offers a dream of perfection, a philosophic ideal for human aspiration. The latter depicts the optimum present reality, which calls for work illuminated by a sense of social purpose, with the former as the guiding standard. Eldorado provides happiness for an entire society; the garden, for a few. Eldorado is another world sufficient unto itself, hence can have no actual connection with this world, except by way of inspiration. The garden is very much a part of this world, and is dedicated to influencing it. Such are the basic differences; but there are resemblances, too, which help to clarify the author's design. Both Eldorado and the garden are *model societies* whose inhabitants have learned the value of *settling down* to *dynamic activity:* in one case for perpetuation, in the other for pursuit, of the ideal. At the very beginning of the Eldorado episode Voltaire strikes the keynote of his message, for the first thing which he has Candide notice is that the country is *cultivated* 'pour le plaisir comme pour le besoin.' He thereby subtly prefigures the cultivation of the garden. And the *vow* of the Eldoradans adumbrates, not only the decision at the end to settle down, but also *the gesture of philosophic disdain*.

The contention has been put forward by Kahn that Candide leaves Eldorado partly because of his yearning for Cunégonde, but basically because 'Eldorado prove[s] unsatisfactory and [can] provide neither an end nor a consummation' (p. 888). It has also been maintained by Flandrin that Candide, though he leaves for[120] the sake of his beloved, appreciates 'à sa valeur cette merveilleuse contrée'[13] (p. 724). Voltaire gives several reasons for Candide's departure: 1) his hope of happiness with Cunégonde, 2) his hankering for superiority and power through wealth, 3) his restlessness, 4) his desire to boast of his travels. The first two reasons are restated together at the moment of leavetaking, as Candide speaks of ransoming Cunégonde and then buying a kingdom. Nowhere in the tale does Voltaire say or imply that any of these motivations are laudable. In fact he makes it his

---

11 ["The land where all goes well."]
12 ["If our friend Pangloss had seen Eldorado, he would no longer have said that the Castle of Thunder-ten-trunckh was the best in the world ..."]
13 ["That marvelous country at its proper worth."]

business to purge his hero of them. Immediately after listing the reasons he makes the following comment: 'les deux heureux résolurent de ne plus l'être ...'[14] He thus already warns the reader that Candide and Cacambo lack the philosophic maturity to appreciate Eldorado at its real worth, and that their reasons for leaving it are wrong. In the course of his subsequent travels Candide refers on six occasions to Eldorado, and his references are uniformly favorable (Cxix, p. 134; Cxxi, p. 143; Cxxii, pp. 167, 170; Cxxiv, pp. 176, 177).[15] To clinch matters, at the end he has been shocked out of his sentimental quixotism, has lost his wealth, has learned the dangers of power, has settled down, and is at work with his friends in a situation of modest fraternal equality. Thus Candide's several reasons for departure are utterly invalidated (see Green, *Contes*, p. xxix, and Falke, p. 38). There is, in addition, a reason which is not his, but Voltaire's. Candide *must* leave Eldorado because it is a myth, a dream, and, as such, unreal. Imperfect man cannot successfully inhale the rarefied air of the heights of perfection. He must redescend to the grosser atmosphere of this world. On the other hand, having scaled the Eldoradan plateau, he will eventually realize that, though its air is humanly unbreathable, its way of life offers the only model worthy of human aspiration. By returning from utopia and establishing himself in the garden, Candide comes to understand what his ideal should be, how it differs from the actual, and how its perfections may at least be approached by imperfect man in this imperfect world.[121]

But such an ideal is more easily conceived in the abstract than imagined in sensuously concrete form. Voltaire the artist has surmounted the difficulty by presenting Eldorado as a vision far-distant and half-lost in a luminous haze.

A general effect of haziness is found throughout the episode. Naves notes that the entry into Eldorado, which others would have treated at length and very colourfully, is passed over in silence; and suggests that the author thereby evinces his disdain for 'l'émotion toute faite et la résonance facile'[16] (*Candide*, pp. 22–23). To this explanation may be added Voltaire's deliberate vaporization of the miraculous, which would account as well for his refusal to handle descriptively: the departure, the cultivation of the country, the dwellings and public monuments, the conversation with the other diners at the inn and at the king's table, the social and economic organization, the intellectual and artistic activity. It is apparently for the same reason that he refuses to name a single Eldoradan; and for the same reason plus the one already given that he omits all particulars of the political structure.

This general haziness is countered, and therefore reinforced, by

---

14 ["The two happy men resolved to be so no longer ..."]
15 [Page references here are to the André Morize edition of *Candide*. See pp. 39; 42; 50, 50; and 52, 53 of the Frame translation reprinted in this book.]
16 ["Ready-made emotion and easy resonance."]

a few physical descriptions and oral discourses which Voltaire has chosen to present in some, though not much, detail because of the impression they make on Candide and should make on the reader. The description of the children at play illustrates the unreality of Eldorado, parodies actual and extraordinary voyages, and satirizes by contrast human notions of wealth. The meal at the inn repeats in its way the themes of unreality and parody. The host's discourse develops the satire on wealth; the king's does the same, and also attacks by indirection human restlessness and tyranny; the old sage's varies the motif of parody, aims satiric hits at restlessness, wealth, and war, and voices an ironic indictment of institutional religion. All of these discourses, moreover, re-emphasize the theme of unreality. Morize has criticized the old sage's exposition of deism as being brief and superficial in respect of fundamentals (p. 116, n. 1). By way of explanation it may be suggested that Voltaire intentionally avoids a systematic exposition[122] because he wants, as if in the natural course of a conversation, to indict institutional religion by stressing its embarrassingly obvious aberrations in the light of deism, which is just as obviously the one true faith—for Eldoradans and *philosophes*.

The haze is further complicated by an admixture of *filtered* luminosity. Gleaming highways and carriages, big red sheep, singularly good-looking men and women; clothing made of gold fabric; children playing with gold, emeralds, and rubies, which turn out to be worthless pebbles there; palatial inns and private dwellings; an indescribedly vast and magnificent royal palace; public works to match, including even skyscrapers; a wondrously elaborate machine for lowering the two travelers back to reality. Along with these dazzling material phenomena, countless irradiations of 'bienfaisance': utility blended with charm; disregard for wealth as ordinarily understood by humans; general affability and co-operation; general courtesy and consideration; unanimous acceptance of deism; absence of courts and prisons, as well as of a military organization; encouragement of the mathematical and physical sciences; cultivation of the arts of peace; a king who is every inch a *philosophe*. These imaginary splendours, as Voltaire does not fail to point out, appropriately amaze even the self-possessed Cacambo.

Among the material phenomena two stand out because they are put to special use: the precious pebbles and the big red sheep. Price interprets them symbolically as Frederick's (the king of Eldorado's) literary works, 'securely encased in red-bound sheepskin,' which Voltaire (Candide) is forced to surrender at Francfort (Surinam), where the pebbles also represent 'large sums of money, the equivalence of all that Voltaire had obtained from Frederick during his stay in Prussia' (pp. 209, 211). Unfortunately, this interpretation exploits certain fanciful analogies without adequate regard for consistency or for correspondence to Voltairean thought-processes and literary methods.

Both the sheep and the pebbles are apparently made to serve a double purpose. On the one hand they definitely have a literal[123] value, for they spring from the author's interest in touches of picturesque realism. As Morize points out, Garcilaso and Raleigh harp on the precious-pebble theme in their travel accounts (pp. 107, n. 1; 109, n. 2; 110, n. 1; 112, n. 2; etc.); and Garcilaso describes a beast of burden called the 'huanacu,' and notes that the wild species is 'de couleur baie'[17] (p. 106, n. 3). The *Encyclopédie*, moreover, in volumes published in 1765, applies the colours 'rougeâtre'[18] (ix.177: art. 'Laine') and 'roux'[19] (x.827: art. 'Mouton') to the fleece of sheep. On the other hand it would seem that they also acquire a symbolic value, for they are so handled as to suggest the unreality of Eldorado.

The pebbles become unreal by reason of their profusion and worthlessness. In chapter xix almost all of them are lost as the travelers come back down to this world, so that Candide, with unconscious irony, remarks to Cacambo: 'Mon ami, vous voyez comme les richesses de ce monde sont périssables ...'[20] The remaining pebbles dwindle away more slowly, in part to prolong the satire on human greed, which has no geographical boundaries, in part to make the conclusion just possible. Their final disappearance is nicely timed: it occurs at the precise moment when Candide is about to make his great affirmation in favour of productive activity.

As for the sheep, unreal ones go grazing through pastoral romances whose heroes, like Candide in chapter xix, rapturously carve the names or initials of their sweethearts on trees. At the end of chapter xviii, Candide obsessively resolves to go offer his sheep to Cunégonde. But along with the pebbles, most of the bearers disappear during the descent from Eldorado back to earth. In chapter xx Candide recovers one of the sheep, and, caressing it, expresses the hope that he will also someday recover Cunégonde. In chapter xxiv, after hearing Paquette's story, he reiterates this hope: 'il se pourra bien faire qu'ayant rencontré mon mouton rouge & Paquette, je rencontre aussi Cunégonde.'[21] The association of the sheep with his dream of amorous bliss thus occurs three times—which strengthens the possibility of a symbolic overtone; for though the dream will eventually lead him to Cunégonde,[124] it will prove to have been a sentimentally quixotic yearning incapable of taking root and fructifying in the world of objective reality. Finally, in chapter xxii, there is Candide's donation of his last Eldoradan sheep to the Academy of Science at Bordeaux. The subject of that year's prize competition provides a delightful opportunity for ridiculing the unreality of a certain Northern scholar's metaphysical formulations.

---

17 ["Of reddish-brown color."]
18 ["Reddish."]
19 ["Reddish-brown."]
20 ["My friend, you see how perishable are the riches of this world ..."]
21 ["It may well be that having met my red sheep and Paquette again, I shall also meet Cunégonde again."]

The impression of distance is driven home by stress on the extreme inaccessibility and isolation of Eldorado. It is elevated, both physically and spiritually, far above the surrounding territory, so that the two travelers 'de l'autre Monde'[22] reach it by a miracle, and leave it with the aid of a unique mechanical invention, the work of three thousand engineers. The old man's historical account of a withdrawal from the world sealed by solemn vows adds a voluntary note to this effect of remoteness.

Unreality, haziness, and parody are variously combined in the indications of incredible hugeness which Voltaire scatters through his depiction of the model society. The two travelers discover, upon arriving, 'un horison immense.' The royal palace displays a portal 'de deux cent vingt pieds de haut, & de cent de large.'[23] The capital has 'les édifices publics élevés jusqu'aux nuës, les marchés ornés de mille colonnes,'[24] and a Hall of Science containing 'une galerie de deux mille pas, toute pleine d'instruments de Mathématique & de Physique.'[25] These indications of hugeness are rounded out by analogous effects of exaggeration, such as: the meal at the inn; the old man's age; the five or six thousand musicians at morning services; the two rows of a thousand musicians each, lining the approach to the king's apartment; the royal witticisms which retain their point in translation; the labour and cost involved in constructing the hoist.

This brings us inevitably to the device of satiric humour, which takes several forms in the episode. There is, to begin with, sustained irony of contrast between the ideal and the actual (McGhee, p. 116; Bellessort, p. 262; Havens, *Candide,* pp. lii, 125 and *Age of ideas,* p. 201). There is also irony directed against Candide, who[125] fails to appreciate the genuine happiness of life in Eldorado and leaves it of his own accord because he thinks he can buy his way to happiness in this world (Falke, p. 38; Green, *Contes,* p. xxix). There is parody of popular fiction, with emphasis on its 'unreality and exaggeration'; and of real and imaginary voyages, with emphasis on their idealization of the exotic (Morize, pp. xlix ff.; Havens, *Candide,* pp. xlix–lii). The satiric humour of the episode finds expression in stylistic details as well as in more general procedures, and an analysis will shortly be made of those details. In an overall view it seems especially significant that, while Voltaire jocosely dwells on the unreality of his utopia, at no point does he mock the ideal itself.

Mention has been made of his refusal to name any of the Eldoradans. This is doubtless because, whether individually or in groups, they are doubly unreal—as instrumental personages and as utopian

22 ["From the other world."]

23 ["Two hundred twenty feet high and one hundred wide."]

24 ["Public buildings rising to the very clouds, the market-places ornamented with a thousand columns."]

25 ["A gallery two thousand feet long, filled with instruments of mathematics and physics."]

figments. The people riding in the carriages; the school-master and his pupils; the fellow-diners, the waiters, the waitresses, and the hostess at the inn; the court officials and attendants; the other guests at the king's table; the musicians; the engineers—all appear barely visible through the haze. Only three persons seem to stand out with any distinctness: the host, the old man, and the king. They have apparently been chosen to typify, on the ideal level, the willing follower, the intellectual leader, and the active leader: the commoner, the sage, and the statesman. More specifically, the host sets the tone for Eldoradan courtesy, consideration, affability, and contempt of lucre. The old man, a traditional figure in imaginary voyages, serves as a venerable fount of historical information and of civilized wisdom, with particular attention to deism. The king, a ruler such as never was, proves democratic of access, miraculously witty, and graciously libertarian. Thus all three are mouthpieces for the author, their goodness is totally abstracted from personality, and they, too, are half-hidden in the luminous haze. It is a point of special interest that the theme of woman is muted throughout the episode. We are told that Candide and Cacambo see 'des hommes & des femmes[126] d'une beauté singulière'[26] riding in carriages; that Candide and the old sage discuss women in the course of their long conversation; and that several ladies sit with His Majesty and the travelers at the palace dinner—nothing more. Other females lower in the social hierarchy appear, but just as incidentally. The reason suggests itself at once. It simply would not do for Candide to become involved with an Eldoradan belle. The design of the tale demands that our callow hero leave to resume the chase after Cunégonde, so Voltaire has him perforce remain blind to the superior allurements of utopian femininity.

The language utilized to convey this manifold of ideas and devices is in general simple, sober, concise, swift, and lucid yet subtle. There is an effective counterpoint, to be sure, of neutral, colourless, and abstract terminology, such as accords with a philosophic recital, and of concrete, localized, picturesque vocabulary (Lanson, *Voltaire*, p. 154, and *Prose*, p. 171; Petit, i.9), such as will lend glamour to the ideal, substantiate the unreal, and parody the South-American voyage. Naves, however, wisely warns against exaggerating the extent of the latter (*Candide*, pp. 21–23). Voltaire does not luxuriate in exotic particulars. He deftly selects just enough of them to produce a passing illusion. In sum, the *picture* of the model society far-distant and half-lost in a luminous haze is to the *conception* of the ideal as *means* to *end*, and the style reflects this proportionally, not only in the description of the setting, but also in the report of events and the manipulation of character.

Within this broad linguistic pattern there are several devices of

---

26 ["Singularly beautiful men and women."]

detail which help to project the picture and to communicate the conception. One such device is accentuation through repetition with variation: Candide's four mentions of the difference in quality between Eldorado and Westphalia; the smiles of the school-master and the old sage, the laughter of the host and hostess and the king; the blushes of the old sage; the excuses offered by the host and the old sage; the light pastel sketches of the inn, the old sage's home, and the royal palace.[127]

A second is contrast between things Eldoradan and things terrestrial. Mention has already been made of Candide's remarks on Westphalia. There are several further examples. The big red sheep surpass in speed the finest horses of Andalusia, Tetuân, and Mequinez. The least of the precious pebbles would be the greatest ornament on the Mogul's throne. The inn resembles a European palace. The greed of the nations of Europe would drive them to massacre the Eldoradans, if they could lay hands on them. The building material of the royal palace is inexpressibly superior to the pebbles and sand we call gold and gems. And the king cannot understand what the Europeans find so attractive in the yellow mud of this country.

A third, which is a variation of the preceding one, involves contrast between Eldoradan and terrestrial standards of valuation, and goes beyond, though it prominently includes, the methodical reduction of gold and gems to mud and pebbles (Havens, *Candide*, p. lviii). The 'Précepteur de la Famille Royale'[27] is actually a village school-master, and 'leurs Altesses Royales'[28] are little ragamuffins. Candide and Cacambo are escorted into the king's presence between two rows of a thousand musicians each, 'selon l'usage ordinaire.'[29]

A fourth is the game of easy familiarity played by the author with his readers to induce an affectation of belief in the impossibly fantastic. Thus, upon entering Eldorado, the travelers are described as 'nos deux hommes de l'autre Monde';[30] upon leaving it, as 'nos deux Voyageurs.'[31] At one point Voltaire speaks of 'ces cailloux & ... ce sable que nous nommons or & pierreries.'[32] At another, to back up Cacambo's knowledge of the Peruvian language spoken by the Eldoradans, he begins his mischievous explanation with the words: 'car tout le monde sait que ...'[33]

A fifth is the 'unexpected conclusion' or surprise twist, which Havens illustrates by quoting the host's comment: 'Je suis fort ig-

---

27 ["Tutor of the Royal Family."]
28 ["Their Royal Highnesses."]
29 ["According to the usual custom."]
30 ["Our two men from the other world."]
31 ["Our two voyagers."]
32 ["Those pebbles and ... that sand we call gold and gems."]
33 ["For everyone knows that ..."]

norant, & je m'en trouve bien';[34] and part of the author's sketch of
the old sage's home: 'Ils entrèrent dans une maison fort simple, car la
porte n'était que d'argent, & les lambris des apartements[128] n'étaient
que d'or'[35] (Candide, p. lvii). The full sketch also exemplifies ironic
understatement. Additional instances of the surprise twist are: Candide's inference, unconsciously chaffing the unreality of the ideal, after
learning of utopian deism and declaring Eldorado superior to Westphalia: 'il est certain qu'il faut voyager';[36] the answer given to Cacambo's question caricaturing elaborate court ceremonial: 'L'usage ... est
d'embrasser le Roi & de le baiser des deux côtés';[37] the revelation regarding His Majesty's wit, which astounds Candide by its ultramun-
dane flexibility: 'Cacambo expliquait les bons mots du Roi à Candide,
& quoique traduits ils paraissaient toujours des bons mots.'[38]

A sixth is delayed-action irony. Candide recognizes again and
again the inferiority of Westphalia to Eldorado, yet leaves to resume
his pursuit of Cunégonde. Also, when the children abandon their
precious quoits, he exclaims: 'il faut que les enfans des Rois de ce
pays soient bien élevés, puisqu'on leur aprend à mépriser l'or & les
pierreries.'[39] Nonetheless, he takes away with him a great load of these
base minerals for the sake of base objectives.

A seventh is foreshadowing by means of a key word subtly
dropped in passing: notably, the 'cultivé' at the beginning of the
episode, which prefigures the conclusion of the tale, and the 'vaga-
bonds' at the end, which suggests that the two travelers will suffer for
their restlessness.

Finally, there is the quintessential set speech or dialogue wherein,
without even a pretense of characterization, Voltaire makes use of
uniform utterance to put across his message. Examples are: the
speeches of the host and the king, the old sage's historical account,
and his dialogue with Candide on deism.

Few value judgments have been made on the Eldorado episode.
Le Breton condemns it in a phrase: 'rien de plus froid'[40] (p. 212). But
Candide is a philosophic tale, not a novel. One demands of a novel
that it generate fictional incandescence; of a philosophic tale, that it
irradiate a steady phosphorescence. There is well-nigh unanimous
agreement on the phosphorescent effect of Candide as a whole. This
discussion has tried to show that the same effect[129] suffuses the El-

---

34 ["I am very ignorant and am all the better for it."]
35 ["They entered a very simple house, for the door was only of silver, and
the panelling of the rooms was only of gold."]
36 ["It is certain that one must travel."]
37 ["The custom ... is to embrace the King and to kiss him on both cheeks."]
38 ["Cacambo explained the King's witty remarks to Candide and though
translated they still appeared witty."]
39 ["Royal children in this country must be well brought up, since they are
taught to despise gold and precious stones."]
40 ["Nothing more frigid."]

dorado episode. Toldo (pp. 173–74) and Faguet (*Voltaire,* pp. 194–95) take a condescending view of the entire presentation because they find it more or less derivative and very deficient in imagination. Their criticism is answerable partly on the same ground as Le Breton's; partly by invoking the nature of methodical parody; partly by pointing out that neither of them takes the episode seriously enough to give it his sustained attention. A comparison of Voltaire's utopia with others would reveal that he has risen far above the merely derivative level to create an episode as imaginatively original as the character and possibilities of the philosophic tale allow. Only Bellessort is favourably disposed: he considers the episode highly effective in bringing out the contrast between illusion and reality (p. 262). This comment is certainly true as far as it goes. The present analysis has of necessity gone much farther in probing the meaning of the episode in relation to the whole and the artistic devices by which that meaning is conveyed—far enough, it is hoped, to prove that Voltaire has fused form and substance so successfully as to produce a miniature masterpiece.[130]

Works Mentioned in Bottiglia's "Theme: Eldorado" Not Listed in Bibliography

Bellessort, André. *Essai sur Voltaire.* Paris, 1925.

Faguet, Emile. *Voltaire.* Paris, 1895.

Lanson, Gustave. *L'Art de la prose.* 13th ed. Paris, 1908?

——————. *Voltaire.* 2nd ed. Paris, 1910.

Le Breton, André. *Le Roman au dix-huitième siècle.* Paris, 1898.

Mornet, Daniel. *Histoire de la littérature et de la pensée française.* Paris, 1924.

——————. *Histoire des grandes œuvres de la littérature française.* Paris, 1925.

Naves, Raymond. *De Candide à Saint-Preux.* Paris, 1940.

Pellissier, Georges. *Voltaire philosophe.* Paris, 1908.

Pomeau, René. *La Religion de Voltaire.* Paris, 1956.

Toldo, Pietro. "Voltaire conteur et romancier," *Zeitschrift für französische sprache und litteratur* (Oppeln, etc., Feb. 1913), XL, 131–185.

Voltaire, François-Marie Arouet de. *Choix de contes,* ed. Frederick C. Green. Cambridge, England, 1951.

——————. *Contes,* ed. Roger Petit. Classiques Larousse. 2 vols. Paris, 1941.

——————. *Contes et romans,* ed. Philippe Van Tieghem. 4 vols. Paris, 1930.

——————. *Œuvres choisies, ed.* Louis Flandrin. 6th ed. Paris, 1930.

ON RE-READING *CANDIDE**
Aldous Huxley

The furniture vans had unloaded their freight in the new house. We were installed, or, at least, we were left to make the best of an unbearable life in the dirt and the confusion. One of the Pre-Raphaelites, I forget at the moment which, once painted a picture called "The Last Day in the Old Home." A touching subject. But it would need a grimmer, harder brush to depict the horrors of "The First Day in the New Home." I had sat down in despair among the tumbled movables when I noticed—with what a thrill of pleased recognition—the top of a little leather-bound book protruding from among a mass of bulkier volumes in an uncovered case. It was *Candide,* my treasured little first edition of 1759, with its discreetly ridiculous title-page, "*Candide ou L'Optimisme,* Traduit de l'Allemand de Mr. le Docteur Ralph."

Optimism—I had need of a little at the moment, and as Mr. le Docteur Ralph is notoriously one of the preachers most capable of inspiring it, I took up the volume and began to read: "Il y avait en Westphalie, dans le Château de[12] Mr. le Baron de Thunder-ten-tronckh. ..." I did not put down the volume till I had reached the final: "Il faut cultiver notre jardin." I felt the wiser and the more cheerful for Doctor Ralph's ministrations.

But the remarkable thing about re-reading *Candide* is not that the book amuses one, not that it delights and astonishes with its brilliance; that is only to be expected. No, it evokes a new and, for me at least, an unanticipated emotion. In the good old days, before the Flood, the history of Candide's adventures seemed to us quiet, sheltered, middle-class people only a delightful phantasy, or at best a high-spirited exaggeration of conditions which we knew, vaguely and theoretically, to exist, to have existed, a long way off in space and time. But read the book to-day; you feel yourself entirely at home in its pages. It is like reading a record of the facts and opinions of 1922; nothing was ever more applicable, more completely to the point. The world in which we live is recognizably the world of Candide and Cunégonde, of Martin and the Old Woman who was a Pope's[13]

---

* From *On the Margin* by Aldous Huxley (London: Chatto & Windus Ltd., 1923), pp. 12–17. Copyright 1923 by Aldous Huxley. Reprinted by permission of Harper & Brothers. Also by permission of Chatto & Windus Ltd., London.

daughter and the betrothed of the sovereign Prince of Massa-Carrara. The only difference is that the horrors crowd rather more thickly on the world of 1922 than they did on Candide's world. The manœuvrings of Bulgare and Abare, the intestine strife in Morocco, the earthquake and *auto-da-fé* are but pale poor things compared with the Great War, the Russian Famine, the Black and Tans, the Fascisti, and all the other horrors of which we can proudly boast. "Quand Sa Hautesse envoye un vaisseau en Egypte," remarked the Dervish, "s'embarrasse-t-elle si les souris qui sont dans le vaisseau sont à leur aise ou non?"[1] No; but there are moments when Sa Hautesse, absentmindedly no doubt, lets fall into the hold of the vessel a few dozen of hungry cats; the present seems to be one of them.

Cats in the hold? There is nothing in that to be surprised at. The wisdom of Martin and the Old Woman who was once betrothed to the Prince of Massa-Carrara has become the everyday wisdom of all the world since 1914. In the happy Victorian and Edwardian past, Western Europe, like Candide, was surprised at[14] everything. It was amazed by the frightful conduct of King Bomba, amazed by the Turks, amazed by the political chicanery and loose morals of the Second Empire—(what is all Zola but a prolonged exclamation of astonishment at the goings-on of his contemporaries?). After that we were amazed at the disgusting behaviour of the Boers, while the rest of Europe was amazed at ours. There followed the widespread astonishment that in this, the so-called twentieth century, black men should be treated as they were being treated on the Congo and the Amazon. Then came the war: a great outburst of indignant astonishment, and afterwards an acquiescence as complete, as calmly cynical as Martin's. For we have discovered, in the course of the somewhat excessively prolonged *histoire à la Candide* of the last seven years, that astonishment is a supererogatory emotion. All things are possible, not merely for Providence, whose ways we had always known, albeit for some time rather theoretically, to be strange, but also for men.

Men, we thought, had grown up from the brutal and rampageous hobbledehoyism[15] of earlier ages and were now as polite and genteel as Gibbon himself. We now know better. Create a hobbledehoy environment and you will have hobbledehoy behaviour; create a Gibbonish environment and every one will be, more or less, genteel. It seems obvious, now. And now that we are living in a hobbledehoy world, we have learnt Martin's lesson so well that we can look on almost unmoved at the most appalling natural catastrophes and at exhibitions of human stupidity and wickedness which would have aroused us in the past to surprise and indignation. Indeed, we have left Martin behind and are become, with regard to many things, Pococurante.

---

1 [When his highness sends a ship to Egypt, does he worry about whether the mice in the ship are comfortable or not?]

And what is the remedy? Mr. le Docteur Ralph would have us believe that it consists in the patient cultivation of our gardens. He is probably right. The only trouble is that the gardens of some of us seem hardly worth cultivating. The garden of the bank clerk and the factory hand, the shop-girl's garden, the garden of the civil servant and the politician—can one cultivate them with much enthusiasm? Or, again, there[16] is my garden, the garden of literary journalism. In this little plot I dig and delve, plant, prune, and finally reap—sparsely enough, goodness knows!—from one year's end to another. And to what purpose, to whom for a good, as the Latin Grammar would say? Ah, there you have me.

There is a passage in one of Tchekov's letters which all literary journalists should inscribe in letters of gold upon their writing desks. "I send you," says Tchekov to his correspondent, "Mihailovsky's article on Tolstoy. ... It's a good article, but it's strange: one might write a thousand such articles and things would not be one step forwarder, and it would still remain unintelligible why such articles are written."

Il faut cultiver notre jardin. Yes, but suppose one begins to wonder why?[17]

VOLTAIRE*
André Maurois

VOLTAIRE'S PHILOSOPHY

Legend is not wrong in seeing the Voltaire of Ferney as the true Voltaire. Before Ferney, what was he? A very famous poet and playwright, a much-discussed historian, a populariser of science: France regarded him as a brilliant writer, not as an intellectual force. It was Ferney that freed him, and so made him great. Under cover of his quadrilateral of 'dens,' he was now to have the daring to say everything. The battle for freedom of thought which his friends the

* From *Voltaire* by André Maurois, translated by Hamish Miles (New York: D. Appleton & Company, 1932), pp. 93–104. Copyright, 1932, by D. Appleton & Company; copyright, 1960, by Hamish Miles. Reprinted by permission of Appleton-Century-Crofts.

Encyclopaedists had engaged upon, and could not carry on in Paris without danger, was to be directed by him from his retreat. To that struggle he contributed wit and fancy, an infinite variety in forms, a deliberate uniformity in ideas.

For twenty years Ferney discharged over Europe a hail of pamphlets printed under scores of names, forbidden, confiscated, disowned, denied, but hawked, read, admired,[93] and digested by all the thinking heads of that time. Voltaire at Ferney was no longer the 'fashionable man'; he was a Benedictine of rationalism. He believed in his apostolic mission: 'I have done more in my own time,' he said, 'than Luther and Calvin.' And further: 'I am tired of hearing it declared that twelve men sufficed to establish Christianity, and I want to prove to them that it only needs one to destroy it.' Nearly all his letters ended with the famous formula: *'Ecrasons l'infâme'*—'We must crush the vile thing'—or, as he wrote it with ingenuous caution, *'Ecr. l'inf.'* What was the vile thing? Religion? The Church? To be more exact, it was Superstition. He hounded it down because he had suffered from it, and because he believed that bigotry makes men more unhappy than they need be.

A great part of Voltaire's work at Ferney, then, was destructive. He wanted to show: (*a*) that it is absurd to suppose that an omnipotent God, creator of Heaven and Earth, had chosen the Jews, a small tribe of Bedouin nomads, as His chosen people; (*b*) that the chronicles of that race (the Bible) was packed with incredible facts, obscenities, and contradictions (he took the trouble to publish under[94] the title of *La Bible Expliquée,* a survey of the biblical text with countless notes); (*c*) that the Gospels, although more moral than the Old Testament, were nevertheless full of the gossipings of illiterate nobodies; and finally (*d*) that the disputes which set the sects at each other's throats throughout eighteen centuries were foolish and unavailing.

The Voltairean criticism has been itself criticised. It has been said that Voltaire lacks sympathy and proportion, and that in any case his own historical science was often at fault. But we must be fair. Voltaire often made particular effort to be so himself. 'It cannot be too often repeated,' he said, 'that we must not judge these centuries by the measure of our own, nor the Jews by that of Frenchmen or Englishmen.' If we are prepared to view the Bible as a collection of legends compiled by barbarian tribes, then he is prepared to admit that it is 'as captivating as Homer.' If we claim to find therein a divine utterance and superhuman thoughts, then he claims the right to quote the prophets, and show their cruel savagery.

What is Voltaire's positive philosophy? It is an agnosticism tempered by a deism. 'It[95] is natural to admit the existence of a God as soon as one opens one's eyes. ... The creation betokens the Creator. It is by virtue of an admirable art that all the planets dance round the sun. Animals, vegetables, minerals—everything is ordered with proportion, number, movement. Nobody can doubt that a painted landscape or drawn animals are works of skilled artists. Could copies possibly spring from an intelligence and the originals not?'

Regarding the nature of God he has little to teach us. 'Fanatics tell us: God came at such-and-such a time; in a certain small town God preached, and He hardened the hearts of His listeners so that they might have no faith in Him; He spoke to them and they stopped their ears. Now, the whole world should laugh at these fanatics. I shall say as much of all the gods that have been invented. I shall be no more merciful to the monsters of the Indies than to the monsters of Egypt. I shall blame every nation that has abandoned the universal God for all these phantoms of private gods.'

What, then, is to be believed? That is rather vague. 'The great name of theist is the only one that should be borne; the only[96] book that should be read is the great book of nature. The sole religion is to worship God and to be an honourable man. This pure and everlasting religion cannot possibly produce harm.' And certainly it would seem difficult for this theism to produce harm; but is it capable of producing much good? It is incomprehensible how so hollow and abstract a belief will maintain the weight of a moral system, and the moral system of Voltaire is not actually based on his theism. It is a purely human morality.

A theist in name, a humanist in fact—that is Voltaire. When he wishes seriously to justify a moral precept, he does so through the idea of society. Moreover, as God is everywhere, morality is in nature itself. 'There is something of divinity in a flea.' At all times and in all places man has found a single morality in his own heart. Socrates, Jesus, and Confucius have differing metaphysics, but more or less the same moral system. Replying to Pascal, who found it 'pleasing' that men such as robbers, who have renounced all the laws of God, should contrive other laws which they scrupulously obey, Voltaire wrote: 'That is more useful than pleasing to consider, for it proves that no[97] society can live for a single day without laws. In this all societies are like games: without rules, they do not exist.' Here the historian has seen aright, and with a penetrating phrase has pointed out what modern observers of primitive societies have since described.

Stern judgment has been passed on this Voltairean philosophy. Faguet defined it as 'a chaos of clear ideas'; Taine remarked that 'he dwarfed great things by dint of bringing them within reach'; and a woman once said: 'What I cannot forgive him, is having made me understand so many things which I shall never understand.' It is certain that a system imbued with perfect clarity has few chances of being a truthful image of an obscure and mysterious world. But still, it remains probable that this world is in part intelligible, for otherwise there would be neither physics or mechanics.

Voltaire himself indicated better than any one the limitations of clarity, and how much madness and confusion there are in human destinies. Let doubters turn back to the second part of the article on 'Ignorance' in the *Philosophical Dictionary*: 'I am ignorant of how I was formed and how I was born. Through a[98] quarter of my lifetime I was absolutely ignorant of the reasons for everything I saw and heard and felt, and was merely a parrot prompted by other parrots. ... When I sought to advance along that infinite course, I could neither find one single footpath nor fully discover one single object, and from the upward leap I made to contemplate eternity I fell back into the abyss of my ignorance.' Here Voltaire touched hands with Pascal, but only half-way; and this troubled Voltaire is the best Voltaire, for he is the Voltaire of *Candide*.[99]

CANDIDE

The author of *Zaïre* and the *Henriade* would doubtless have been prodigiously surprised had he been assured that the only book (or nearly the only book) of his which would be read in 1950, and held as a masterpiece of man's wit, would be a short novel written at the age of sixty-five, and bearing the title of *Candide*.

He wrote it to ridicule the optimism of Leibniz. 'Everything is for the best in the best of worlds ...' said the optimists. Voltaire had observed men's lives; he had lived, battled, suffered, and seen suffering. No, emphatically: this world of stakes and scaffolds, battles and disease, was not the best of possible worlds. Some historians—Michelet especially—have attributed the pessimism of *Candide* to particular occurrences: the dreadful earthquake at Lisbon (on which Voltaire wrote a poem), or the Seven Years' War and its victims, or the greed of Mme. Denis. These petty reasons[100] seem useless. Voltaire denied the perfection of the world because, to an intelligent old man, it did not look perfect.

His theme was simple. It was a novel of apprenticeship, that is, the shaping of an adolescent's ideas by rude contact with the universe. Candide learned to know armies and the Jesuits of Paraguay; murder, theft, and rape; France, England, and the Grand Turk. Everywhere his observation showed him that man was rather a wicked animal. Optimist philosophy was personified in Pangloss; pessimism, in Martin, who thinks that man 'is born to live amid the convulsions of anxiety and the lethargy of ennui.' But the author accepted neither Martin's pessimism nor Pangloss's optimism at their face values. The last words of the book were: 'We must cultivate our garden'; that is to say: the world is mad and cruel; the earth trembles and the sky hurls thunderbolts; Kings fight and Churches rend each other. Let us limit our activity and try to do as well as we can the small task that seems to be within our powers.

It is, as René Berthelot remarks, an eminently scientific and bourgeois conclusion. Action is necessary. All is not well, but all things[101] can be bettered. Man 'cannot obliterate the cruelty of the universe, but by prudence he can shield certain small confines from that cruelty.' What Voltaire sets up against Martin's pessimism and Pangloss's optimism, what he opposes to Christian theology and to the stoic optimism resumed by Leibniz, is Newtonian science, the science that limits itself to nature, that makes us grasp only certain connexions, but at least assures us thereby of our power over certain natural phenomena.

No work shows better than *Candide* how fully Voltaire remains a great classic and a man of the eighteenth century, while Rousseau is already a romantic and a man of the nineteenth. Nothing would have been easier than to make *Candide* into a *Childe Harold*. Let Candide take on the semblance of a projection of Voltaire's own personality, let him accuse the Universe of having robbed him of Mlle. Cunégonde, let him conceive of a personal struggle between himself and Destiny —and he would be a romantic hero. But Candide is universal as a character of Molière's is universal, and it was the reading of *Candide* that shaped the second Byron, the anti-romantic, the Byron of *Don Juan*. That is why all romantics are anti-Voltairean,[102] even Michelet, whose political fervour ought to have made him stand aligned with Voltaire, and that is why, on the other hand, all the minds which accept the world and recognise its irony and indifference are Voltairean. M. Jacques Bainville has said that M. Charles Maurras re-reads his *Candide* once a year, and as he closes it, says to himself: 'The road is clear'—'that is to say, that Voltaire sweeps earthly illusions boldly aside, drives away the clouds and all that is interposed between reality and understanding.'

One reason for the enduring success of *Candide* is that it represents one of the attitudes of the human mind, and perhaps the bravest. But above all, it is admirable as a work of art. Alain has justly observed that the style of *Candide* resembles that of the *Arabian Nights* in Galland's translation. The union of classic French, proving and deducing consequences with such clarity, and the fantastic image of life formed by the fatalist Orient, was bound to produce a novel dissonance, and did in fact produce one. The poetry of a text is largely produced by the fact that the wild chaos of the universe are therein, at one and the same time, expressed and controlled by a rhythm.[103] In *Candide* both characteristics exist. Over every page stream unforeseeable cascades of facts, and yet the swift movement, the regular recurrence of the optimist themes of Pangloss, the pessimist themes of Martin, the narratives of the old woman and the refrains of Candide, afford the mind that troubled, tragic repose which is only given by great poetry.

Alongside the Galland influence, that of Swift should be noted.

Voltaire had read much of Swift, and was fond of him; and from the Dean he had learned how to tell an absurd story in the most natural manner. Of all the classic French texts, *Candide* is certainly the most closely akin to the English humorists. But Swift's rather fierce humour, sometimes too emphatic, is here tempered by the desire to please. In the body of every writer's creation there are things of sheer delight: *Candide* was the best of such in Voltaire's.[104]

COUNTERIRRITANTS AND CONSOLATIONS*
Norman L. Torrey

The development of counterirritants for his irritable and deeply emotional temperament was of capital importance. Otherwise he would have become misanthropic with Swift and Rousseau or cynical along with Fontenelle, Frederick the Great, and D'Alembert. The last two mentioned tried to persuade him in their letters that men were stupid and ignorant and that nothing could be done about it; while on a more philosophical plane, the optimism of Pope and Leibnitz maintained that all degrees of stupidity and ignorance entered necessarily into God's plan for this best of all possible worlds —that monkeys should not try to be men, nor men, angels, lest a necessary link in the chain of degrees[48] between imperfection and perfection be broken—a most hopeless and desolate doctrine, thought Voltaire, in spite of its consoling name. So he wrote his racy *Candide, ou l'Optimisme,* which completely demolished a philosophical system that ponderously asserted that all was for the best and that man's efforts to make it better were not only useless but sacrilegious. It was not *Candide,* in spite of its form, that was frivolous, it was the devitalizing optimism of Leibnitz. There is, too, the more popular form of optimism which refuses to see the physical and moral evils of this world. As an answer to this the naïve Candide is conducted on a tour of misery over the whole western world and hardly misses a spot where the wounds of humanity are particularly festering or where nature is at her worst. The only land where men are wise and happy is El-

---

* Reprinted from Norman L. Torrey, *The Spirit of Voltaire* (New York: Columbia University Press, 1938), pp. 48–51, by permission of Norman L. Torrey. Professor Torrey's later remarks, found on p. x of his edition of *Candide* (New York: Appleton-Century-Crofts, 1946), should also be noted.

dorado, which does not exist. After having lost one illusion after another Candide receives the final stunning blow when he discovers that his beloved Cunégonde, whom he has spent so much time and effort seeking, has lost all her beauty and is now an old hag with red-lidded eyes and yellow, sagging skin. What is left, then, in life for the completely disillusioned man? Nothing but to cultivate his garden.

Candide being one of the better known of Voltaire's works, the conclusion—"Cultivate your garden!"—has been widely discussed. Some have interpreted it as an expression of pessimism, a counsel of inaction and of withdrawal from all efforts to better the lot of mankind. This conclusion is so obviously[49] in contrast with Voltaire's own way of life that others have sought an allegorical interpretation and have seen in the words an exhortation to enter the fight for humanity. Voltaire's tales have a way, however, of summing up certain periods of his existence and certain problems with which he was then faced. Zadig has a definite and unmistakable bearing on his struggles to enter the French Academy and on his ideas concerning destiny, or Providence. Candide sums up the period of personal discouragement after his departure from Berlin until his settlement near Geneva, where he found peace and repose and, above all, a beautiful garden overlooking the lake in which were reflected the mountains beyond. He had suffered many a personal rebuff, many a heartache over the Lisbon earthquake, and, while reading in preparation for his general history, many a desolate moment over the stories of human stupidity. After every emotional crisis came the period of calm and, during these last years, of quiet cultivation of his garden. The following verse, borrowed by Waller from Tasso, which Voltaire picked up in England, to which he often referred and which he incorporated as the only genuinely lyric passage in his tragedy Mahomet, appealed to him very evidently because it touched so closely his own experience with life:

> Our passions gone, and reason on her throne,
> Amaz'd we see the mischief we have done.
> After a tempest, when the winds are laid,
> The calm sea wonders at the wrecks it made.[50]

His letters from this period on show very definitely that the exhortation at the end of Candide meant literally what it said, but that it was meant only for those periods when he had reached the bottom of his. emotional curve.[51]

TOPICS FOR DISCUSSION AND RESEARCH PAPERS

Some of the following topics can be used for class discussion and some for research papers, but most of them can be used for both purposes. Although the topics are grouped according to the divisions of this book, the student should not hesitate to make use of any of the sections of the book when searching for the answers to a question. He should also use the library.

Topics Related to Part One: *Candide* and Its Background

1. How does Voltaire use irony and paradox in *Candide*?
2. How does Voltaire use understatement in *Candide*?
3. How does Voltaire use parody in *Candide*?
4. Explain with illustrations why Voltaire moves back and forth between the past and historical present tenses in *Candide*.
5. How accurate a picture of Leibniz is Pangloss?
6. How does Voltaire satirize romantic primitivism in *Candide*?
7. How is *Candide* foreshadowed by Voltaire's *The Story of Scarmentado's Travels*?
8. Is it more accurate to classify *Candide* as a novel or as a philosophic tale? Explain why.
9. How is Frederick the Great satirized in *Candide*?
10. In what ways does Pococurante resemble Voltaire?
11. What specific persons are satirized in *Candide,* and how are they satirized?
12. How is religion satirized in *Candide*?
13. How does *Candide* develop the theme of initiation?
14. Write a critical essay on the universality of *Candide*.
15. What and how does Voltaire satirize in *Candide*?
16. What is Voltaire's attitude toward human nature as revealed in *Candide*?
17. What is Voltaire's attitude toward civilization as revealed in *Candide*?

Topics Related to Part Two: Comments on *Candide* as a Work of Art

1. What are the principal objections of eighteenth-century writers to *Candide*? What parts of *Candide* probably caused these objections?

2. Explain why Edward Young says to Voltaire in lines 153–154 of Part II of "Resignation": "Your trash, with mine, at open war,/ Is obstinately bent." How did these two friends differ philosophically?

3. Attack or defend Boswell's statement about the difference between Johnson's *Rasselas* and Voltaire's *Candide* with illustrations from both works.

4. What are the values of *Candide* that nineteenth-century British critics praised? What parts of *Candide* probably inspired this praise?

5. Find evidence in some of Wordsworth's poems that would indicate why he reacted so unfavorably to Voltaire's *Candide* in *The Excursion*.

6. Is the word "scoffer" an appropriate epithet for the author of *Candide*? Explain with illustrations.

7. Attack or justify the use of the word "dull" as a description of *Candide*.

8. Friedrich Grimm and Thomas Carlyle express contrasting opinions about the order in Voltaire's fiction. Using *Candide* for illustrations, explain which you agree with and why.

9. Thomas Carlyle and Henry Brougham disagree about Voltaire's use of wit and humor. Using *Candide* for illustrations, explain which you agree with and why.

10. Analyze the economy of language in *Candide*.

11. Henry Brougham and John Morley speak of the caricature in *Candide*. Explain and illustrate what they mean.

12. Explain Lytton Strachey's idea that "Voltaire's meaning is deep in proportion to the lightness of his writing"; use *Candide* to illustrate.

13. Explain why Lytton Strachey compares Voltaire's style to a rapier and a pirouette; use *Candide* to illustrate.

Topics Related to Part Three: The Problem of Evil

1. How did the Lisbon Earthquake of 1755 affect French intellectuals in the eighteenth century?

2. Why and how did Voltaire satirize the idea of a predestined harmonious order in *Candide*?

3. Which writers side with Voltaire in his dispute with the optimists, and which side with the optimists? What reasons do these writers give for their partisanship?

4. How have twentieth-century writers evaluated Voltaire's handling of the problem of evil?

5. What are the arguments for taking *Candide* lightly, seriously, or both ways?

6. How does Voltaire combine wit and deep seriousness in *Candide?*

7. What evidence is there to indicate that Voltaire was or was not a pessimist?

8. What evidence of Voltaire's humanitarianism is there in *Candide* and the controversy over optimism?

9. Analyze the ambiguity of *Candide.*

10. Attack or defend Wade's statement that "every judgment of *Candide* is bound to be partial, one sided, contradictory, and vague, just like every judgment we make of life or of our individual lives."

11. Was Voltaire attacking philosophers or a philosophy in *Candide?* Explain.

12. Compare *Candide* with one or more other books that deal with the problem of evil, such as the Book of Job, Melville's *Moby Dick,* Hawthorne's *The Marble Faun,* Sophocles' *Oedipus Rex,* Shakespeare's *King Lear,* or Dostoevsky's *The Idiot.*

Topics Related to Part Four: Eldorado

1. Contrast Voltaire's style in the Eldorado episode with his style in the rest of *Candide.*

2. What is the significance of the social customs that Voltaire describes in Eldorado?

3. Explain Voltaire's method of characterizing the Eldoradans and his reason for doing it this way.

4. Explain the symbolism of the pebbles and sheep that Candide brings from Eldorado.

5. Does Voltaire present Eldorado as an unattainable ideal or as a way of life that man can attain? How have critics treated this question?

6. How is eighteenth-century deism illustrated in *Candide?*

7. What is Voltaire's attitude toward nature as revealed in *Candide* and the controversy over optimism?

8. Explain what Bottiglia means by the phosphorescence of *Candide.*

9. How do Bottiglia and Kahn differ in interpreting the Eldorado episode in *Candide?* Which one is more convincing and why?

10. How does Eldorado contrast with the real eighteenth-century world that Voltaire knew?

11. Compare Voltaire's Eldorado episode with other utopian writings, such as Plato's *Republic,* Thomas More's *Utopia,* Francis Bacon's *The New Atlantis,* Thomas Hobbes's *Leviathan,* Edward Bellamy's *Looking Backward,* or H. G. Wells's *A Modern Utopia.*

Topics Related to Part Five: Cultivating Our Garden

1. How is the eighteenth-century ideal of common sense illustrated in *Candide?*

2. How is the eighteenth-century ideal of moderation illustrated in *Candide?*

3. What is Voltaire's doctrine of work, and how is it related to *Candide* and the controversy over optimism?

4. What is the relationship between *Candide* and Newtonian science?

5. Candide's remark "but we must cultivate our garden" has been interpreted in various ways. Summarize and discuss them.

6. Contrast the philosophical positions represented by Pangloss, Martin, and Candide.

7. Explain what is meant by Manicheism and how Voltaire uses this religious system in Candide.

8. In what ways is Voltaire's thought similar to and different from that of Leibniz?

9. Why is Candide less obviously, less physically marred by misfortunes than his companions at the end of the book? Is this fact inconsistent with Voltaire's attack on optimism?

10. How does Voltaire make use of similar ideas in *Candide* and the *Ignorant Philosopher?*

11. Select a distinct period in human history, as Huxley does with the post-World War I era in "On Re-reading *Candide*," and show the relevance of *Candide* to that period. Or show the relevance of *Candide* to the present.

12. Explain how Voltaire's life at Ferney parallels Candide's remark that "we must cultivate our garden."

General Topics

1. Read Voltaire's *Poem on the Lisbon Earthquake* found in *The Works of Voltaire,* trans. and ed. Tobias Smollett and others (Paris: E. R. Du Mont, 1901), XXXVI, 5–18, or in *The Portable Voltaire,* ed. Ben Ray Redman (New York: Viking Press, 1949). In what ways does it foreshadow *Candide?*

2. Contrast Voltaire's view of life in *The Poem on the Lisbon Earthquake* and in *Candide* with Alexander Pope's in *An Essay on Man.*

3. Read "Summary of the Controversy Reduced to Formal Arguments" in Gottfried W. Leibniz, *Theodicy,* trans. E. M. Huggard (London: Routledge and Kegan Paul, Ltd., 1952), pp. 377–388. Contrast Voltaire's view of evil in *The Poem on the Lisbon Earthquake* and in *Candide* with Leibniz's in this selection.

4. If you read French, read Rousseau's *Letter on Providence* (Jean-Jacques Rousseau, Letter 112, à M. de Voltaire, 18 août 1756, *Œuvres de J. J. Rousseau,* ed. Mussay Pathay, Paris: Werdet et Lequien Fils, 1826, pp. 224–247). How is the dispute between Voltaire and Rousseau related to *Candide?*

5. What are the various causes that critics have suggested for Voltaire's writing *Candide?*

6. What major ideas of Voltaire's are revealed to us in some of his philosophic tales, such as *Candide, Zadig, Micromégas, Memnon, The World as It Is, Story of a Good Brahman, Ingenuous,* and *Bababec?*

7. What evidence is there in the life and writings of Voltaire that he was a humanitarian reformer?

8. What was the total impact of *Candide* on eighteenth-century thought?

9. Relate Voltaire's use of the idea of nature in *Candide* to other eighteenth-century concepts of nature.

10. How is *Candide* related to other books of travel and adventure that were popular in the eighteenth century, such as Abbé Prévost's *Cleveland,* Swift's *Gulliver's Travels,* or Johnson's *Rasselas?*

11. Analyze the role of optimism in the thought of some leading eighteenth-century thinkers.

12. Compare *Candide* with one or more other works that deal with the theme of initiation, such as Fielding's *Joseph Andrews* or *Tom Jones,* Byron's *Don Juan,* Twain's *Huckleberry Finn,* Conrad's *The Secret Sharer* or *Lord Jim,* Crane's *The Red Badge of Courage,* Hemingway's *In Our Time,* Faulkner's *The Bear,* or Salinger's *The Catcher in the Rye.*

13. The bibliography of this book lists translations of *Candide* by Richard Aldington, Lowell Bair, John Butt, Norman Cameron, Donald Frame (whose translation is used in this book), Henry Morley, and Tobias Smollett (along with James Thornton who revised Smollett's translation). If you read French, compare and evaluate two or more of these translations, checking them against André Morize's edition of *Candide* in French.

BIBLIOGRAPHY*

The following bibliographical works will guide the student to other works on *Candide* not listed in this selected bibliography:

"Annual Bibliography," *PMLA*. Published usually in the April or May issue. See subsection, "Eighteenth Century," under "French Language and Literature Including Provençal."

Barr, Mary-Margaret H. "Bibliographical Data on Voltaire from 1931–1940," *Modern Language Notes,* LVI (December 1941), 563–582. Lists biographical and critical books and articles on Voltaire. Should be used in conjunction with the following two entries.

——————. "Bibliographical Data on Voltaire from 1926–1930," *Modern Language Notes,* XLVIII (May 1933), 292–307.

——————. *A Century of Voltaire Study; a Bibliography of Writings on Voltaire, 1825–1925.* New York: Publications of the Institute of French Studies, 1929.

Havens, George R., and Donald F. Bond. "Eighteenth Century," in *A Critical Bibliography of French Literature,* ed. David C. Cabeen. 4 vols. Syracuse: Syracuse University Press, 1951. Vol. IV. An annotated bibliography that includes brief summaries of books and articles on *Candide*.

Editions of *Candide*

Voltaire, François-Marie Arouet de. *The Works of Voltaire,* trans. and ed. Tobias Smollett and others. 42 vols. Paris: E. R. Du Mont, 1901. Volume I contains *Candide,* a biographical introduction by Oliver H. G. Leigh, commentaries on Voltaire by Oliver Goldsmith and Victor Hugo, and the so-called Part II of *Candide,* which is not by Voltaire, but which has been attributed to Thorel de Campigneulles.

——————. *Candide, ou l'Optimisme, Edition Critique avec un Introduction et un Commentaire,* ed. André Morize. Paris: Hachette, 1913. Thorough and authoritative study of the sources, background, form, and ideas of *Candide.* Reissued in 1931 and 1957.

——————. *Candide, or the Optimist,* trans. Henry Morley. London: George Routledge and Sons, 1922. The introduction by Henry Morley compares *Candide* with Samuel Johnson's *Rasselas.*

——————. *Candide and Other Romances,* trans. and introd. Richard Aldington. New York: E. P. Dutton and Co., 1927. Mr. Aldington's introduction summarizes the philosophical origins of *Candide* and Voltaire's argument with Rousseau about optimism and providence. Mr. Aldington's translation is also available in an edition published by Doubleday and Company in 1959.

---

* Titles preceded by an asterisk are excerpted in this book and therefore are not annotated.

——————————. *Candide and Other Philosophical Tales,* ed. Morris Bishop. New York: Charles Scribner's Sons, 1929. An introduction by Mr. Bishop summarizes Leibnizianism and describes Voltaire's attack on it. Warns against taking Voltaire's pessimism in *Candide* too literally.

——————————. *Candide, ou l'Optimisme,* ed. Lawrence Levin. New York: Prentice-Hall, Inc., 1929. Mr. Levin's introduction stresses Voltaire's antioptimism and doctrine of work.

——————————. *Candide, or All for the Best,* ed. Walter Jerrold. New York: Tree and Jacobs, 1930. The introduction reviews early reactions to *Candide.*

——————————. *Candide, ou l'Optimisme,* ed. George R. Havens. New York: Henry Holt and Co., 1934. Includes a full introduction on the life of Voltaire and the origin, background, satire, style, reputation, and meaning of *Candide.*

——————————. *Candide and Other Tales,* ed. Henry N. Brailsford, trans. Tobias Smollett, revised by James C. Thornton. New York: E. P. Dutton and Co., 1937. In the introduction to this Everyman edition Mr. Brailsford discusses Voltaire's satiric style and doctrine of work. Reissued in 1955.

——————————. *Candide, or Optimism,* ed. Norman L. Torrey. New York: Appleton-Century-Crofts, 1946. In the introduction to this Crofts Classics edition Professor Torrey discusses Voltaire's treatment of the problem of evil and his meliorism in *Candide.*

——————————. *Candide, or Optimism,* trans. Norman Cameron. Toronto: Musson Book Co., 1947. Brief introduction on the purpose of *Candide.*

——————————. *The Portable Voltaire,* ed. Ben Ray Redman. New York: Viking Press, 1949. An introductory biographical sketch stresses Voltaire's greatness as a spokesman for his age. Besides *Candide* the book contains selections from Voltaire's *Philosophical Dictionary,* novels, letters, an essay, and the "Poem on the Lisbon Earthquake."

——————————. *Candide,* trans. John Butt. Baltimore: Penguin Books, Inc., 1956. Mr. Butt's introduction discusses Voltaire's handling of the problem of evil, the controversy concerning optimism, and contemporary allusions in *Candide.*

——————————. *Candide, ou l'Optimisme,* ed. Lester G. Crocker. London: University of London Press, 1958. A carefully annotated edition.

——————————. *Candide,* trans. Lowell Bair, introd. André Maurois. New York: Bantam Books, Inc., 1959. A recent translation. The introduction by Mr. Maurois is the same as the selection reprinted in this book.

——————————. *Candide, Zadig and Selected Stories,* trans. and introd. Donald M. Frame. New York: The New American Library, 1961. The translation reprinted in this book. The introduction deals with Voltaire's life, character, and works.

Books and Articles Related to *Candide*

Aldington, Richard. *Voltaire.* London: George Routledge and Sons, Ltd., 1925. A biography and analysis of Voltaire's writings that deals with his strengths and weaknesses as man and writer.

Barber, William H. *Leibniz in France, from Arnauld to Voltaire: A Study in French Reactions to Leibnizianism, 1670–1760.* Oxford: The Clarendon Press, 1955. Carefully reviews Voltaire's hostility to Leibnizian optimism before, during, and after his writing of *Candide.* See especially pp. 228–243.

*——————. *Voltaire: Candide.* London: Edward Arnold Ltd., 1960.

Becker, Carl. *The Heavenly City of the Eighteenth-Century Philosophers.* New Haven: Yale University Press, 1932. On the meaning of "nature" and "reason" in the eighteenth century. Describes Voltaire as a man of faith rather than a skeptic. Refers to *Candide* on pp. 36–37.

Bottiglia, William F. "Candide's Garden," *PMLA,* LXVI (September 1951), 718–733. Reviews interpretations of ". . . but we must cultivate our garden." Stresses Voltaire's meliorism or belief in the value of work.

——————. "Eldorado Episode in *Candide,*" *PMLA,* LXXIII (September 1958), 339–347.

*——————. *Voltaire's Candide: Analysis of a Classic,* Vol. VII of *Studies on Voltaire and the Eighteenth Century,* ed. Theodore Besterman. Geneva: Institut et Musée Voltaire, 1959.

Brailsford, Henry N. *Voltaire.* New York: Henry Holt and Co., 1935. Praises Voltaire's liberalism and discusses his influence on the French revolution. Admires the way Voltaire combines fantasy and realism.

Brandes, Georg. *Voltaire,* trans. Otto Kruger and Pierce Butler. 2 vols. New York: Albert and Charles Boni, 1930. The section on *Candide* in this lengthy biography stresses Voltaire's antioptimism but maintains that he is not a pessimist.

*Brougham, Henry. "Voltaire," in *Lives of Men of Letters of the Time of George III.* London: Richard Griffin and Co., 1856.

*Carlyle, Thomas. "Voltaire," in *Critical and Miscellaneous Essays.* London: Chapman and Hall, Ltd., 1869. Vol. II.

Carr, Herbert W. *Leibniz.* Boston: Little, Brown and Co., 1929. (Reprinted as Dover Publication paperback, 1960.) Discusses the ideas of Leibniz and the philosophical background of *Candide.*

Cassirer, Ernst. *The Philosophy of the Enlightenment,* trans. Fritz C. A. Koelin and James P. Pettegrove. Princeton: Princeton University Press, 1951. On intellectual currents in the eighteenth century. Refers to *Candide* on pp. 147–148.

Clifford, James L. "Some Remarks on Candide and Rasselas," in *Bicentenary Essays on Rasselas,* ed. Magdi Wahba. Cairo: Société Orientale de Publicité, 1959. Compares the two books, stresses their antioptimism and relevance to modern times.

Crane, Ronald S. "The Diffusion of Voltaire's Writings in England, 1750–1800," *Modern Philology,* XX (February 1923), 261–274. Reviews the great popularity of *Candide* and other works of Voltaire in England during the eighteenth century.

Crocker, Lester G. "Voltaire's Struggle for Humanism," in *Studies on Voltaire and the Eighteenth Century*, Theodore Besterman, ed. Geneva: Institut et Musée Voltaire, 1957, IV, 137–170. About Voltaire's inner conflict concerning religion and humanism. Sees Voltaire as essentially a humanist because he finds value only in human nature, even though he sometimes depreciates man.

Falke, Rita. "Eldorado: le meilleur des mondes possible," in *Studies on Voltaire and the Eighteenth Century*, Theodore Besterman, ed. Geneva: Institut et Musée Voltaire, 1956, II, 25–41. Compares Voltaire's Eldorado favorably with other utopias.

Fitch, Robert Elliot. "A Tale of Two Pilgrims, A Comparison of Bunyan's *Pilgrim's Progress* and Voltaire's *Candide*," *The Hibbert Journal*, XLVIII (July 1950), 388–393. Contrasts *Candide* unfavorably with *Pilgrim's Progress*. Stresses Eldorado episode and Voltaire's doctrine of work.

——————. *Voltaire's Philosophic Procedure: A Case-Study in the History of Ideas*. Forest Grove, Oregon: The News-Times Publishing Co., 1935. Chapter VIII deals with Voltaire's antioptimism in *Candide*.

Flowers, Ruth C. *Voltaire's Stylistic Transformation of Rabelaisian Satirical Devices*. Studies in Romance Languages and Literatures, vol. 41. Washington, D.C.: 1951. Catholic University of America Press. Compares the satire of Rabelais and Voltaire and shows the influence of Rabelais on Voltaire.

Gay, Peter. *Voltaire's Politics: The Poet as Realist*. Princeton: Princeton University Press, 1959. Pages 18–32, "Overweening Confidence, Infallible Rationality," stress Voltaire's value as a reformer.

Hall, Evelyn B. (pseud. Stephen G. Tallentyre). *The Life of Voltaire*, 3rd ed. New York: G. P. Putnam's Sons, 1910. Chapter XXXIII gives an account of the origin of *Candide*, including a discussion of the "Poem on the Lisbon Earthquake" and Rousseau's letter on Providence.

Hamley, Edward B. *Voltaire*. Philadelphia: J. B. Lippincott and Co., 1877. Brief biography with some discussion of Voltaire's works.

Harper, Henry H. *Voltaire*. Boston: Bibliophile Society, 1934. Strictly biographical with no literary criticism. Gives details of Voltaire's involvement with Madame du Châtelet, her husband, and St. Lambert.

Havens, George R. "The Composition of Voltaire's *Candide*," *Modern Language Notes*, XLVII (April 1932), 225–234. Attacks story that *Candide* was written in three days. Discusses the influence of Frederick the Great on the writing of *Candide*.

——————. "The Conclusion of Voltaire's *Poème sur le désastre de Lisbonne*," *Modern Language Notes*, LVI (June 1941), 422–426. Maintains that the conclusion of the poem should be interpreted as an expression of pessimism.

*——————. "Nature Doctrine of Voltaire," *PMLA*, XL (December 1925), 852–862.

——————. *Selections from Voltaire*. New York: The Century Co., 1925. Contains brief discussions of the "Poem on the Lisbon Earthquake" and *Candide*.

180   BIBLIOGRAPHY

——————. "Taking Counsel with Candide," in *Age of Ideas.* New York: Henry Holt & Co., 1955. Summarizes and analyzes Voltaire's philosophical tales. Stresses the doctrine of work in *Candide.*

——————. "Voltaire, Rousseau, and the *Lettre sur la Providence,*" *PMLA,* LIX (March 1944), 109–130. On the controversy between Voltaire and Rousseau over the Lisbon earthquake and the problem of evil.

——————. "Voltaire's Marginal Comments upon Pope's *Essay on Man,*" *Modern Language Notes,* XLIII (November 1928), 429–439. On Voltaire's opposition to Pope's ideas as indicated by marginal comments.

——————. "Voltaire's Pessimistic Revision of the Conclusion of his *Poème sur le désastre de Lisbonne,*" *Modern Language Notes,* XLIV (December 1929), 489–492. Points out that the conclusion to the poem is only partly optimistic.

*Huxley, Aldous. "On Re-reading *Candide,*" in *On the Margin.* London: Chatto and Windus, 1923. Pp. 12–17.

Josephson, Matthew. *Jean-Jacques Rousseau.* New York: Harcourt, Brace and Co., 1931. Discusses the argument between Rousseau and Voltaire about the Lisbon earthquake and the problem of evil.

*Kahn, Ludwig W. "Voltaire's *Candide* and the Problem of Secularization," *PMLA,* LXVII (September 1952), 886–888.

*Kendrick, Thomas D. *The Lisbon Earthquake.* London: Methuen & Co. Ltd., 1956.

Lanson, Gustave. *Voltaire, ed., rev. et mise à jour par René Pomeau.* Paris: Hachette, 1960. Short study of Voltaire's life and writings by a highly respected authority.

Latta, Robert. *Leibniz, the Monadology and Other Philosophical Writings.* Oxford: Oxford University Press, 1898. Introduces Leibniz's philosophy and presents the text of several of his chief works.

Lewis, Joseph. *Voltaire, the Incomparable Infidel.* New York: The Freethought Press Association, 1929. Mainly on Voltaire's life and character.

Lovejoy, Arthur O. *The Great Chain of Being.* Cambridge: Harvard University Press, 1936. Chapter VII, "Eighteenth Century Optimism," provides background for understanding Voltaire's reaction to optimism.

——————. "Optimism and Romanticism," *PMLA,* XLII (December 1927), 921–945. Includes a discussion of Voltaire's opposition to optimism.

MacDonald, Wilbert L. *Pope and His Critics.* London: J. M. Dent and Sons, 1951. Contains an analysis of Pope's *Essay on Man.*

McGhee, Dorothy M. *Voltairian Narrative Devices as Considered in the Author's Contes Philosophiques.* Menasha, Wisconsin: George Banta, 1933. A study of the form and style of Voltaire's philosophical novels.

Maurois, André. "Voltaire," in Romain Rolland, André Maurois, and Edouard Herriot, *French Thought in the Eighteenth Century.* London: Cassell and Co., Ltd., 1953. A biographical sketch of Voltaire with emphasis on *Candide.*

*———————. *Voltaire,* trans. Hamish Miles. New York: D. Appleton and Co., 1932.

Meyer, Adolph E. *Voltaire: Man of Justice.* London: Quality Press, Ltd., 1952. Laudatory biography stressing Voltaire's liberalism. Describes the controversy between Voltaire and Rousseau. Summarizes *Candide* and comments on the reactions to it.

Moore, C. A. "Did Leibniz Influence Pope's *Essay?" Journal of English and Germanic Philology,* XVI (January 1917), 84–102. Moore finds absolutely no evidence that Leibniz influenced Pope directly, but he concedes that Leibniz might have influenced him slightly through Bolingbroke.

Morley, John. *Rousseau and His Era.* London: Macmillan and Co., Ltd., 1923.

*———————. *Voltaire.* London: Macmillan and Co., Ltd., 1923.

Noyes, Alfred. *Voltaire.* New York: Sheed and Ward, 1936. Discusses Voltaire's religious faith in relationship to *Candide.* Attacks John Morley's interpretation of Voltaire's "Poem on the Lisbon Earthquake." Comments on the controversy between Voltaire and Rousseau.

Parton, James. *Life of Voltaire.* 2 vols. Boston: Houghton Mifflin Co., 1882. Full biography, including discussion of Voltaire's argument with Rousseau and the origin of *Candide.*

"The Philosophy of Voltaire's Romances," *The Temple Bar,* LXXX (May 1887), 91–110. Summarizes *Candide* and interprets the ideas set forth in it. Also deals with other tales by Voltaire.

Robertson, James M. *Voltaire.* London: Watts and Co., Ltd., 1922. Short study of Voltaire's life and writings by a liberal who values Voltaire's independent thought.

Rockett, K. "An Optimistic Streak in Voltaire's Thought," *Modern Language Review,* XXXIX (January 1944), 24–27. Sees evidence in the "Poem on the Lisbon Earthquake" that Voltaire was really an optimist who was fighting against a temptation to be pessimistic.

Rousseau, Jean-Jacques. *Confessions.* London: Gibbings and Co., Ltd., 1901. In "Book IX, 1756" (Vol. III, pp. 131–133) Rousseau recalls his argument with Voltaire about the Lisbon earthquake and Providence and claims that *Candide* was Voltaire's answer to Rousseau's "Letter on Providence."

———————. Lettre à M. de Voltaire, le 18 août 1756, in *Œuvres de J. J. Rousseau,* ed. Mussay Pathay. Paris: Werdet et Lequien fils, 1826. XVII, 224–247. Rousseau's famous "Letter on Providence," in which he attacks Voltaire's pessimistic philosophy on the problem of evil as set forth in *The Poem on the Lisbon Earthquake.*

Saintsbury, George. "Voltaire," *Encyclopaedia Britannica,* Eleventh Edition, 1911. Biographical and critical article covering Voltaire's virtues and faults. Praises Voltaire's use of irony.

Schlegel, Dorothy B. *Shaftesbury and the French Deists.* Chapel Hill, North Carolina: University of North Carolina Press, 1956. Discusses Voltaire's antagonism to Shaftesbury's optimism and Voltaire's doctrine of work as set forth in *Candide.*

Shilling, Bernard N. *Conservative England and the Case Against Voltaire.* New York: Columbia University Press, 1950. On unfavorable reactions to Voltaire in England because of his attacks on religion and his paving the way for the French Revolution.

*Strachey, G. Lytton. *Landmarks in French Literature.* New York: Henry Holt and Co., 1912.

Thaddeus, Victor. *Voltaire, Genius of Mockery.* New York: Brentano's, 1928. Pages 198–203 of "The Battle Cry of Voltaire" deal with *Candide,* especially Voltaire's use of venereal disease in the novel.

Topazio, W. "Voltaire, Philosopher of Human Progress," *PMLA,* LXXIV (September 1959), 356–364. Opposes idea that Voltaire is a destructive or negative thinker. Appraises the constructive elements in Voltaire's works.

Torrey, Norman L. "The Date of Composition of *Candide,* and Voltaire's Corrections," *Modern Language Notes,* XLIV (November 1929), 445–447. Establishes July 1758 as the date of composition of *Candide.* Cites evidence to deny that it was written in three days.

*————. *The Spirit of Voltaire.* New York: Columbia University Press, 1938.

————. *Voltaire and the English Deists.* New Haven: Yale University Press, 1930. Argues that Voltaire's deism was caused partly by his being influenced by English thinkers.

Triebel, L. A. "Bicentenary of *Candide,*" *Contemporary Review,* CXCV (March 1959), 181–183. Identifies reason as Voltaire's chief ideal. Emphasizes Voltaire's doctrine of work and the applicability of *Candide* to today.

*Tsanoff, Radoslav A. *The Nature of Evil.* New York: The Macmillan Co., 1931.

Van Doren, Mark, ed. "Voltaire: *Candide,*" in *New Invitation to Learning.* New York: Random House, 1942. A transcription of a radio panel discussion in which Irvin Edman, André Maurois, and Mark Van Doren talked about *Candide.* Aspects of the novel discussed include anti-optimism, the doctrine of work, and the meaning of the Eldorado episode.

Vulliamy, Colwyn E. *Voltaire.* New York: Dodd, Mead and Co., 1930. Mainly biographical, based to a great extent on Voltaire's letters. Prefers Rousseau's character to Voltaire's.

Wade, Ira O. *The Search for a New Voltaire: Studies in Voltaire Based upon Material Deposited at the American Philosophical Society,* Philadelphia: American Philosophical Society, 1958. Includes, on pages 42–48, an analysis of the impact of the Lisbon Earthquake on Voltaire and its relationship to *Candide.* Much use is made of Voltaire's correspondence.

*————. *Voltaire and Candide.* Princeton: Princeton University Press, 1959.

Weightman, J. G. "The Quality of *Candide,*" in *Essays Presented to C. M. Girdlestone,* ed. E. T. Dubois and others. Newcastle Upon Tyne: University of Durham, 1960. Interpretation and evaluation of *Candide* with stress on Voltaire's doctrine of work.